04
`ION

Department 56 Villages

GREENBOOK

Includes All Buildings and Accessories for All Department 56® Villages.

- ✤ *The Original Snow Village® Series*
- ✤ *Dickens' Village Series®*
- ✤ *New England Village® Series*
- ✤ *Alpine Village Series®*
- ✤ *Christmas In The City® Series*
- ✤ *The Holy Land® Collection*
- ✤ *North Pole Series™*
- ✤ *Small Collections*
  (Includes: Historical Landmark Series®, Meadowland, Literary Classics® Collection, Disney Parks Village™ Series, North Pole Woods™ Collection, Seasons Bay® Series)
- ✤ *Profiles Department 56®*
- ✤ *And Other Related Series*

Featuring Secondary Market Values, Historical Facts, Information, and Trivia that will make collecting more enjoyable than ever.

Personal Collection of

_____

GREENBOOK®

The Definitive Reference & Secondary Market Guide To

Department 56®Villages

56 Freeway Drive, Cranston, RI 02920

Order Line: 1-877-212-4356 (Toll-Free Inside the U.S.)
Inquiries: 401-467-9343
Fax: 401-467-9359

www.greenbooks.com
www.villagechronicle.com

© Copyright 2004, The Collectible Source, Inc.

Published by The Collectible Source, Inc. & the Village Chronicle®

ISBN 0-9649032-8-8

First Printing, March, 2004

Printed and bound in Canada.

Table Of Contents

On the Cover...
Clockwise from top left: Christmas In The City The Doctor's Office,
North Pole Santa's Sleigh Launch, Snow Village McGuire's Irish Pub,
Dickens' Village The Horse And Hounds Pub, and Profiles Series Spam
Museum.

Getting The Most From This Guide

Sections

Each village has its own section. Its accessories immediately follow the lighted pieces.

The **Heritage Village** section contains porcelain pieces that were not necessarily designed for a specific village series and may be appropriate for two or more Heritage Villages.

The **Small Collection** section consists of collections that are too small in number to warrant their own individual sections.

The **Special Design**s section features buildings and accessories that were produced for a particular retailer, company, or organization.

Chronological Order

We're often asked why the collections are placed in chronological order. There are several reasons. One is that its sequence follows that of printed materials produced by Department 56, Inc. such as its History List. Another is that it's the only way a collector can get a complete grasp of a collection. It allows one to see how the designs, creativity, and technology developed over the years. It also makes it possible to see all the pieces made in one year (or a series of years) at a glance. For instance, say you want to see all the Dickens' Village® Series buildings from 1991…there they are.

Values

Another question that is often asked is how we determine values. Simply put, we don't…actual sales from around the country determine them. We canvass various sources of secondary market sales throughout the nation, from East to West, from auctions, to brokers, to swap & sells, to the traditional retail stores. Pricing structures in each of these sources differ, making a one-price-fits-all value unrealistic.

With That In Mind, It's More Than Just A Secondary Market Guide

This guide is designed to do more than present a pictorial representation of the collections with current values to accompany them. It's meant to offer you the facts, data, background, and yes, trivia in a concise, easy-to-follow manner. It's our goal to provide a guide that makes collecting the villages more exciting than ever before. It's our hope that we have accomplished this goal. If you have comments or ideas, please contact us at 401-467-9343 or at www.greenbooks.com.

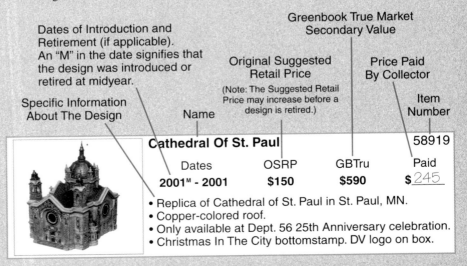

Dates of Introduction and Retirement (if applicable). An "M" in the date signifies that the design was introduced or retired at midyear.

Specific Information About The Design

Name

Original Suggested Retail Price

(Note: The Suggested Retail Price may increase before a design is retired.)

Greenbook True Market Secondary Value

Price Paid By Collector

Item Number

Cathedral Of St. Paul   58919

Dates	OSRP	GBTru	Paid
2001ᴹ - 2001	$150	$590	$ 245

- Replica of Cathedral of St. Paul in St. Paul, MN.
- Copper-colored roof.
- Only available at Dept. 56 25th Anniversary celebration.
- Christmas In The City bottomstamp. DV logo on box.

The Original Snow Village® Collection

The matriarch of the winter villages, the Original Snow Village® Collection debuted in 1976. The only ceramic community, it is the largest village, annually introducing and retiring the most pieces. The buildings are generally larger and more vividly colored than any of the porcelain villages. The detail and exceptional craftsmanship in recent years are in contrast to the early years.

This is Americana through the years, and patriotic pieces and Classic Cars confirm that focus. Licensing agreements have resulted in buildings with such familiar names as Coca-Cola®, McDonald's®, Starbucks®, Harley-Davidson®, Lionel®, Ford®, and Krispy Kreme®. Among the most eye-catching buildings are several of an art deco nature. Retail establishments abound, but so do residences and churches. Among the homes is a subseries, the American Architecture Series that replicates various architectural styles. Popular pieces such as fire stations, lighthouses, and schools have been re-introduced to meet the demands of new collectors.

While figures have never been in scale, the original contrast was even greater than today as downsizing took place in the late 1980s. Children are featured in the accessories to a much greater extent than any other village. Animals are also a very popular theme in the family-oriented designs. The Buck's County Series reflects an emphasis on the more rural lifestyle.

The number of Halloween pieces has increased, and a separate section has been added to this publication at the end of the regular collection. Valentine's, Easter, and St. Patrick's Day have also expanded this village to more than a winter setting.

Mountain Lodge 50013

Dates	OSRP	GBTru	Paid
1976 - 1979	**$20**	**$375**	$_____

- Colors on roof often vary.
- Must have a sunburst face on the end of the building to be authentic.
- Skis are sometimes broken or detached.

Gabled Cottage 50021

Dates	OSRP	GBTru	Paid
1976 - 1979	**$20**	**$275**	$_____

- Color varies to the point where no two are alike.

The Inn 50039

Dates	OSRP	GBTru	Paid
1976 - 1979	**$20**	**$425**	$_____

- Colors on roof often vary to the point where no two are alike.
- Watch for cracks in the porch supports.

Country Church 50047

Dates	OSRP	GBTru	Paid
1976 - 1979	**$18**	**$325**	$_____

- Also known as Wayside Chapel.
- This is one of the most frequently imitated pieces in Snow Village. The lettering on the walls must be hand painted (as opposed to stamped on) to be authentic.

Steepled Church 50054

Dates	OSRP	GBTru	Paid
1976 - 1979	**$25**	**$450**	$_____

- Colors on roof often vary.

Small Chalet 50062

Dates	OSRP	GBTru	Paid
1976 - 1979	**$15**	**$375**	$_____

- Also known as Gingerbread Chalet.
- An often imitated design, it is difficult to authenticate.
- The color varies from tan to brown, and the number of flowers in window box varies.

Victorian House   50070

Dates	OSRP	GBTru	Paid
1977 - 1979	**$30**	**$345**	$_____

- Color of building varies among rust/white, salmon/white, pink/white, and orange/yellow (no tree attached).
- Birds are often broken off, leaving lack of paint and glazing where the birds should be.

Mansion   50088

Dates	OSRP	GBTru	Paid
1977 - 1979	**$30**	**$450**	$_____

- Color of roof often varies from forest green (first shipments) to turquoise.
- The amount of glaze on the forest green version varies while the turquoise version sometimes has flaking paint.

Stone Church (Version 1)   50096

Dates	OSRP	GBTru	Paid
1977 - 1979	**$35**	**$575**	$_____

- Pale mint green building with very glossy finish.
- Right sides of front steps are flush.
- Steeple is approximately 10½" high as opposed to the 1979 version which is approximately 8½" high.

(Version 2)

GBTru	Paid
$490	$_____

- Greenish-yellow building with less glossy finish.
- Right side of top front step is indented from bottom one.
- Both versions have felt glued to the bottom.
- The bell is sometimes missing from the bell tower.

Homestead   50112

Dates	OSRP	GBTru	Paid
1978 - 1984	**$30**	**$195**	$_____

- Sometimes not painted or glazed well.
- Porch pillars, garland, and chimney are easily damaged.

General Store

50120

Dates	OSRP	GBTru	Paid
1978 - 1980	$25	See below	

- Variations: white with gray roof (first shipments), tan with red roof, and gold with brown roof.
- Signs: on white "General Store Y & L Brothers," on tan "General Store S & L Brothers," on gold "General Store."

	GBTru	Paid
White	$375	$_____
Tan	$440	$_____
Gold	$450	$_____

Cape Cod

50138

Dates	OSRP	GBTru	Paid
1978 - 1980	$20	$330	$_____

- The snow around the bottom of the piece detaches easily.

Nantucket

50146

Dates	OSRP	GBTru	Paid
1978 - 1986	$25	$225	$_____

- Some pieces were manufactured with garland above front windows; others were not. Still others had the garland broken off. This is usually easy to determine.

Skating Rink/Duck Pond Set

50153

Dates	OSRP	GBTru	Paid
1978 - 1979	$16	$825	$_____

- The trees are attached directly to the bases where their size and weight caused frequent breakage.
- The pieces in this set are often sold separately on the secondary market.
- Do not confuse this set with the 1982 Skating Pond set.
- Set of 2 includes the Skating Rink (features a snowman and a lighted tree) and the Duck Pond (features a bench, blue birds, and a lighted tree).

Small Double Trees (Blue Birds) — 50161

Dates	OSRP	GBTru	Paid
1978 - 1989	$13.50	$145	$____

- Pieces with blue birds were shipped first.

(Red Birds Version)

	GBTru	Paid
	$40	$____

- Pieces with red birds began to appear in late 1979.
- Throughout the years there were mold changes with the design becoming more and more detailed.
- Amount of snow on the trees varies greatly.

Victorian — 50542

Dates	OSRP	GBTru	Paid
1979 - 1982	$30	See below	

- Peach (1st year) often has peeling paint.
- Gold with smooth walls (2nd year) ⎫ Defects are often
- Gold with clapboard walls (3rd year) ⎭ located along the bottom edges.

	GBTru	Paid
Peach	$325	$____
Gold - S	$350	$____
Gold - C	$355	$____

Knob Hill (Gray) — 50559

Dates	OSRP	GBTru	Paid
1979 - 1981	$30	$280	$____

- This color is considered to be the first shipped.
- The paint on this version is commonly thin and bubbly.
- Cracks on the bottom are also common.
- Beware of chips along the steps.

(Yellow Version)

	GBTru	Paid
	$250	$____

- Beware of chips along the steps.
- The chimneys on both colors are very fragile.

Brownstone 50567

Dates	OSRP	GBTru	Paid
1979 - 1981	$36	See below	

		GBTru	Paid
• Gray roof (first year)		$495	$_____
• Red roof (second year)		$425	$_____

• Beware of cracks near windows and chipped steps.

Log Cabin 50575

Dates	OSRP	GBTru	Paid
1979 - 1981	$22	$480	$_____

• The skis by the door are very fragile and are often broken off.

Countryside Church 50583

Dates	OSRP	GBTru	Paid
1979 - 1984	$27.50	$210	$_____

Stone Church 50591

Dates	OSRP	GBTru	Paid
1979 - 1980	$32	$840	$_____

• Similar to 1977 Stone Church, this steeple is approximately 8½" high.
• Felt was glued to the bottom at the factory to conceal cracks and chips.

School House 50609

Dates	OSRP	GBTru	Paid
1979 - 1982	$30	$370	$_____

• Varies from reddish-brown to dark brown.
• American flag is separate in box.

Tudor House 50617

Dates	OSRP	GBTru	Paid
1979 - 1981	$25	$295	$_____

• Another design with the same name was issued in this village in 2001.

Mission Church

50625

Dates	OSRP	GBTru	Paid
1979 - 1980	$30	$1575	$_____

• The bell is sometimes missing.

Mobile Home

50633

Dates	OSRP	GBTru	Paid
1979 - 1980	$18	$1495	$_____

• The paint is usually thin and bubbly.
• The trailer hitch is easily broken off and, therefore, is sometimes missing.

Giant Trees

50658

Dates	OSRP	GBTru	Paid
1979 - 1982	$20	$250	$_____

Adobe House

50666

Dates	OSRP	GBTru	Paid
1979 - 1980	$18	$2350	$_____

• Factory imperfections such as dents and fingerprints are common.
• The extended roof beams are fragile.

Cathedral Church

50674

Dates	OSRP	GBTru	Paid
1980 - 1981	$36	$2700	$_____

• Inspired by St. Paul Cathedral in St. Paul, MN.
• Prone to crazing.
• Felt is sometimes glued on at the factory to conceal chips and cracks.

Stone Mill House

50682

Dates	OSRP	GBTru	Paid
1980 - 1982	$30	$470	$_____

• Separate bag of oats (intended to be hung from block and tackle) is often missing and decreases value.
• Window areas are often thin and fragile.

Colonial Farm House 50709

Dates	OSRP	GBTru	Paid
1980 - 1982	$30	$240	$_____

• All Saints Church (1986) was also issued with this item number.

Town Church 50717

Dates	OSRP	GBTru	Paid
1980 - 1982	$33	$375	$_____

• Carriage House (1986) was also issued with this item number.

Train Station With 3 Train Cars 50856

Dates	OSRP	GBTru	Paid
1980 - 1985	$100	$300	$_____

• In the first year, the set included a Station with 6 windows in front (top, left). A year later, the Station was larger with 8 windows in front (bottom, left), and the OSRP increased to $110. Set of 4. All pieces light.

Train Station 50873

Dates	OSRP	GBTru	Paid
1980 - 1981	$42	$150	$_____

• Station has 6 windows in front and 1 in the door.
• It was sold individually as well as part of the above set.

3 Train Cars 50865

Dates	OSRP	GBTru	Paid
1980 - 1982	$65	$150	$_____

• It was sold individually as well as part of the above set.
• Set of 3. All pieces light.

Wooden Clapboard 50725

Dates	OSRP	GBTru	Paid
1981 - 1984	**$32**	**$220**	$_____

English Cottage 50733

Dates	OSRP	GBTru	Paid
1981 - 1982	**$25**	**$290**	$_____

• Toy Shop (1986) was also issued with this item number.

Barn 50741

Dates	OSRP	GBTru	Paid
1981 - 1984	**$32**	**$290**	$_____

• The cow at the side of the barn often has its ears and/or horns broken off.

Corner Store 50768

Dates	OSRP	GBTru	Paid
1981 - 1983	**$30**	**$210**	$_____

• Apothecary (1986) was also issued with this item number.

Bakery 50776

Dates	OSRP	GBTru	Paid
1981 - 1983	**$30**	**$220**	$_____

• Bakery (1986) was also issued with this item number.

English Church 50784

Dates	OSRP	GBTru	Paid
1981 - 1982	**$30**	**$315**	$_____

• Diner (1986) was also issued with this item number.
• Cross is separate in box.

Large Single Tree 50806

Dates	OSRP	GBTru	Paid
1981 - 1989	**$17**	**$40**	$_____

- Throughout the years there were mold changes with the design becoming more and more detailed.
- Amount of snow on the trees varies greatly.

Skating Pond 50172

Dates	OSRP	GBTru	Paid
1982 - 1984	**$25**	**$290**	$_____

- Snowman easily breaks off.
- Set of 2 includes pond and separate lighted trees.
- Do not confuse this piece with the 1978 Skating Pond/Duck Set.

Street Car 50199

Dates	OSRP	GBTru	Paid
1982 - 1984	**$16**	**$330**	$_____

- The "electrical hook-up" on roof often causes collectors to believe a pole should be included, but this is not so.
- Cathedral Church (1987) was also issued with this item number.

Centennial House 50202

Dates	OSRP	GBTru	Paid
1982 - 1984	**$32**	**$275**	$_____

- The front steps and extension are fragile.

Carriage House 50210

Dates	OSRP	GBTru	Paid
1982 - 1984	**$28**	**$230**	$_____

- Another design with the same name was issued in this village in 1986.

Pioneer Church 50229

Dates	OSRP	GBTru	Paid
1982 - 1984	**$30**	**$325**	$_____

- The front steps are fragile.

Swiss Chalet
50237

Dates	OSRP	GBTru	Paid
1982 - 1984	**$28**	**$375**	$____

- Sometimes came from the factory with uneven and bubbly paint on the roof.

Bank
50245

Dates	OSRP	GBTru	Paid
1982 - 1983	**$32**	**$490**	$____

- Check areas around the staircase and revolving door.
- Dentist sign at stairway is often broken off.
- Cumberland House (1987) was also issued with this item number.

Gabled House
50814

Dates	OSRP	GBTru	Paid
1982 - 1983	**$30**	**$320**	$____

- Early samples are rust color; production pieces are white.
- Early release to GCC dealers.
- Red Barn (1987) was also issued with this item number.

Flower Shop
50822

Dates	OSRP	GBTru	Paid
1982 - 1983	**$25**	**$400**	$____

- Window frames vary from brown to green.
- Flowers are fragile.
- Jefferson School (1987) was also issued with this item number.

New Stone Church
50830

Dates	OSRP	GBTru	Paid
1982 - 1984	**$32**	**$350**	$____

- This is often not as glossy as most Snow Village pieces.
- Early release to GCC dealers.

Town Hall
50008

Dates	OSRP	GBTru	Paid
1983 - 1984	**$32**	**$260**	$____

- Metal weathervane is separate in box. It is rare to find a Town Hall with its weathervane.

Grocery

50016

Dates	OSRP	GBTru	Paid
1983 - 1985	$35	$285	$_____

• The staircase is very fragile.

Victorian Cottage

50024

Dates	OSRP	GBTru	Paid
1983 - 1984	$35	$345	$_____

Governor's Mansion

50032

Dates	OSRP	GBTru	Paid
1983 - 1985	$32	$260	$_____

• The ironwork for the cupola is separate in box and is often missing.

Turn Of The Century

50040

Dates	OSRP	GBTru	Paid
1983 - 1986	$36	$230	$_____

• Bottom inscription reads "Turn The Time Of Century."
• The three chimneys are very fragile, especially the one on the center peak.

Gingerbread House

50253

Dates	OSRP	GBTru	Paid
1983 - 1984	$24	$380	$_____

• Besides lighted version, there is also a very rare non-lighted bank with a coin slot that was sold as a giftware item as opposed to part of Snow Village.

Village Church

50261

Dates	OSRP	GBTru	Paid
1983 - 1984	$30	$445	$_____

• Very similar to Parish Church (1984).
• Early release to GCC dealers.

Gothic Church

50288

Dates	OSRP	GBTru	Paid
1983 - 1986	$36	$210	$_____

• The cross at the top is easily broken off.

Parsonage

50296

Dates	OSRP	GBTru	Paid
1983 - 1985	$35	$320	$_____

• The cross atop the gable is easily broken off.

Wooden Church

50318

Dates	OSRP	GBTru	Paid
1983 - 1985	$30	$345	$_____

Fire Station

50326

Dates	OSRP	GBTru	Paid
1983 - 1984	$32	$360	$_____

• Varies with and without Dalmatian. Close examination should reveal whether a piece without a Dalmatian was made that way or if the dog was broken off.

English Tudor

50334

Dates	OSRP	GBTru	Paid
1983 - 1985	$30	$225	$_____

• Chimneys are fragile.

Chateau

50849

Dates	OSRP	GBTru	Paid
1983 - 1984	$35	$380	$_____

• This is often not as glossy as most Snow Village pieces.
• Early release to GCC dealers.

Main Street House

50059

Dates	OSRP	GBTru	Paid
1984 - 1986	$27	$200	$_____

• Early release to GCC dealers.

Stratford House

50075

Dates	OSRP	GBTru	Paid
1984 - 1986	$28	$155	$_____

Haversham House

50083

Dates	OSRP	GBTru	Paid
1984 - 1987	$37	$200	$_____

• Early release to GCC dealers. These are larger, heavier, more impressive, and subject to more defects than those shipped later. **GBTru: $215** Paid: **$_____**

Galena House

50091

Dates	OSRP	GBTru	Paid
1984 - 1985	$32	$335	$_____

• The front steps are fragile.

River Road House

50105

Dates	OSRP	GBTru	Paid
1984 - 1987	$36	$160	$_____

• Early release to GCC dealers. These have window above door and transoms above lower front windows cut out. Later ones do not.

Delta House

50121

Dates	OSRP	GBTru	Paid
1984 - 1986	$32	$245	$_____

• Ironwork for the top of the tower is separate in box and is often missing.

Bayport

50156

Dates	OSRP	GBTru	Paid
1984 - 1986	$30	$180	$_____

Congregational Church

50342

Dates	OSRP	GBTru	Paid
1984 - 1985	$28	$525	$_____

• It is rare to find one with a straight steeple.
• The steeple is easily broken.

Trinity Church

50350

Dates	OSRP	GBTru	Paid
1984 - 1986	$32	$280	$_____

Summit House

50369

Dates	OSRP	GBTru	Paid
1984 - 1985	$28	$375	$_____

• The porch columns are crooked on almost all examples of this design.
• Do not handle by porch columns.

New School House

50377

Dates	OSRP	GBTru	Paid
1984 - 1986	$35	$250	$_____

• American flag is separate in box.

Parish Church

50393

Dates	OSRP	GBTru	Paid
1984 - 1986	$32	$285	$_____

• Very similar to Village Church (1993).

Stucco Bungalow

50458

Dates	OSRP	GBTru	Paid
1985 - 1986	$30	$345	$_____

Williamsburg House

50466

Dates	OSRP	GBTru	Paid
1985 - 1988	$37	$120	$_____

• Entryway attachment is fragile.
• The paint on the building is known to suddenly develop cracks under the glaze after a period of time.

Plantation House

50474

Dates	OSRP	GBTru	Paid
1985 - 1987	$37	$100	$_____

• Do not handle by porch columns.

Church Of The Open Door

50482

Dates	OSRP	GBTru	Paid
1985 - 1988	$34	$115	$_____

• Despite its name, the door on this design is closed.

Spruce Place

50490

Dates	OSRP	GBTru	Paid
1985 - 1987	$33	$210	$_____

• The area around the porch and steps is easily damaged.

Duplex

50504

Dates	OSRP	GBTru	Paid
1985 - 1987	$35	$125	$_____

Depot And Train With 2 Train Cars

50512

Dates	OSRP	GBTru	Paid
1985 - 1988	$65	$110	$_____

- There are 3 variations:
  1. Brown Depot with gray cornerstones (top) and Train Car with yellow windows.
  2. Brick Depot without cornerstones and Train Car with yellow windows (bottom).

  3. Brick Depot without cornerstones and Train Car with white windows.
- Though referred to as a set of 2, it includes the Depot, 2-piece train, and a ceramic track.

Ridgewood

50520

Dates	OSRP	GBTru	Paid
1985 - 1987	$35	$145	$_____

- Do not handle by porch columns.

Waverly Place

50415

Dates	OSRP	GBTru	Paid
1986 - 1986	$35	$310	$_____

- Inspired by Gingerbread Mansion in Ferndale, CA.
- Early release to GCC dealers.
- Squirrel is often missing.

Twin Peaks

50423

Dates	OSRP	GBTru	Paid
1986 - 1986	$32	$365	$_____

- The peaks are easily damaged.
- Early release to GCC dealers.

2101 Maple

50431

Dates	OSRP	GBTru	Paid
1986 - 1986	$32	$285	$_____

- The turret peak is easily damaged.
- Early release to GCC dealers.

Lincoln Park Duplex

50601

Dates	OSRP	GBTru	Paid
1986 - 1988	$33	$125	$_____

Sonoma House

50628

Dates	OSRP	GBTru	Paid
1986 - 1988	$33	$130	$_____

• Early release to GCC dealers.

Highland Park House

50636

Dates	OSRP	GBTru	Paid
1986 - 1988	$35	$140	$_____

• The chimney is fragile.
• Early release to GCC dealers.

Beacon Hill House

50652

Dates	OSRP	GBTru	Paid
1986 - 1988	$31	$150	$_____

• This design is often confused with the Pacific Heights House because they were mislabeled in the Department 56 Snow Village Collectors Album.

Pacific Heights House

50660

Dates	OSRP	GBTru	Paid
1986 - 1988	$33	$95	$_____

• This design is often confused with the Beacon Hill House because they were mislabeled in the Department 56 Snow Village Collectors Album.

Ramsey Hill House

50679

Dates	OSRP	GBTru	Paid
1986 - 1989	$36	$95	$_____

• Early release to GCC dealers. Pieces in early release are brighter than those shipped later.

Saint James Church

50687

Dates	OSRP	GBTru	Paid
1986 - 1988	**$37**	**$125**	$_____

• The cross on the center peak is easily broken off.

All Saints Church

50709

Dates	OSRP	GBTru	Paid
1986 - 1997	**$38**	**$50**	$_____

• Colonial Farm House (1980) was also issued with this item number.

Carriage House

50717

Dates	OSRP	GBTru	Paid
1986 - 1988	**$29**	**$110**	$_____

• Town Church (1980) was also issued with this item number.
• Another design with the same name was issued in this village in 1982.

Toy Shop

50733

Dates	OSRP	GBTru	Paid
1986 - 1990	**$36**	**$95**	$_____

• Inspired by the Finch Building in Hastings, MN.
• Decorative attachments on the roof are fragile.
• English Cottage (1981) was also issued with this item number.

Apothecary

50768

Dates	OSRP	GBTru	Paid
1986 - 1990	**$34**	**$80**	$_____

• Sleeves often read "Antique Shop."
• Inspired by the former City Hall in Hastings, MN.
• Corner Store (1981) was also issued with this item number.

Bakery

50776

Dates	OSRP	GBTru	Paid
1986 - 1991	**$35**	**$75**	$_____

• Inspired by the Scofield Building in Northfield, MN.
• The awnings are fragile.
• Bakery (1981) was also issued with this item number.

Diner
50784

Dates	OSRP	GBTru	Paid
1986 - 1987	$22	$555	$_____

- Also known as Mickey's and Mickey's Diner.
- Inspired by Mickey's Diner in St. Paul, MN.
- English Church (1981) was also issued with this item number.

St. Anthony Hotel & Post Office
50067

Dates	OSRP	GBTru	Paid
1987 - 1989	$40	$90	$_____

- American flag is separate in box.

Snow Village Factory
50130

Dates	OSRP	GBTru	Paid
1987 - 1989	$45	$115	$_____

- Smokestack is a separate piece from building.
- The dark burgundy paint on the building is known to suddenly develop cracks under the glaze after a period of time.

Cathedral Church
50199

Dates	OSRP	GBTru	Paid
1987 - 1990	$50	$80	$_____

- Street Car (1982) was also issued with this item number.

Cumberland House
50245

Dates	OSRP	GBTru	Paid
1987 - 1995	$42	$55	$_____

- Do not handle by the columns.
- Bank (1982) was also issued with this item number.

Springfield House
50270

Dates	OSRP	GBTru	Paid
1987 - 1990	$40	$85	$_____

Lighthouse

50300

Dates	OSRP	GBTru	Paid
1987 - 1988	$36	$390	$_____

- There are 2 variations:
  Tower painted white and unglazed.
  Tower painted off-white and glazed.
- Do not handle by the tower.

Red Barn

50814

Dates	OSRP	GBTru	Paid
1987 - 1992	$38	$90	$_____

- Early release to GCC dealers.
- Gabled House (1982) was also issued with this item number.

Jefferson School

50822

Dates	OSRP	GBTru	Paid
1987 - 1991	$36	$130	$_____

- Early release to GCC dealers.
- Bell is sometimes missing from tower.
- Flower Shop (1982) was also issued with this item number.

Farm House

50890

Dates	OSRP	GBTru	Paid
1987 - 1992	$40	$60	$_____

- Do not handle by porch columns or railings.

Fire Station No. 2

50911

Dates	OSRP	GBTru	Paid
1987 - 1989	$40	$150	$_____

- Staircase is easily damaged.
- Early release to GCC dealers.

Snow Village Resort Lodge

50920

Dates	OSRP	GBTru	Paid
1987 - 1989	$55	$120	$_____

Village Market

50440

Dates	OSRP	GBTru	Paid
1988 - 1991	**$39**	**$80**	$_____

• Color varies from mint green to cream.
• Sisal tree on top of roof is packaged separately in the box and is often missing.
• Early release to GCC dealers.

Kenwood House

50547

Dates	OSRP	GBTru	Paid
1988 - 1990	**$50**	**$125**	$_____

• Do not handle by porch columns.
• Early release to GCC dealers.

Maple Ridge Inn

51217

Dates	OSRP	GBTru	Paid
1988 - 1990	**$55**	**$60**	$_____

• Inspired by the actual Maple Ridge Inn in Cambridge, NY. The home once belonged to relatives of painter Grandma Moses who visited there often.
• Early release to GCC dealers.

Village Station And Train

51225

Dates	OSRP	GBTru	Paid
1988 - 1992	**$65**	**$90**	$_____

• Train cars do not light.
• Set of 4.

Cobblestone Antique Shop

51233

Dates	OSRP	GBTru	Paid
1988 - 1992	**$36**	**$65**	$_____

• On rare occasion, the silk-screened windows detach.

Corner Cafe

51241

Dates	OSRP	GBTru	Paid
1988 - 1991	**$37**	**$80**	$_____

• On rare occasion, the silk-screened windows detach.

Single Car Garage

51250

Dates	OSRP	GBTru	Paid
1988 - 1990	**$22**	**$40**	$_____

• In many cases, the box must be broken in order to safely remove the piece.
• The tree attached to the back is indeed supposed to have holes drilled in it.

Home Sweet Home

51268

Dates	OSRP	GBTru	Paid
1988 - 1991	**$60**	**$100**	$_____

• Inspired by the East Hampton, NY historic home of John Howard Payne, composer of "Home Sweet Home."
• The windmill blades are packaged separately in the box and are made of metal.
• Set of 2.

Redeemer Church

51276

Dates	OSRP	GBTru	Paid
1988 - 1992	**$42**	**$55**	$_____

Service Station

51284

Dates	OSRP	GBTru	Paid
1988 - 1991	**$37.50**	**$160**	$_____

• Also known as Big Bill's Service Station which is the inscription on the bottom.
• Set of 2 includes Station and pumps.

Stonehurst House 51403

Dates	OSRP	GBTru	Paid
1988 - 1994	$37.50	$50	$_____

Palos Verdes 51411

Dates	OSRP	GBTru	Paid
1988 - 1990	$37.50	$55	$_____

• A small potted tree is packaged separately in the box.

Jingle Belle Houseboat 51144

Dates	OSRP	GBTru	Paid
1989 - 1991	$42	$175	$_____

• Bell is packaged separately in box and is often missing.

Colonial Church 51195

Dates	OSRP	GBTru	Paid
1989 - 1992	$60	$65	$_____

• The gray paint at steps and porch sometimes curls up and peels off.
• Do not handle by the columns.
• Early release to GCC dealers.

North Creek Cottage 51209

Dates	OSRP	GBTru	Paid
1989 - 1992	$45	$55	$_____

• Do not handle by the columns.
• Early release to GCC dealers.

Paramount Theater 51420

Dates	OSRP	GBTru	Paid
1989 - 1993	$42	$150	$_____

• Decals make cleaning this piece a delicate job.

Doctor's House
51438

Dates	OSRP	GBTru	Paid
1989 - 1992	$56	$110	$_____

• Do not handle by columns.

Courthouse
51446

Dates	OSRP	GBTru	Paid
1989 - 1993	$65	$180	$_____

• Inspired by the Gibson County Courthouse in Princetown, IN.
• Do not handle by tower.

Village Warming House
51454

Dates	OSRP	GBTru	Paid
1989 - 1992	$42	$50	$_____

• Includes 4 removable sisal trees.

J. Young's Granary
51497

Dates	OSRP	GBTru	Paid
1989 - 1992	$45	$80	$_____

Pinewood Log Cabin
51500

Dates	OSRP	GBTru	Paid
1989 - 1995	$37.50	$60	$_____

• Do not handle by porch columns.
• Early release to GCC dealers.

56 Flavors Ice Cream Parlor
51519

Dates	OSRP	GBTru	Paid
1990 - 1992	$42	$150	$_____

• Stem on cherry is often broken off and is often missing.
• "Parlor" decal comes off easily.
• Early release to GCC dealers.

Morningside House 51527

Dates	OSRP	GBTru	Paid
1990 - 1992	$45	$75	$___

• Includes 5 removable sisal trees.

Mainstreet Hardware Store 51535

Dates	OSRP	GBTru	Paid
1990 - 1993	$42	$70	$___

• Sample pieces have blue awnings and window trim. They were changed to green for the actual production.

Village Realty 51543

Dates	OSRP	GBTru	Paid
1990 - 1993	$42	$60	$___

Spanish Mission Church 51551

Dates	OSRP	GBTru	Paid
1990 - 1992	$42	$80	$___

• Inspired by the then-named Enga Memorial Chapel in Minneapolis, MN.
• Bell in tower is easily lost.
• Crosses on roof and in graveyard are fragile.

Prairie House 51560

Dates	OSRP	GBTru	Paid
1990 - 1993	$42	$70	$___

• American Architecture Series.
• Includes 2 removable sisal trees.

Queen Anne Victorian 51578

Dates	OSRP	GBTru	Paid
1990 - 1996	$48	$55	$___

• American Architecture Series.
• Do not handle by columns.

The Christmas Shop

50970

Dates	OSRP	GBTru	Paid
1991 - 1996	**$37.50**	**$55**	$_____

• Early release to GCC and Showcase dealers.

Oak Grove Tudor

54003

Dates	OSRP	GBTru	Paid
1991 - 1994	**$42**	**$55**	$_____

• Early release to Showcase dealers.

The Honeymooner Motel

54011

Dates	OSRP	GBTru	Paid
1991 - 1993	**$42**	**$85**	$_____

• The moon and stars symbol on the peak are easily damaged.
• Early release to Showcase dealers.

Village Greenhouse

54020

Dates	OSRP	GBTru	Paid
1991 - 1995	**$35**	**$50**	$_____

• The greenhouse "glass" often discolors with age.

Southern Colonial

54038

Dates	OSRP	GBTru	Paid
1991 - 1994	**$48**	**$70**	$_____

• American Architecture Series.
• 2 small sisal trees are separate in the box.
• Do not handle by columns or railings.

Gothic Farmhouse

54046

Dates	OSRP	GBTru	Paid
1991 - 1997	**$48**	**$65**	$_____

• American Architecture Series.
• Do not handle by columns.

Finklea's Finery: Costume Shop

54054

Dates	OSRP	GBTru	Paid
1991 - 1993	$45	$50	$____

• Some decals detach easily.

Jack's Corner Barber Shop

54062

Dates	OSRP	GBTru	Paid
1991 - 1994	$42	$75	$____

• The turret is easily damaged.

Double Bungalow

54070

Dates	OSRP	GBTru	Paid
1991 - 1994	$45	$55	$____

Grandma's Cottage

54208

Dates	OSRP	GBTru	Paid
1992 - 1996	$42	$70	$____

• Do not handle by columns or railings.
• Early release to GCC dealers.

St. Luke's Church

54216

Dates	OSRP	GBTru	Paid
1992 - 1994	$45	$55	$____

• Early release to GCC dealers.

Village Post Office

54224

Dates	OSRP	GBTru	Paid
1992 - 1995	$35	$70	$____

• Early release to Showcase dealers.

Al's TV Shop

54232

Dates	OSRP	GBTru	Paid
1992 - 1995	**$40**	**$45**	$_____

• Television antenna is packaged separately in the box.

Good Shepherd Chapel & Church School

54240

Dates	OSRP	GBTru	Paid
1992 - 1996	**$72**	**$65**	$_____

• Though designed to do so, the two pieces do not always fit together well.
• Decals fall off easily.
• Set of 2.

Print Shop & Village News

54259

Dates	OSRP	GBTru	Paid
1992 - 1994	**$37.50**	**$65**	$_____

• Do not handle by columns.

Hartford House

54267

Dates	OSRP	GBTru	Paid
1992 - 1995	**$55**	**$70**	$_____

• Do not handle by columns or railings.

Village Vet And Pet Shop

54275

Dates	OSRP	GBTru	Paid
1992 - 1995	**$32**	**$80**	$_____

• Early pieces read "Vetrinary."
• Decals fall off easily.

Craftsman Cottage

54372

Dates	OSRP	GBTru	Paid
1992 - 1995	**$55**	**$70**	$_____

• American Architecture Series.

Village Station

54380

Dates	OSRP	GBTru	Paid
1992 - 1997	$65	$80	$_____

• Decals fall off easily.

Airport

54399

Dates	OSRP	GBTru	Paid
1992 - 1996	$60	$90	$_____

• Loudspeaker and propeller are easily damaged.
• Do not handle by tower.

Nantucket Renovation

54410

Dates	OSRP	GBTru	Paid
1993 - 1993	$55	$65	$_____

• First limited (year of production) Snow Village design.
• Concept is how a "remodeled" Nantucket might appear
  15 years after the original one was issued.
• Packaged in special "blueprint" sleeve.

Mount Olivet Church

54429

Dates	OSRP	GBTru	Paid
1993 - 1996	$65	$85	$_____

• Crosses on peaks are easily damaged.

Village Public Library

54437

Dates	OSRP	GBTru	Paid
1993 - 1997	$55	$75	$_____

• Do not handle by columns.

Woodbury House

54445

Dates	OSRP	GBTru	Paid
1993 - 1996	$45	$60	$_____

• Do not handle by columns or railing.

Hunting Lodge

54453

Dates	OSRP	GBTru	Paid
1993 - 1996	$50	$145	$_____

• Antlers are easily damaged.

Dairy Barn

54461

Dates	OSRP	GBTru	Paid
1993 - 1997	$55	$80	$_____

• Weathervane is packaged separately in the box.

Dinah's Drive-In

54470

Dates	OSRP	GBTru	Paid
1993 - 1996	$45	$110	$_____

• The name "Dinah" was inspired by the line "Someone's in the kitchen with Dinah" in the song "I've Been Working on the Railroad."
• The straw in the rooftop milk shake is easily damaged.

Snowy Hills Hospital

54488

Dates	OSRP	GBTru	Paid
1993 - 1996	$48	$115	$_____

• A portion of the proceeds benefited AmFAR—the American Foundation for AIDS Research.
• Do not handle by columns.

Fisherman's Nook Cabins

54615

Dates	OSRP	GBTru	Paid
1994 - 1999	$50	$80	$_____

• Cabins differ only by names "Bass" and "Trout."
• Railings are very fragile.
• Set of 2.

Fisherman's Nook Resort

54607

Dates	OSRP	GBTru	Paid
1994 - 1999	$75	$85	$_____

• Sign on side is very fragile.

Snow Village Starter Set

54623

Dates	OSRP	GBTru	Paid
1994 - 1996	$50	$60	$_____

• First available at GCC Open House event in November 1994.
• Set of 6 includes **Shady Oak Church** (named for street adjacent to Department 56's office complex), "Sunday School Serenade," trees, and snow.

Wedding Chapel

54640

Dates	OSRP	GBTru	Paid
1994 - 2001	$55	$60	$_____

• Bell is attached in tower.

Federal House

54658

Dates	OSRP	GBTru	Paid
1994 - 1997	$50	$65	$_____

• American Architecture Series.
• Do not handle by columns.

Carmel Cottage

54666

Dates	OSRP	GBTru	Paid
1994 - 1997	$48	$55	$_____

Skate & Ski Shop

54674

Dates	OSRP	GBTru	Paid
1994 - 1998	**$50**	**$55**	$_____

• Sign and snow extending from front are easily damaged.

Glenhaven House

54682

Dates	OSRP	GBTru	Paid
1994 - 1997	**$45**	**$65**	$_____

• Do not handle by columns.

Coca–Cola® brand Bottling Plant

54690

Dates	OSRP	GBTru	Paid
1994 - 1997	**$65**	**$100**	$_____

• First pieces do not have soda cases on loading platform, though some later pieces have lost theirs. Close examination should reveal this.
• Licensed by Coca-Cola®.

Marvel's Beauty Salon

54704

Dates	OSRP	GBTru	Paid
1994 - 1997	**$37.50**	**$45**	$_____

Christmas Cove Lighthouse

54836

Dates	OSRP	GBTru	Paid
1995ᴹ - 2001	**$60**	**$70**	$_____

• First lighthouse with separate bulb at top of tower.
• The top comes off easily and is susceptible to damage because it is a separate piece and does not fit tightly.

Coca–Cola® brand Corner Drugstore

54844

Dates	OSRP	GBTru	Paid
1995ᴹ - 1998	**$55**	**$85**	$_____

• Early samples have red "label" around the bottle at the top of the sign.
• Licensed by Coca-Cola®.

Peppermint Porch Day Care

54852

Dates	OSRP	GBTru	Paid
1995ᴹ - 1997	$45	$65	$_____

- Early samples read "Peppermint Place."
- Do not handle by columns.

Snow Carnival Ice Palace

54850

Dates	OSRP	GBTru	Paid
1995 - 1998	$95	$120	$_____

- Inspired by the snow castles constructed during carnivals in Minnesota.
- Acrylic turrets can become unglued or yellow with age.
- Set of 2 includes building and gate.

Pisa Pizza

54851

Dates	OSRP	GBTru	Paid
1995 - 1998	$35	$60	$_____

Village Police Station

54853

Dates	OSRP	GBTru	Paid
1995 - 1998	$48	$70	$_____

- Acrylic light globes are easily dislodged.
- Do not handle by attached doughnut shop.

Holly Brothers Garage

54854

Dates	OSRP	GBTru	Paid
1995 - 1998	$48	$70	$_____

- Do not handle by columns or gas pumps.

Ryman Auditorium

54855

Dates	OSRP	GBTru	Paid
1995 - 1997	$75	$100	$_____

- Inspired by country music's Ryman Auditorium in Nashville, TN, once home to the Grand Ole Opry.
- Licensed by Opryland USA, Inc.

Dutch Colonial

54856

Dates	OSRP	GBTru	Paid
1995 - 1996	**$45**	**$50**	$_____

• American Architecture Series.

Beacon Hill Victorian

54857

Dates	OSRP	GBTru	Paid
1995 - 1998	**$60**	**$65**	$_____

• Do not handle by columns or railing.

Bowling Alley

54858

Dates	OSRP	GBTru	Paid
1995 - 1998	**$42**	**$55**	$_____

Starbucks Coffee®

54859

Dates	OSRP	GBTru	Paid
1995 - 2000	**$48**	**$90**	$_____

• Do not handle by roof pediment.
• Licensed by Starbucks Coffee®.

Nick's Tree Farm

54871

Dates	OSRP	GBTru	Paid
1996ᴹ - 1999	**$40**	**$45**	$_____

• Set of 10 includes Nick, hut, and 8 sisal trees.
• The coat, hat, and lantern hanging on the hut often come unglued.

Smokey Mountain Retreat

54872

Dates	OSRP	GBTru	Paid
1996ᴹ - 2000	**$65**	**$70**	$_____

• Chimney "smokes" when used with Village Magic Smoke®. Smoking element sometimes leaks, requiring something being placed under it for protection.
• Do not handle by railings or columns.

Boulder Springs House

54873

Dates	OSRP	GBTru	Paid
1996^M - 1997	$60	$55	$_____

• Do not handle by columns or railing.

Reindeer Bus Depot

54874

Dates	OSRP	GBTru	Paid
1996^M - 1997	$42	$55	$_____

• Do not handle by columns, sign, or bench.

Rockabilly Records

54880

Dates	OSRP	GBTru	Paid
1996 - 1998	$45	$55	$_____

Christmas Lake High School

54881

Dates	OSRP	GBTru	Paid
1996 - 1999	$52	$60	$_____

• Attached basketball hoop is easily damaged.

Birch Run Ski Chalet

54882

Dates	OSRP	GBTru	Paid
1996 - 1999	$60	$75	$_____

• Do not handle by columns or railings.

Rosita's Cantina

54883

Dates	OSRP	GBTru	Paid
1996 - 1999	$50	$65	$_____

• Lighting fixtures are easily damaged when removing piece from box.

Shingle Victorian

54884

Dates	OSRP	GBTru	Paid
1996 - 1999	$55	$60	$_____

• American Architecture Series.
• Do not handle by columns or railings.

The Secret Garden Florist

54885

Dates	OSRP	GBTru	Paid
1996 - 2001	$50	$45	$_____

• The awning is cloth.
• Sign is separate in box.
• A similar design was produced for Bachman's in 1997. See the Special Design section.

Harley-Davidson® Motorcycle Shop

54886

Dates	OSRP	GBTru	Paid
1996 - 2002	$65	$75	$_____

• The gray paint on the front overhang's supports often peels. They are also very fragile.
• Licensed by Harley-Davidson®.

Mainstreet Gift Shop

54887

Dates	OSRP	GBTru	Paid
1997ᴹ - 1997	$50	$50	$_____

• To commemorate the 20th Anniversary of GCC, this design was available only through GCC member stores.
• Two signs are included—one with the GCC logo, and a blank one so dealers could personalize the design.

Snow Village Start A Tradition Set

54902

Dates	OSRP	GBTru	Paid
1997ᴹ - 1998	$100	$85	$_____

• It was first available for $75 during the 1997 Homes for the Holidays event.
• Set of 8 includes **Kringles Toy Shop**, **Nikki's Cocoa Shop**, "Saturday Morning Downtown" accessory, trees, snow, and road.
• Nikki's Cocoa Shop's hangtag reads "Kringle's Cocoa Shop."
• The handle on the mug is fragile.

Old Chelsea Mansion 54903

Dates	OSRP	GBTru	Paid
1997ᴹ - 1998	$85	$85	$_____

• Inspired by the New York, NY home of Clement C. Moore, author of "A Visit from St. Nicholas." Includes a book containing the classic poem and information about Moore and the mansion.

New Hope Church 54904

Dates	OSRP	GBTru	Paid
1997ᴹ - 1998	$60	$65	$_____

Ronald McDonald® House, The House That ♥ Built 08960

Dates	OSRP	GBTru	Paid
1997ᴹ - 1997	Promo	$265	$_____

• A limited edition design, this was made available as a fund raiser during the November 1997 Homes for the Holidays event. Proceeds benefited Ronald McDonald® House Charities.

Christmas Barn Dance 54910

Dates	OSRP	GBTru	Paid
1997 - 1999	$65	$70	$_____

Italianate Villa 54911

Dates	OSRP	GBTru	Paid
1997 - 2001	$55	$60	$_____

• American Architecture Series.
• Spire is separate in box.
• Do not handle by columns.

Farm House 54912

Dates	OSRP	GBTru	Paid
1997 - 2000	$50	$60	$_____

• Do not handle by columns.

Hershey's® Chocolate Shop
54913

Dates	OSRP	GBTru	Paid
1997 - 2000	$55	$70	$_____

• The billboard on the roof is very fragile.
• Licensed by Hershey Foods.

McDonald's®
54914

Dates	OSRP	GBTru	Paid
1997 - 1999	$65	$110	$_____

• First time people were included as an attachment.
• Because of the attachments and the arches, extra care should be taken when handling this piece.
• Licensed by McDonald's®.

Gracie's Dry Goods & General Store
54915

Dates	OSRP	GBTru	Paid
1997 - 2000	$70	$75	$_____

• Do not handle by columns.
• Set of 2 includes Store and gas pumps.
• Licensed by Rapala.

Rollerama Roller Rink
54916

Dates	OSRP	GBTru	Paid
1997 - 1999	$56	$60	$_____

• The lights on the building are functional.
• Do not handle by the front entryway.

Linden Hills Country Club
54917

Dates	OSRP	GBTru	Paid
1997 - 2001	$60	$65	$_____

• Metal lanterns light from within.
• Linden Hills is an area near downtown Minneapolis, close to Lake Harriet.
• Set of 2 includes building and sign.

The Brandon Bungalow
54918

Dates	OSRP	GBTru	Paid
1997 - 1999	$55	$65	$_____

• Brandon is a small resort town in northern Minnesota.

Rock Creek Mill House

54932

Dates	OSRP	GBTru	Paid
1998ᴹ - 1998	$64	$80	$_____

- Early samples have a glossy finish. Production pieces have a matte finish.
- The water wheel comes loose on occasion.

Glossy edition GBTru = $85 $_____

Carnival Carousel

54933

Dates	OSRP	GBTru	Paid
1998ᴹ - 2001	$150	$160	$_____

- Images on screen created by carousel inside building.
- Plays 30 songs.
- Includes AC adapter. Optional lights enhance appearance.

Snowy Pines Inn Exclusive Gift Set

54934

Dates	OSRP	GBTru	Paid
1998ᴹ - 1998	$65	$90	$_____

- Available during the 1998 Homes for the Holiday event.
- Set of 9 includes building, a 2 piece accessory "Decorate The Tree," trees, road, and snow.

Ronald McDonald® House, The House That ♥ Built

02210

Dates	OSRP	GBTru	Paid
1998ᴹ - 1998	Promo	$260	$_____

- Limited to only 5,600 pieces, this was made available as a fund raiser during the November 1998 Homes for the Holidays event. Proceeds benefited Ronald McDonald® House Charities.

Center For The Arts

54940

Dates	OSRP	GBTru	Paid
1998 - 2000	$64	$65	$_____

- Sign for Art Center is separate in box.

Uptown Motors Ford® 54941

Dates	OSRP	GBTru	Paid
1998 - 2002	$95	$110	$____

- Working turntable inside building displays red Mustang.
- Set of 3 incudes building, car, and sign.
- Pennants and hanging sign packaged separately in box.
- Licensed by Ford Motor Co.

Fire Station #3 54942

Dates	OSRP	GBTru	Paid
1998 - 2003	$70	$70	$____

- Turret peak is susceptible to damage when removing the piece from its box.

Stick Style House 54943

Dates	OSRP	GBTru	Paid
1998 - 2000	$60	$60	$____

- American Architecture Series.
- Do not handle by columns.

Hidden Ponds House 54944

Dates	OSRP	GBTru	Paid
1998 - 2001	$50	$50	$____

...Another Man's Treasure Garage 54945

Dates	OSRP	GBTru	Paid
1998 - 2001	$60	$60	$____

- Set of 22 includes building, items to be sold, and a string of pennants.

The Farmer's Co-Op Granary

54946

Dates	OSRP	GBTru	Paid
1998 - 2000	$64	$75	$_____

• Lamp is separate in box.

Lionel® Electric Train Shop

54947

Dates	OSRP	GBTru	Paid
1998 - 2000	$55	$65	$_____

• A similar design was produced for Allied Model Trains. See the Special Design section.
• Licensed by Lionel®.

Harley-Davidson® Manufacturing

54948

Dates	OSRP	GBTru	Paid
1998 - 2000	$80	$115	$_____

• The address reflects that of Harley-Davidson's Milwaukee, WI headquarters.
• Set of three includes building and two motorcycles.
• Licensed by Harley-Davidson®.

The Secret Garden Greenhouse

54949

Dates	OSRP	GBTru	Paid
1998 - 2001	$60	$60	$_____

• In addition to bulb and cord arrangement, interior lights along ceiling also light.
• A similar design was produced for Bachman's. See the Special Design section.

2000 Holly Lane

54977

Dates	OSRP	GBTru	Paid
1999ᴹ - 1999	$65	$110	$_____

• Limited to year of production.
• This is the first Snow Village design to include a three-dimensional scene in the house.
• First available during the November 1999 Discover Department 56 event.
• Set of 11 includes house, gate, hedges, and snowman.

Cinema 56

54978

Dates	OSRP	GBTru	Paid
1999ᴹ - 2001	$85	$100	$_____

- Marquee is interchangeable with optional accessory marquees.
- The lights around the marquee are functional.
- Do not handle by marquee.

A Home In The Making

54979

Dates	OSRP	GBTru	Paid
1999ᴹ - 2001	$95	$85	$_____

- A portion of the proceeds benefited Habitat for Humanity.
- Midyear introduction to select stores.
- Set of 5 includes the house, man climbing ladder, two men cutting board, two women carrying lumber, and sign.

Champsfield Stadium

55001

Dates	OSRP	GBTru	Paid
1999 - 2001	$195	$170	$_____

- Set of 24 includes two seating sections; two teams; two referees; fans; field; two goal posts; two billboards; U.S., Canadian, NFC, and AFC flags; and stickers and lettering for collector customization.
- Players' arms and waists move.
- Licensed by NFLP.

Village Bank & Trust

55002

Dates	OSRP	GBTru	Paid
1999 - 2001	$75	$75	$_____

- Lanterns on either side of the main entrance are functional.

Holy Spirit Church

55003

Dates	OSRP	GBTru	Paid
1999 - 2002	$70	$65	$_____

- Cross and plaque that can be personalized are separate in box.
- Do not handle by columns.
- Set of 2 includes church and sign.

Super Suds Laundromat

55006

Dates	OSRP	GBTru	Paid
1999 - 2001	$60	$55	$_____

Shelly's Diner

55008

Dates	OSRP	GBTru	Paid
1999 -	$110	-	$_____

- Set of 2 includes Diner and lighted sign.

Cedar Point Cabin

55009

Dates	OSRP	GBTru	Paid
1999 - 2002	$66	$70	$_____

- A bird house is separate in box.

WSNO Radio

55010

Dates	OSRP	GBTru	Paid
1999 - 2002	$75	$70	$_____

- The light at the top of the antenna is functional.
- Lamp is separate in box.
- Customized version WCCO used as a promotional item at Twin Cities radio station.

Lucky Dragon Restaurant

55011

Dates	OSRP	GBTru	Paid
1999 - 2000	$75	$75	$_____

- Early sample reads "The Golden Dragon Restaurant."
- 8 lanterns are separate in box.
- The hanging lanterns are fragile.

Last Stop Gas Station
55012

Dates	OSRP	GBTru	Paid
1999 - 2001	**$72**	**$70**	$_____

• Set of 2 includes building and pumps.

Carpenter Gothic Bed & Breakfast
55043

Dates	OSRP	GBTru	Paid
2000ᴹ - 2003	**$75**	**$80**	$_____

• American Architecture Series.
• Do not handle by columns or railings.
• Set of 2 includes building and sign.

Silver Bells Christmas Shop Gift Set
55040

Dates	OSRP	GBTru	Paid
2000ᴹ - 2000	**$75**	**$80**	$_____

• Sold during the 2000 Discover Department 56 event.
• Limited to year of production.
• Silver bells commemorate Dept. 56's 25th anniversary.
• The lamppost at the tree lot is functional.
• Set of 4 includes Shop, "Oh, Christmas Tree" accessory, tree, and snow.

Elvis Presley's Graceland Gift Set
55041

Dates	OSRP	GBTru	Paid
2000ᴹ - 2001	**$165**	**$170**	$_____

• Sold during the 2000 Discover Department 56 event.
• Retired on January 8, 2001, Elvis' 66th birthday.
• Set of 6 includes Graceland, 1955 Pink Cadillac Fleetwood, wrought iron gate, original lawn decorations, and 2 sets of mylar twinkling trees.
• Licensed by EPE and GM.

Village Town Hall 55044

Dates	OSRP	GBTru	Paid
2000 - 2003	$96	$95	$_____

- 6 "add-on" garland pieces and sign allow holiday decor to be added to this non-snow building.
- U. S. and Canadian flags are separate in box.
- Spires and lampposts are fragile.

Candlerock Lighthouse Restaurant 55045

Dates	OSRP	GBTru	Paid
2000 - 2001	$110	$110	$_____

- 25th Anniversary Limited Edition of 30,000.
- The top of the light tower is separate and can easily fall and be damaged.
- Flag and 3 lanterns are separate in box.

Palm Lounge Supper Club 55046

Dates	OSRP	GBTru	Paid
2000 - 2001	$95	$90	$_____

- Set of 2 includes building and walkway.
- Posts on the walkway are fragile.

Frost And Sons 5 & Dime 55047

Dates	OSRP	GBTru	Paid
2000 - 2002	$68	$65	$_____

- Do not handle by sign.
- Licensed by SWIMC, Inc. and Eveready Battery Co., Inc.

The Holiday House 55048

Dates	OSRP	GBTru	Paid
2000 -	$90	-	$_____

- Santa and 4 reindeer are separate in box.

Buck's County™ Horse Barn 55049

Dates	OSRP	GBTru	Paid
2000 - 2002	$72	$75	$_____

- Weathervane and lantern are separate in box.

Buck's County™ Farmhouse

55051

Dates	OSRP	GBTru	Paid
2000 - 2002	**$75**	**$75**	$_____

• Weathervane is separate in box.
• Tree limbs are very fragile and are easily broken when removing or putting the piece in its box.

Abner's Implement Co.

55052

Dates	OSRP	GBTru	Paid
2000 - 2003	**$85**	**$85**	$_____

• Buck's County Series.
• Set of 2 includes building and gas pump.
• Flag and lantern are separate in box.
• Licensed by Deere & Co.

Totem Town Souvenir Shop

55053

Dates	OSRP	GBTru	Paid
2000 - 2002	**$68**	**$65**	$_____

• Sign and lantern are separate in box.

Timberlake Outfitters

55054

Dates	OSRP	GBTru	Paid
2000 - 2002	**$75**	**$70**	$_____

• Block and tackle is separate in box.
• Oars are extremely fragile.
• Licensed by Bob Timberlake, Inc.

Crosby House

55056

Dates	OSRP	GBTru	Paid
2000 - 2002	**$50**	**$50**	$_____

Lowell Inn

55059

Dates	OSRP	GBTru	Paid
2001ᴹ - 2001	**$85**	**$145**	$_____

• Depicts the Stillwater, MN inn where the concept of the villages was conceived.
• Only available at Dept. 56's silver anniversary event.
• 16 flags (13 colonies, MN, US, D56) are separate in box.

Christmas Lake Chalet

55061

Dates	OSRP	GBTru	Paid
2001ᴹ - 2001	$75	$85	$_____

- First available during the 2001 Holiday Discover Department 56 event.
- Fireplace flickers, and lanterns on porch light.
- Set of 5 includes Chalet, "The Final Touch" accessory, 2 sisal trees, and a bag of snow.

Tudor House

55062

Dates	OSRP	GBTru	Paid
2001ᴹ - 2002	$60	$65	$_____

- American Architecture Series.
- Another design with the same name was issued in this village in 1979.

Stardust Drive-In Theater

55064

Dates	OSRP	GBTru	Paid
2001ᴹ - 2003	$68	$65	$_____

- Animated screen with 12 different images.

Stardust Refreshment Stand

55065

Dates	OSRP	GBTru	Paid
2001ᴹ - 2003	$50	$55	$_____

- Set of 7 includes Refreshment Stand and 6 speakers.

Juliette's School Of French Cuisine

55063

Dates	OSRP	GBTru	Paid
2001 - 2002	$65	$65	$_____

- Mother's Day Spring promotion.
- Set of 4 includes School, sign, 2 potted shrubs, and extra sign which can be personalized.
- 5% of proceeds goes to fight against breast cancer.

McGuire's Irish Pub

55066

Dates	OSRP	GBTru	Paid
2001 -	$50	-	$____

• Designed to celebrate St. Partick's Day.
• Front banner is removable.
• Two lanterns are separate in the box.

Gus's Drive-In

55067

Dates	OSRP	GBTru	Paid
2001 - 2003	$95	$105	$____

• Set of 7 includes Drive-In, "Car Hop" accessory, 2 trays, 2 menus, and a sandwich board.

Woodlake Chapel Starter Set

55068

Dates	OSRP	GBTru	Paid
2001 - 2003	$65	$70	$____

• Set of 2 includes Chapel and 2 piece accessory "On Our Wedding Day."
• Cross and brass plaque which can be engraved are separate in the box.
• Cross attached to roof is very fragile.

Cedar Ridge School

55070

Dates	OSRP	GBTru	Paid
2001 -	$60	-	$____

• Flag, lantern, and brass plaque which can be engraved are separate in the box.

Krispy Kreme Doughnut Shop

55071

Dates	OSRP	GBTru	Paid
2001 -	$85	-	$_____

• Set of 2 includes Shop and sign.
• Licensed by HDN Development Corporation.

Country Quilts And Pies

55072

Dates	OSRP	GBTru	Paid
2001 -	$65	-	$_____

• Buck's County Series.
• Set of 2 includes building and "Handmade Quilts For Sale" accessory.

Polaris Snowmobile Dealership

55078

Dates	OSRP	GBTru	Paid
2001 - 2003	$85	$75	$_____

• Sign is separate in the box.
• Licensed by Polaris Industries, Inc.

Village Legion Hall

55080

Dates	OSRP	GBTru	Paid
2001 - 2003	$55	$55	$_____

• Set of 2 includes Hall and 2-piece accessory "Cannon And Flag."
• Second flag (with short staff) and lamppost are separate in the box.

Armed Forces Recruiting Station

55081

Dates	OSRP	GBTru	Paid
2001 - 2002	**$55**	**$55**	$_____

• Two signs and 2 flags are separate in the box.

Happy Easter House

55090

Dates	OSRP	GBTru	Paid
2001 -	**$50**	-	$_____

• Easter Series.
• "Happy Easter" sign is removable.
• Set of 3 includes house, 2-piece accessory "Egg Hunt."

Moonlight Bay Bunk And Breakfast

55074

Dates	OSRP	GBTru	Paid
2002ᴹ -	**$75**	-	$_____

• Set of 2 includes building and sign.

1224 Kissing Claus Lane

55091

Dates	OSRP	GBTru	Paid
2002ᴹ - 2002	**$75**	**$85**	$_____

• Holiday 2002 Special Edition.
• Animated and musical. Plays "I Saw Mommy Kissing Santa Claus."
• Set of 4 includes house, "Christmas Eve Delivery" accessory, a frosted topiary, and a bag of snow.
• Spires on roof are fragile.

Lily's Nursery & Gifts

55095

Dates	OSRP	GBTru	Paid
2002ᴹ -	$65	-	$_____

- Easter Series.
- Set of 3 includes building and 2 piece accessory, "Gifts For Easter."

Hearts & Blooms Cottage

55097

Dates	OSRP	GBTru	Paid
2002ᴹ -	$50	-	$_____

- Intended to be used as a Valentine's Day design.
- Set of 2 includes Cottage and "Young Love" accessory.

The Cocoa Stop

55096

Dates	OSRP	GBTru	Paid
2002ᴹ - 2002	$65	$120	$_____

- Club 56 dealer exclusive. Limited to 5,600 pieces.
- Many boxes and sleeves have a rippled effect.
- Certificate of authenticity and hot cocoa recipe are included in the box.

Red Owl Grocery Store

55303

Dates	OSRP	GBTru	Paid
2002 - 2003	$70	$70	$_____

- Named after a Midwest grocery store.
- Licensed by Supervalu, Inc.

The Sweet Shop (Regular Issue)   55300

Dates	OSRP	GBTru	Paid
2002 -	$65	-	$_____

• The Shop's hanging sign is extremely fragile.

(Early Release)   05923

Dates	OSRP	GBTru	Paid
2002ᴹ - 2002	$75	$130	$_____

• This was an early release to department stores.
• Set of 5 includes the Shop, 2-piece lit accessory "Sampling The Treats" (pictured at left), frosted topiary with candy canes, and snow.

Harmony House   55302

Dates	OSRP	GBTru	Paid
2002 -	$50	-	$_____

• Set of 3 includes the House, and 2 piece accessory, "Snowman Sonata And Fence."
• Can be personalized.

Rocky's 56 Filling Station   55305

Dates	OSRP	GBTru	Paid
2002 -	$80	-	$_____

• Set of 3 includes the Station and 2 piece accessory, "56 Gasoline Pump And Sign."

Bungalow

55304

Dates	OSRP	GBTru	Paid
2002 -	$55	-	$_____

• American Architecture Series.

Main Street Medical

55306

Dates	OSRP	GBTru	Paid
2002 -	$68	-	$_____

• Can be personalized.

Jonathan The Bear Man's Carving Studio

55307

Dates	OSRP	GBTru	Paid
2002 - 2003	$75	$65	$_____

• Limited to year of production.
• Named for an artist in Wyoming.

Dairy Land Creamery

55308

Dates	OSRP	GBTru	Paid
2002 -	$75	-	$_____

Campbell's® Soup Counter

55309

Dates	OSRP	GBTru	Paid
2002 -	$60	-	$_____

• Licensed by The Campbell Soup Co®.

The Frozen Swirl

55318

Dates	OSRP	GBTru	Paid
2002 -	$65	-	$_____

Wright Bike Shop
55314

Dates	OSRP	GBTru	Paid
2002 - 2003	**$65**	**$65**	$_____

- Spring Gift Set.
- Set of 5 includes the Shop, "Let's Get A New Bike" accessory, 2 shrubs, and a summer tree.
- Can be personalized.
- Named for the Wright brothers.

Home For The Holidays Express
55320

Dates	OSRP	GBTru	Paid
2003ᴹ - 2003	**$110**	**$95**	$_____

- Holiday 2003 Special Edition.
- Musical. Plays "Home For The Holidays" and train sounds.
- Set of 11 includes train, station, "Welcoming Christmas To Town" accessory, vinyl track, birch tree, and a bag of snow.
- A special edition Home For The Holidays Caboose was issued in 2004 as a complementary piece.

Year Round Holiday House
55321

Dates	OSRP	GBTru	Paid
2003ᴹ -	**$75**	-	$_____

- Christmas Lane Series.
- Includes attachable decorations for five holidays.

American Hero Comics
55322

Dates	OSRP	GBTru	Paid
2003ᴹ - 2003	**$65**	**$100**	$_____

- Club 56 dealer exclusive. Limited to 5,600 pieces.

Sweetheart Candy Shop

55323

Dates	OSRP	GBTru	Paid
2003ᴹ -	$50	-	$_____

• Intended to be used as a Valentine's Day design.
• Candy decorations light up and flash.

Hard Rock Café Snow Village

55324

Dates	OSRP	GBTru	Paid
2003ᴹ -	$85	-	$_____

• Includes pin.
• Licensed by Hard Rock Cafe International (USA), Inc.

Happy Easter Church

55325

Dates	OSRP	GBTru	Paid
2003ᴹ -	$65	-	$_____

• Easter Series.
• Set of 3 includes Church, "Joyful Greetings" accessory, and 2 removable banners.

High Roller Riverboat Casino

55330

Dates	OSRP	GBTru	Paid
2003ᴹ -	$110	-	$_____

• Special lighting effect on paddle wheel.

Village Train Station

55331

Dates	OSRP	GBTru	Paid
2003 -	$85	-	$_____

Mission Style House

55332

Dates	OSRP	GBTru	Paid
2003 -	$75	-	$_____

• American Architecture Series.

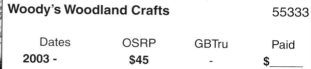

Woody's Woodland Crafts

55333

Dates	OSRP	GBTru	Paid
2003 -	$45	-	$_____

• Set of 2 includes building and "Wood Carvings For Sale" accessory.

Midtown Shops

55334

Dates	OSRP	GBTru	Paid
2003 -	$70	-	$_____

Lot 56, Christmas Court

55335

Dates	OSRP	GBTru	Paid
2003 -	$65	-	$_____

KBRR TV

55337

Dates	OSRP	GBTru	Paid
2003 -	$80	-	$_____

• Can be personalized.
• Includes adapter.

Roosevelt Park Band Shell
55338

Dates	OSRP	GBTru	Paid
2003 -	$65	-	$_____

- Set of 2 includes Band Shell and "Village Musicians" accessory.
- Adapter included.
- Christmas and Fourth Of July decorations are separate in box.

Vineland Estates Winery
55339

Dates	OSRP	GBTru	Paid
2003 -	$70	-	$_____

- Numbered limited edition of 20,000.
- Can be personalized.

Friendly Used Car Sales
55340

Dates	OSRP	GBTru	Paid
2003 -	$60	-	$_____

Pillsbury Doughboy™ Bake Shop
55342

Dates	OSRP	GBTru	Paid
2003 -	$75	-	$_____

- Set of 2 includes Bake Shop and "Pillsbury Doughboy™" accessory.
- Licensed by The Pillsbury Company.

The Noel House

55341

Dates	OSRP	GBTru	Paid
2003 -	**$85**	-	$_____

• Christmas Lane Series.
• Includes an adapter.

Home For The Holidays Caboose

Dates	OSRP	GBTru	Paid
2004 - 2004	**n/a**	-	$_____

• Limited to 1,000 pieces, it was distributed to collectors whose 2003 Homes For The Holidays Gift Set boxes contained special Department 56 holograms.

Use the space(s) below to update your guide when the midyear introductions are announced.

Photos of the midyear introductions will be included in the July-August issue of *the Village Chronicle* magazine.

Dates	OSRP	GBTru	Paid
_____ - _____	$_____	-	$_____

Dates	OSRP	GBTru	Paid
_____ - _____	$_____	-	$_____

Dates	OSRP	GBTru	Paid
_____ - _____	$_____	-	$_____

	Dates	OSRP	GBTru	Paid
	_____ - _____	$_____	-	$_____

	Dates	OSRP	GBTru	Paid
	_____ - _____	$_____	-	$_____

	Dates	OSRP	GBTru	Paid
	_____ - _____	$_____	-	$_____

	Dates	OSRP	GBTru	Paid
	_____ - _____	$_____	-	$_____

	Dates	OSRP	GBTru	Paid
	_____ - _____	$_____	-	$_____

	Dates	OSRP	GBTru	Paid
	_____ - _____	$_____	-	$_____

Carolers

50641 - Set of 4

1979 - 1986

OSRP: $12

GBTru: $110

Paid: $_____

Ceramic Car

50690

1980 - 1986

OSRP: $5

GBTru: $40

Paid: $_____

Ceramic Sleigh

50792

1981 - 1986

OSRP: $5

GBTru: $40

Paid: $_____

Snowman With Broom

50180

1982 - 1990

OSRP: $3

GBTru: $8

Paid: $_____

• This is the first mixed media accessory. It's made of ceramic and straw.

Monks-A-Caroling

64599

1983 - 1984

OSRP: $6

GBTru: $40

Paid: $_____

• Blush on cheeks is lighter and diffused.
• 1982 giftware line had unglazed set (64602) w/paper books and cord sashes. **GBTru: $175**

Monks-A-Caroling

50407

1984 - 1988

OSRP: $6

GBTru: $40

Paid: $_____

• 1st: Bright red speckled rash on cheeks. 2nd: Blush on cheeks is a defined dot. Taller.

Scottie With Tree

50385

1984 - 1985

OSRP: $3

GBTru: $175

Paid: $_____

• Is also available with a white star on top of the tree.

Singing Nuns

50539

1985 - 1987

OSRP: $6

GBTru: $115

Paid: $_____

Auto With Tree

(Squashed Version)

50555

1985 - 2001

OSRP: $5

GBTru: $8

Paid: $_____

• The first pieces are less round and less detailed. See picture to the right.

GBTru: $110

Paid: $_____

Snow Kids Sled, Skis

50563 - Set of 2

1985 - 1987

OSRP: $11

GBTru: $40

Paid: $_____

• In 1987, this set was reduced in size and combined with Girl/ Snowman, Boy to form Snow Kids.

Family Mom/Kids, Goose/Girl

50571 - Set of 2

1985 - 1988

OSRP: $11

GBTru: $30

Paid: $_____

• The first year's pieces were larger and less detailed than those produced in the later years.

Santa/Mailbox

50598 - Set of 2

1985 - 1988

OSRP: $11

GBTru: $45

Paid: $_____

• The first year's pieces were larger and less detailed than those produced in the later years.

Kids Around The Tree

50946

1986 - 1990

OSRP: $15

GBTru: $35

Paid: $_____

• The first year's pieces were larger and less detailed than those produced in the later years.

Girl/Snowman, Boy

50954 - Set of 2

1986 - 1987

OSRP: $11

GBTru: $35

Paid: $_____

• In 1987, this set was reduced in size and combined with Snow Kids Sled, Skis to form Snow Kids.

Shopping Girls With Packages

50962 - Set of 2

1986 - 1988

OSRP: $11

GBTru: $30

Paid: $_____

• The first year's pieces were larger and less detailed than those produced in the later years.

3 Nuns With Songbooks

51020
1987 - 1988
OSRP: $6
GBTru: $120
Paid: $_____

Praying Monks

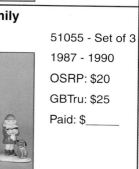

51039
1987 - 1988
OSRP: $6
GBTru: $35
Paid: $_____

Children In Band

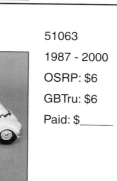

51047
1987 - 1989
OSRP: $15
GBTru: $20
Paid: $_____

Caroling Family

51055 - Set of 3
1987 - 1990
OSRP: $20
GBTru: $25
Paid: $_____

Taxi Cab

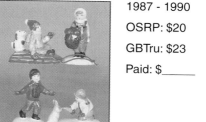

51063
1987 - 2000
OSRP: $6
GBTru: $6
Paid: $_____

Christmas Children

51071 - Set of 4
1987 - 1990
OSRP: $20
GBTru: $23
Paid: $_____

House For Sale Sign

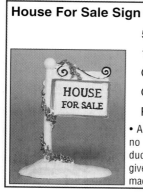

51080
1987 - 1989
OSRP: $3.50
GBTru: $5
Paid: $_____

• A similar design with no writing was produced for GCC and given to collectors who made $100 purchases.

Snow Kids

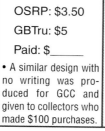

51136 - Set of 4
1987 - 1990
OSRP: $20
GBTru: $30
Paid: $_____

• This set combines smaller versions of Snow Kids Sled, Skis (1985) and Girl/ Snowman, Boy (1986).

Snow Village House For Sale Sign

Promo

1987 - 1987

OSRP: Promo

GBTru: $25

Paid: $_____

• This was free to dealers who placed their orders at Department 56 showrooms. It is a very rare accessory.

Man On Ladder Hanging Garland

51160

1988 - 1992

OSRP: $7.50

GBTru: $10

Paid: $_____

• Includes mixed media —ceramic man, wooden ladder, and sisal garland.

Hayride

51179

1988 - 1990

OSRP: $30

GBTru: $45

Paid: $_____

School Children

51187 - Set of 3

1988 - 1990

OSRP: $15

GBTru: $28

Paid: $_____

Apple Girl/Newspaper Boy

51292 - Set of 2

1988 - 1990

OSRP: $11

GBTru: $20

Paid: $_____

Woodsman And Boy

51306 - Set of 2

1988 - 1991

OSRP: $13

GBTru: $25

Paid: $_____

Doghouse/Cat In Garbage Can

51314 - Set of 2

1988 - 1992

OSRP: $15

GBTru: $25

Paid: $_____

• Box reads "Cat And Dog."

Fire Hydrant & Mailbox

51322 - Set of 2

1988 - 1998

OSRP: $6

GBTru: $10

Paid: $_____

Water Tower

51330

1988 - 1991

OSRP: $20

GBTru: $65

Paid: $_____

• Similar designs were produced for retailers. See the Special Design section.

Nativity

51357

1988 - 2000

OSRP: $7.50

GBTru: $8

Paid: $_____

Woody Station Wagon

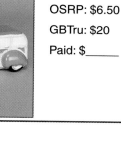

51365

1988 - 1990

OSRP: $6.50

GBTru: $20

Paid: $_____

School Bus, Snow Plow

51373 - Set of 2

1988 - 1991

OSRP: $16

GBTru: $50

Paid: $_____

Tree Lot

51381

1988 - 1999

OSRP: $33.50

GBTru: $32

Paid: $_____

• Includes mixed media —small ceramic shed, wooden fence, and 7 sisal trees.

Sisal Tree Lot

81833

1988 - 1991

OSRP: $45

GBTru: $65

Paid: $_____

Village Gazebo

51462

1989 - 1995

OSRP: $27

GBTru: $25

Paid: $_____

Choir Kids

51470

1989 - 1992

OSRP: $15

GBTru: $25

Paid: $_____

Special Delivery

51489 - Set of 2

1989 - 1990

OSRP: $16

GBTru: $48

Paid: $_____

• Retired after one year due to unauthorized use of red, white, and blue colors of U.S. Postal Service.

For Sale Sign

51667

1989 - 1998

OSRP: $4.50

GBTru: $5

Paid: $_____

• Similar designs were produced for retailers. See the Special Design section.

Street Sign

51675 - Set of 6

1989 - 1992

OSRP: $7.50

GBTru: $8

Paid: $_____

• Includes stickers (with street names and blank ones) for signs.
• Metal.

Kids Tree House

51683

1989 - 1991

OSRP: $25

GBTru: $28

Paid: $_____

• This was the first all resin accessory.

Bringing Home The Tree

51691

1989 - 1992

OSRP: $15

GBTru: $24

Paid: $_____

• Includes mixed media —ceramic sleigh and people with sisal tree.

Skate Faster Mom

51705

1989 - 1991

OSRP: $13

GBTru: $21

Paid: $_____

Crack The Whip

51713 - Set of 3

1989 - 1996

OSRP: $25

GBTru: $25

Paid: $_____

Through The Woods

51721 - Set of 2

1989 - 1991

OSRP: $18

GBTru: $24

Paid: $_____

Statue Of Mark Twain

51730

1989 - 1991

OSRP: $15

GBTru: $27

Paid: $_____

Calling All Cars

51748 - Set of 2

1989 - 1991

OSRP: $15

GBTru: $55

Paid: $_____

Village Stop Sign

51764 - Set of 2

1989 - 1998

OSRP: $5

GBTru: $5

Paid: $_____

• Metal.

Flag Pole

51772

1989 - 1999

OSRP: $8.50

GBTru: $10

Paid: $_____

• Metal, ceramic, and cloth.

Village Parking Meter

51780 - Set of 4

1989 - 1999

OSRP: $6

GBTru: $9

Paid: $_____

• Metal.

Mailbox

51799

1989 - 1990

OSRP: $3.50

GBTru: $15

Paid: $_____

• Retired after one year due to unauthorized use of red and blue colors of U.S.P.S.

Snow Village Promotional Sign

99481

1989 - 1990

OSRP: Promo

GBTru: $17

Paid: $_____

• Used as a promotional piece by Dept. 56 retailers.

Kids Decorating The Village Sign

51349

1990 - 1993

OSRP: $12.50

GBTru: $20

Paid: $_____

Down The Chimney He Goes

51586

1990 - 1993

OSRP: $6.50

GBTru: $7

Paid: $_____

• Adhesive strip allows this piece to be mounted on a building's roof.

Sno-Jet Snowmobile

51594

1990 - 1993

OSRP: $15

GBTru: $22

Paid: $_____

Sleighride

51608

1990 - 1992

OSRP: $30

GBTru: $45

Paid: $_____

Here We Come A Caroling

51616 - Set of 3

1990 - 1992

OSRP: $18

GBTru: $22

Paid: $_____

Home Delivery

51624 - Set of 2

1990 - 1992

OSRP: $16

GBTru: $32

Paid: $_____

Fresh Frozen Fish

51632 - Set of 2

1990 - 1993

OSRP: $20

GBTru: $32

Paid: $_____

A Tree For Me

51640 - Set of 2

1990 - 1995

OSRP: $7.50

GBTru: $10

Paid: $_____

• Ceramic with sisal trees.

A Home For The Holidays

51659

1990 - 1996

OSRP: $6.50

GBTru: $9

Paid: $_____

Special Delivery

51977 - Set of 2

1990 - 1992

OSRP: $16

GBTru: $25

Paid: $_____

• Re-issue of first Special Delivery (1989) after changing the color of the truck to red, white, and green.

Village Mail Box

51985

1990 - 1998

OSRP: $3.50

GBTru: $6

Paid: $_____

• Re-issue of Mailbox (1989) after changing the colors to red and green and putting "S.V. Mail" on front.

Christmas Trash Cans

52094 - Set of 2

1990 - 1998

OSRP: $7

GBTru: $10

Paid: $_____

• Metal, paper, and plastic.

Wreaths For Sale

54089 - Set of 4

1991 - 1994

OSRP: $27.50

GBTru: $30

Paid: $_____

• Ceramic with sisal wreaths.

Winter Fountain

54097

1991 - 1993

OSRP: $25

GBTru: $45

Paid: $_____

• Includes mixed media —ceramic and acrylic.

Cold Weather Sports

54100 - Set of 4

1991 - 1994

OSRP: $27.50

GBTru: $35

Paid: $_____

Come Join The Parade

54119

1991 - 1992

OSRP: $12.50

GBTru: $15

Paid: $_____

Village Marching Band

54127 - Set of 3

1991 - 1992

OSRP: $30

GBTru: $45

Paid: $_____

Christmas Cadillac

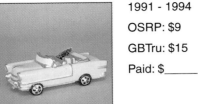

54135
1991 - 1994
OSRP: $9
GBTru: $15
Paid: $_____

Snowball Fort

54143 - Set of 3
1991 - 1993
OSRP: $27.50
GBTru: $34
Paid: $_____

Country Harvest

54151
1991 - 1993
OSRP: $13
GBTru: $18
Paid: $_____

Village Used Car Lot

54283 - Set of 5
1992 - 1997
OSRP: $45
GBTru: $45
Paid: $_____

Village Phone Booth

54291
1992 -
OSRP: $7.50
GBTru: -
Paid: $_____

Nanny And The Preschoolers

54305 - Set of 2
1992 - 1994
OSRP: $27.50
GBTru: $30
Paid: $_____

Early Morning Delivery

54313 - Set of 3
1992 - 1995
OSRP: $27.50
GBTru: $30
Paid: $_____

Christmas Puppies

54321 - Set of 2
1992 - 1996
OSRP: $27.50
GBTru: $33
Paid: $_____

Round & Round We Go!

54330 - Set of 2

1992 - 1995

OSRP: $18

GBTru: $20

Paid: $_____

A Heavy Snowfall

54348 - Set of 2

1992 - 2001

OSRP: $16

GBTru: $20

Paid: $_____

We're Going To A Christmas Pageant

54356

1992 - 1994

OSRP: $15

GBTru: $18

Paid: $_____

Winter Playground

54364

1992 - 1995

OSRP: $20

GBTru: $35

Paid: $_____

Spirit Of Snow Village Airplane

54402

1992 - 1996

OSRP: $32.50

GBTru: $40

Paid: $_____

• This is very difficult to put back in box. See 1993 for item by the same name.

Safety Patrol

54496 - Set of 4

1993 - 1997

OSRP: $27.50

GBTru: $27

Paid: $_____

Christmas At The Farm

54500 - Set of 2

1993 - 1996

OSRP: $16

GBTru: $25

Paid: $_____

Check It Out Bookmobile

54518 - Set of 3

1993 - 1995

OSRP: $25

GBTru: $28

Paid: $_____

Tour The Village

54526

1993 - 1997

OSRP: $12.50

GBTru: $16

Paid: $_____

• Bayport on sign is spelled "Bayqort."

Pint-Size Pony Rides

54534 - Set of 3

1993 - 1996

OSRP: $37.50

GBTru: $45

Paid: $_____

Pick-up And Delivery

54542

1993 - 2001

OSRP: $10

GBTru: $12

Paid: $_____

• See Special Design section.

A Herd Of Holiday Heifers

54550 - Set of 3

1993 - 1997

OSRP: $18

GBTru: $24

Paid: $_____

Windmill

54569

1993 - 1993

OSRP: $20

GBTru: $24

Paid: $_____

Classic Cars

54577 - Set of 3

1993 - 1998

OSRP: $22.50

GBTru: $24

Paid: $_____

Spirit Of Snow Village Airplane

54585

1993 - 1996

OSRP: $12.50

GBTru: $40

Paid: $_____

• Available in blue or yellow. See 1992 for another item by the same name.

Village News Delivery

54593 - Set of 2

1993 - 1996

OSRP: $15

GBTru: $24

Paid: $_____

Caroling At The Farm

54631

1994^M - 2000

OSRP: $35

GBTru: $36

Paid: $_____

Stuck In The Snow

54712 - Set of 3

1994 - 1998

OSRP: $30

GBTru: $32

Paid: $_____

Pets On Parade

54720 - Set of 2

1994 - 1998

OSRP: $16.50

GBTru: $22

Paid: $_____

Feeding The Birds

54739 - Set of 3

1994 - 1997

OSRP: $25

GBTru: $28

Paid: $_____

Mush!

54747 - Set of 2

1994 - 1997

OSRP: $20

GBTru: $24

Paid: $_____

Skaters & Skiers

54755 - Set of 3

1994 - 2001

OSRP: $27.50

GBTru: $28

Paid: $_____

Going To The Chapel

54763 - Set of 2

1994 - 2001^M

OSRP: $20

GBTru: $22

Paid: $_____

Santa Comes To Town, 1995

54771

1994 - 1995

OSRP: $30

GBTru: $28

Paid: $_____

• Limited to year of production.
• First in a series.

Marshmallow Roast

54780 - Set of 3

1994 - 2002

OSRP: $32.50

GBTru: $34

Paid: $_____

• The fire is battery or adapter operated.

Coca–Cola® brand Delivery Truck

54798

1994 - 1998

OSRP: $15

GBTru: $30

Paid: $_____

• Licensed by Coca-Cola.

Coca–Cola® brand Delivery Men

54801 - Set of 2

1994 - 1998

OSRP: $25

GBTru: $33

Paid: $_____

• Licensed by Coca-Cola.

Coca–Cola® brand Billboard

54810

1994 - 1997

OSRP: $18

GBTru: $24

Paid: $_____

• Licensed by Coca-Cola.

Sunday School Serenade

54623

1994 - 1996

OSRP: *

GBTru: *

• Accessory contained in The Original Snow Village Starter Set.

Frosty Playtime

54860 - Set of 3

1995 - 1997

OSRP: $30

GBTru: $35

Paid: $_____

Poinsettias For Sale

54861 - Set of 3

1995 - 1998

OSRP: $30

GBTru: $33

Paid: $_____

Santa Comes To Town, 1996

54862

1995 - 1996

OSRP: $32.50

GBTru: $40

Paid: $_____

• Limited to year of production.
• Second in a series.

Chopping Firewood

54863 - Set of 2

1995 - 2002

OSRP: $16.50

GBTru: $20

Paid: $_____

• This includes mixed media —ceramic and wood.

Firewood Delivery Truck

54864

1995 - 1999

OSRP: $15

GBTru: $20

Paid: $_____

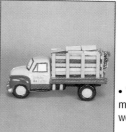

• This includes mixed media —ceramic and wood.

Service With A Smile

54865 - Set of 2

1995 - 1998

OSRP: $25

GBTru: $30

Paid: $_____

Pizza Delivery

54866 - Set of 2

1995 - 1998

OSRP: $20

GBTru: $25

Paid: $_____

Grand Ole Opry Carolers

54867

1995 - 1997

OSRP: $25

GBTru: $35

Paid: $_____

• Licensed by Opry-land USA, Inc.

Snow Carnival Ice Sculptures

54868 - Set of 2

1995 - 1998

OSRP: $27.50

GBTru: $28

Paid: $_____

• Includes mixed media—ceramic and acrylic.

Snow Carnival King & Queen

54869

1995 - 1998

OSRP: $35

GBTru: $40

Paid: $_____

Starbucks Coffee® Cart

54870 - Set of 2

1995 - 2000

OSRP: $27.50

GBTru: $35

Paid: $_____

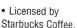

• Licensed by Starbucks Coffee.

Just Married

54879 - Set of 2
1995 -
OSRP: $25
GBTru: -
Paid: $_____

A Ride On The Reindeer Lines

54875 - Set of 3
1996ᴹ - 1997
OSRP: $35
GBTru: $38
Paid: $_____

Treetop Tree House

54890
1996 -
OSRP: $35
GBTru: -
Paid: $_____

• Resin.

On The Road Again

54891 - Set of 2
1996 - 2002
OSRP: $20
GBTru: $17
Paid: $_____

Moving Day

54892 - Set of 3
1996 - 1998
OSRP: $32.50
GBTru: $32
Paid: $_____

Holiday Hoops

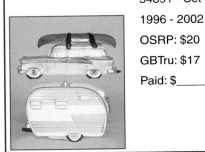

54893 - Set of 3
1996 - 1999
OSRP: $20
GBTru: $28
Paid: $_____

Men At Work

54894 - Set of 5
1996 - 1998
OSRP: $27.50
GBTru: $30
Paid: $_____

Terry's Towing

54895 - Set of 2
1996 - 1999
OSRP: $20
GBTru: $25
Paid: $_____

Caroling Through The Snow

54896

1996 - 1999

OSRP: $15

GBTru: $20

Paid: $_____

Heading For The Hills

54897

1996 - 2002

OSRP: $8.50

GBTru: $9

Paid: $_____

• Available in blue or yellow.

A Harley-Davidson® Holiday

54898 - Set of 2

1996 - 1999

OSRP: $22.50

GBTru: $24

Paid: $_____

• Licensed by Harley-Davidson.

Santa Comes To Town, 1997

54899

1996 - 1997

OSRP: $35

GBTru: $36

Paid: $_____

• Limited to year of production.
• Third in a series.

Harley-Davidson® Fat Boy & Softail

54900

1996 - 2001ᴹ

OSRP: $16.50

GBTru: $22

Paid: $_____

• Licensed by Harley-Davidson.

Harley-Davidson® Sign

54901

1996 - 2002

OSRP: $18

GBTru: $20

Paid: $_____

• Licensed by Harley-Davidson.

Saturday Morning Downtown

54902 - Set of 2

1997ᴹ - 1998

OSRP: *

GBTru: *

* Accessory contained in The Original Snow Village Start A Tradition Set.

The Whole Family Goes Shopping

54905 - Set of 3

1997ᴹ - 1999

OSRP: $25

GBTru: $28

Paid: $_____

A Holiday Sleigh Ride Together

54921

1997 - 2001^M

OSRP: $32.50

GBTru: $32

Paid: $_____

Christmas Kids

54922 - Set of 5

1997 - 1999

OSRP: $27.50

GBTru: $28

Paid: $_____

Let It Snow, Let It Snow

54923

1997 - 2000

OSRP: $20

GBTru: $24

Paid: $_____

Kids Love Hershey's®!

54924 - Set of 2

1997 - 2000

OSRP: $30

GBTru: $28

Paid: $_____

• Licensed by Hershey Foods.

McDonald's®...Lights Up The Night

54925

1997 - 1999

OSRP: $30

GBTru: $30

Paid: $_____

• Sign is battery/adapter operated.
• Licensed by McDonald's.

Kids, Candy Canes...& Ronald McDonald®

54926 - Set of 3

1997 - 1999

OSRP: $30

GBTru: $35

Paid: $_____

• Licensed by McDonald's.

He Led Them Down The Streets Of Town

54927 - Set of 3

1997 - 1999

OSRP: $30

GBTru: $30

Paid: $_____

Everybody Goes Skating At Rollerama

54928 - Set of 2

1997 - 1999

OSRP: $25

GBTru: $28

Paid: $_____

At The Barn Dance, It's Allemande Left

54929 - Set of 2
1997 - 1999
OSRP: $30
GBTru: $35
Paid: $_____

Hitch-Up The Buckboard

54930
1997 - 1999
OSRP: $40
GBTru: $40
Paid: $_____

Farm Accessory Set

54931 - Set of 35
1997 - 2002
OSRP: $75
GBTru: $75
Paid: $_____

• Includes 8 trees, 12 hay bales, 4 fence, and 11 ceramic pieces.

Santa Comes To Town, 1998

54920
1997 - 1998
OSRP: $30
GBTru: $36
Paid: $_____

• Limited to year of production.
• Fourth in a series.

Snow Village Utility Accessories

52775
1998 - 2001
OSRP: $15
GBTru: $12
Paid: $_____

Decorate The Tree

54934 - Set of 2
1998ᴹ - 1998
OSRP: *
GBTru: *

* Accessory contained in the Snowy Pines Inn Gift Set.

First Round Of The Year

54936 - Set of 3
1998ᴹ - 2001ᴹ
OSRP: $30
GBTru: $35
Paid: $_____

Carnival Tickets & Cotton Candy

54938 - Set of 3
1998ᴹ - 2000
OSRP: $30
GBTru: $30
Paid: $_____

• Ceramic and cloth.

Two For The Road

54939

1998^M - 2002

OSRP: $20

GBTru: $24

Paid: $_____

• Available in three color schemes—red, yellow, and blue.
• Licensed by Harley-Davidson.

Uptown Motors Ford® Billboard

52780

1998 - 2001^M

OSRP: $20

GBTru: $20

Paid: $_____

• Licensed by Ford.

1955 Ford® Automobiles

54950

1998 - 2001

OSRP: $10 ea.

GBTru: $10

Paid: $_____

• 6 assorted, each with a sign.
• Licensed by Ford.

1964½ Ford® Mustang

54951

1998 - 2001

OSRP: $10 ea.

GBTru: $18

Paid: $_____

• 3 assorted, each with a sign.
• Licensed by Ford.

Village Fire Truck

54952

1998 - 2003

OSRP: $22.50

GBTru: $24

Paid: $_____

• Lighted headlights and emergency beacon are battery operated.

Fireman To The Rescue

54953 - Set of 3

1998 - 2001^M

OSRP: $30

GBTru: $32

Paid: $_____

Fun At The Firehouse

54954 - Set of 2

1998 -

OSRP: $27.50

GBTru: -

Paid: $_____

Farmer's Flatbed

54955

1998 - 2000

OSRP: $17.50

GBTru: $18

Paid: $_____

The Catch Of The Day

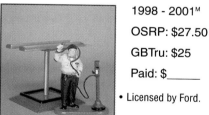

54956

1998 - 2001^M

OSRP: $30

GBTru: $34

Paid: $_____

• Fishing line is easily broken.

Christmas Visit To The Florist

54957 - Set of 3

1998 - 2001

OSRP: $30

GBTru: $33

Paid: $_____

• A similar design was also produced for Bachman's. See the Special Design section.

Santa Comes To Town, 1999

54958

1998 - 1999

OSRP: $30

GBTru: $32

Paid: $_____

• Limited to year of production.
• Fifth in a series.

Village Service Vehicles

54959

1998 - 2001

OSRP: $15 ea.

GBTru: $14

Paid: $_____

• 3 assorted—garbage truck, tow truck, and snow plow were often sold separately.

Quality Service At Ford®

54970 - Set of 2

1998 - 2001^M

OSRP: $27.50

GBTru: $25

Paid: $_____

• Licensed by Ford.

Patrolling The Road

54971

1998 - 2001^M

OSRP: $20

GBTru: $22

Paid: $_____

• Licensed by Harley-Davidson.

Couldn't Wait Until Christmas

54972

1998 - 2000

OSRP: $17

GBTru: $22

Paid: $_____

• Licensed by Lionel.

Uncle Sam's Fireworks Stand

54974 - Set of 2

1998 - 2000

OSRP: $45

GBTru: $40

Paid: $_____

• July 1999 event piece.

Harley-Davidson® Water Tower

54975

1998 - 2002

OSRP: $32.50

GBTru: $35

Paid: $_____

• Licensed by Harley-Davidson.

Another Man's Treasure Accessories

54976 - Set of 3

1998 - 2001ᴹ

OSRP: $27.50

GBTru: $32

Paid: $_____

A Home In The Making Accessories

54979 - Set of 4

1999ᴹ - 2001

OSRP: *

GBTru: *

* This accessory is contained in A Home In The Making.
• Licensed by Habitat For Humanity

Looney Tunes® Film Festival

54983 - Set of 4

1999ᴹ - 2001ᴹ

OSRP: $40

GBTru: $42

Paid: $_____

• Marquee can be placed on Cinema 56.
• Licensed by Warner Bros.

The Backyard Patio

52836 - Set of 2

1999 - 2002

OSRP: $40

GBTru: $40

Paid: $_____

It's Time For An Icy Treat

55013 - Set of 2

1999 - 2001

OSRP: $30

GBTru: $30

Paid: $_____

• Licensed by Good Humor-Breyers Ice Cream.

Welcome To The Congregation

55014

1999 - 2001ᴹ

OSRP: $15

GBTru: $15

Paid: $_____

Santa Comes To Town, 2000

55015

1999 - 2000

OSRP: $37.50

GBTru: $38

Paid: $_____

• Limited to year of production.
• Sixth in a series.

Laundry Day

55017

1999 - 2001^M

OSRP: $13

GBTru: $15

Paid: $_____

Before The Big Game

55019 - Set of 4

1999 - 2001

OSRP: $37.50

GBTru: $36

Paid: $_____

Finding The Bird's Song

55020 - Set of 2

1999 - 2001^M

OSRP: $25

GBTru: $24

Paid: $_____

Send In The Clown!

55021

1999 - 2001^M

OSRP: $13.50

GBTru: $14

Paid: $_____

• Stickers are included so plaque can be personalized.

Holy Spirit Baptistery

55022

1999 - 2001

OSRP: $37.50

GBTru: $30

Paid: $_____

• Music box plays "Jesus Loves The Little Children."

First Deposit

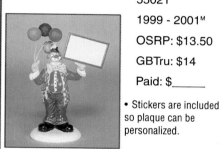

55023

1999 - 2001

OSRP: $14

GBTru: $15

Paid: $_____

Angels In The Snow

55024 - Set of 2

1999 -

OSRP: $30

GBTru: -

Paid: $_____

Santa's Little Helpers

55025

1999 - 2001

OSRP: $27.50

GBTru: $28

Paid: $_____

Is That Frosty?

55030

1999 -

OSRP: $22.50

GBTru: -

Paid: $_____

On The Way To Ballet Class

55031 - Set of 3

1999 - 2001^M

OSRP: $27.50

GBTru: $25

Paid: $_____

The Dragon Parade

55032

1999 - 2001

OSRP: $35

GBTru: $35

Paid: $_____

Gifts On The Go

55035 - Set of 2

1999 -2001^M

OSRP: $30

GBTru: $30

Paid: $_____

Backwoods Outhouse

55036

1999 -

OSRP: $20

GBTru: -

Paid: $_____

• Battery operated.

Oh, Christmas Tree

55040

2000^M - 2000

OSRP: *

GBTru: *

* Accessory contained in the Silver Bells Christmas Shop Gift Set.

1955 Pink Cadillac® Fleetwood™

55041

2000^M - 2000

OSRP: *

GBTru: *

* Accessory contained in the Elvis Presley's Graceland Gift Set.
• Licensed by GM.

Sitting In The Park

55100 - Set of 4

2000^M - 2002

OSRP: $28

GBTru: $26

Paid: $_____

How The Grinch Stole Christmas - Movie Premiere

55103 - Set of 2

2000^M - 2001

OSRP: $17.50

GBTru: $20

Paid: $_____

• Marquee can be placed on Cinema 56.
• Licensed by Dr. Seuss Enterprises.

Windmill By The Chicken Coop

52867

2000 - 2003

OSRP: $55

GBTru: $45

Paid: $_____

• Buck's County Series.

The Old Pickup Truck

52868

2000 - 2002

OSRP: $30

GBTru: $27

Paid: $_____

• Buck's County Series.

Yesterday's Tractor

52869

2000 - 2002

OSRP: $30

GBTru: $25

Paid: $_____

• Buck's County Series.

The Tree Lighting Ceremony

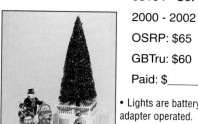

55104 - Set of 3

2000 - 2002

OSRP: $65

GBTru: $60

Paid: $_____

• Lights are battery/ adapter operated.

Now Showing - Elvis Presley Sign

55105

2000 - 2001

OSRP: $30

GBTru: $26

Paid: $_____

• Licensed by Elvis Presley Enterprises.
• Adapter operated.

Elvis Presley's Autograph

55106 - Set of 3

2000 - 2001

OSRP: $25

GBTru: $27

Paid: $_____

• Licensed by Elvis Presley Enterprises.

Pedal Cars For Christmas

55108 - Set of 2

2000 - 2003

OSRP: $27.50

GBTru: $30

Paid: $_____

Roadside Billboards

55109 - Set of 3

2000 - 2003

OSRP: $40

GBTru: $35

Paid: $_____

• Licensed by the Campbell Soup Co., SWIMC, Inc., and Eveready Batt. Co, Inc.
• Battery/adapter.

Christmastime Trimming

55110

2000 -

OSRP: $15

GBTru: -

Paid: $_____

Buck's County™ Water Tower

55111

2000 - 2003

OSRP: $32.50

GBTru: $35

Paid: $_____

• Buck's County Series.

Buck's County™ Stables

55112 - Set of 9

2000 - 2002

OSRP: $65

GBTru: $65

Paid: $_____

• Buck's County Series.

Family Canoe Trip

55116 - Set of 3

2000 - 2002

OSRP: $48

GBTru: $45

Paid: $_____

2001 Space Oddity

55118 - Set of 11

2000 - 2001

OSRP: $125

GBTru: $118

Paid: $_____

• Includes adapter.

On The Beat

55119 - Set of 2

2000 -

OSRP: $35

GBTru: -

Paid: $_____

• Battery/adapter operated.

Santa Comes To Town, 2001

55120

2000 - 2001

OSRP: $40

GBTru: $40

Paid: $_____

• Limited to year of production.
• Seventh in a series.
• Batt./adapt. operated.

The Abandoned Gas Pump

55121

2000 - 2002

OSRP: $37.50

GBTru: $34

Paid: $_____

• Buck's County Series.

1958 Corvette® Roadster

55281

2000 -

OSRP: $20

GBTru: -

Paid: $_____

• Classic Cars Series.
• Licensed by General Motors.

'50's Hot Rod

55282

2000 -

OSRP: $20

GBTru: -

Paid: $_____

• Classic Cars Series.

1957 Chevrolet® Bel Air

55283

2000 -

OSRP: $20

GBTru: -

Paid: $_____

• Classic Cars Series.
• Licensed by General Motors.

1958 John Deere® 730 Diesel Tractor

55284

2000 - 2003

OSRP: $20

GBTru: $22

Paid: $_____

• Classic Cars Series.
• Licensed by Deere & Co.

1950 Ford® F-1 Pickup

55285

2000 - 2003

OSRP: $20

GBTru: $19

Paid: $_____

• Classic Cars Series.
• Licensed by Ford Motor Co and Deere & Co.

Buck's County™ Horse Trailer

55286

2000 - 2002

OSRP: $17.50

GBTru: $18

Paid: $_____

• Buck's County Series.
• Coordinates with 1950 Ford F-1 Pickup.

1954 Willy's CJ3 Jeep®

55287

2000 - 2002

OSRP: $20

GBTru: $18

Paid: $_____

• Classic Cars Series.
• Licensed by Daimler-Chrysler Corp.

1949 Ford® Woody Wagon

55288

2000 -

OSRP: $20

GBTru: -

Paid: $_____

• Classic Cars Series.
• Licensed by Ford Motor Co.

1959 Chevrolet® Impala Convertible

55289

2000 -

OSRP: $20

GBTru: -

Paid: $_____

• Classic Cars Series.
• Licensed by General Motors.

The Final Touch

55061

2001ᴹ - 2001

OSRP: *

GBTru: *

* The accessory contained in the Christmas Lake Chalet Gift Set.

Happy New Year

55124 - Set of 4

2001ᴹ - 2002

OSRP: $25

GBTru: $23

Paid: $_____

• Includes sign that can be placed on Town Hall (#55044).

Fun In The Snow

55125 - Set of 2

2001ᴹ -

OSRP: $25

GBTru: -

Paid: $_____

Holiday Reindeer Run

55126

2001ᴹ - 2002

OSRP: $25

GBTru: $24

Paid: $_____

• Originally was titled Holiday Fun Run.

Car Hop

55067

2001 - 2003

OSRP: *

GBTru: *

* The accessory contained in Gus's Drive-In.

On Our Wedding Day

55068

2001 -

OSRP: *

GBTru: *

* The accessory contained in the Woodlake Chapel Starter Set.

Handmade Quilts For Sale

55072

2001 -

OSRP: *

GBTru: *

* The accessory contained in Country Quilts And Pies.

Cannon And Flag

55080

2001 - 2003

OSRP: *

GBTru: *

* The accessory contained in Village Legion Hall.

Egg Hunt

55090

2001 -

OSRP: *

GBTru: *

* The accessory contained in Happy Easter House.

Feeding The Ducks

55122

2001 - 2003

OSRP: $40

GBTru: $38

Paid: $_____

• Buck's County Series.

Santa Comes To Town, 2002

55127

2001 - 2002

OSRP: $85

GBTru: $60

Paid: $_____

• Limited to year of production, 2002.
• Eighth in a series.
• Battery operated.

Bringing The Irish Cheer

55128

2001 -

OSRP: $12.50

GBTru: -

Paid: $_____

School's Out!

55129

2001 - 2003

OSRP: $20

GBTru: $18

Paid: $_____

Start Your Engines

55132 - Set of 2

2001 - 2003

OSRP: $25

GBTru: $24

Paid: $_____

Hiking In The North Woods

55133
2001 - 2003
OSRP: $20
GBTru: $18
Paid: $_____

Main Street Villagers

55134 - Set of 3
2001 -
OSRP: $25
GBTru: -
Paid: $_____

College Kids At Krispy Kreme

55135
2001 -
OSRP: $17.50
GBTru: -
Paid: $_____

• Licensed by HDN Development Corp.

Snowmobile Racers

55136 - Set of 2
2001 -
OSRP: $15
GBTru: -
Paid: $_____

Oh, Brother!

55137 - Set of 2
2001 - 2003
OSRP: $18
GBTru: $18
Paid: $_____

Door-To-Door Sales

55139 - Set of 2
2001 - 2003
OSRP: $20
GBTru: $18
Paid: $_____

4th of July Celebration

55141 - Set of 3
2001 -
OSRP: $25
GBTru: -
Paid: $_____

Rest Stop?

55142
2001 - 2003
OSRP: $15
GBTru: $15
Paid: $_____

Sunday Football With Dad

55143

2001 - 2003

OSRP: $15

GBTru: $15

Paid: $_____

Ben & Buddy's Lemonade Stand

55144

2001 - 2003

OSRP: $20

GBTru: $25

Paid: $_____

Brand New Recruit

55152

2001 - 2003

OSRP: $20

GBTru: $22

Paid: $_____

Congratulations...Recruit!

55153 - Set of 2

2001 - 2002

OSRP: $17.50

GBTru: $18

Paid: $_____

Snow Village Raising The Flag

55154

2001 -

OSRP: $15

GBTru: -

Paid: $_____

Welcome To Snow Village Population Sign

55155

2001 -

OSRP: $10

GBTru: -

Paid: $_____

School Bus

55292

2001 -

OSRP: $20

GBTru: -

Paid: $_____

• Classic Cars Series.

1950 Studebaker

55293

2001 -

OSRP: $20

GBTru: -

Paid: $_____

• Classic Cars Series.

1951 Custom Mercury

55294

2001 -

OSRP: $20

GBTru: -

Paid: $_____

• Classic Cars Series.
• Licensed by Ford Motor Co.

1959 Cadillac Eldorado

55295

2001 - 2003

OSRP: $20

GBTru: $18

Paid: $_____

• Classic Cars Series.
• Licensed by General Motors.

Sampling The Treats

05923 - Set of 2

2002ᴹ - 2002

OSRP: *

GBTru: *

* The accessory contained in The Sweet Shop.

Christmas Eve Delivery

55091

2002ᴹ - 2002

OSRP: *

GBTru: *

* The accessory contained in 1224 Kissing Claus Lane.

Gifts For Easter

55095 - Set of 2

2002ᴹ -

OSRP: *

GBTru: *

• Easter Series.
* The accessory contained in Lily's Nursery & Gifts.

Young Love

55097

2002ᴹ -

OSRP: *

GBTru: *

* The accessory contained in Hearts & Blooms Cottage.

Nature Walk

55156 - Set of 2

2002ᴹ -

OSRP: $27.50

GBTru: -

Paid: $_____

Lucky's Irish Souvenirs

55157 - Set of 2

2002ᴹ -

OSRP: $45

GBTru: -

Paid: $_____

• Battery/adapter operated.

Mainstreet Snowman

55159

2002^M - 2002

OSRP: $32.50

GBTru: $30

Paid: $_____

• Limited to year of production.
• Available only at Gold Key dealers.

One Hop Walk

55160

2002^M -

OSRP: $40

GBTru: -

Paid: $_____

• Easter Series.

It's The Easter Bunny!

55164 - Set of 2

2002^M -

OSRP: $17.50

GBTru: -

Paid: $_____

• Easter Series.

Krispy Kreme Doughnut Deliveries

55165

2002^M -

OSRP: $20

GBTru: -

Paid: $_____

• Licensed by HDN Development Corp. and General Motors.

1956 Hook & Ladder

55296

2002^M -

OSRP: $30

GBTru: -

Paid: $_____

• Classic Cars Series.

1956 Mainline Police Sedan

55297

2002^M -

OSRP: $20

GBTru: -

Paid: $_____

• Classic Cars Series.
• Box reads "1956 Ford Mainline Police Sedan."
• Licensed by Ford.

Village Snow Clown

55161

2002 - 2003

OSRP: $17.50

GBTru: $17

Paid: $_____

At Your Service

55168

2002 -

OSRP: $12.50

GBTru: -

Paid: $_____

Violin Serenade

55169

2002 -

OSRP: $17.50

GBTru: -

Paid: $_____

Making A House Call

55170

2002 -

OSRP: $12.50

GBTru: -

Paid: $_____

Home Away From Home

55171

2002 -

OSRP: $27.50

GBTru: -

Paid: $_____

• Battery/adapter operated.

Weekend Getaway

55172 - Set of 2

2002 -

OSRP: $25

GBTru: -

Paid: $_____

Let's Play House

55173

2002 -

OSRP: $22.50

GBTru: -

Paid: $_____

• Lighted.

Village Utilities

55175 - Set of 10

2002 -

OSRP: $15

GBTru: -

Paid: $_____

Best Friends

55176

2002 -

OSRP: $20

GBTru: -

Paid: $_____

Car Wash Fundraiser

55177 - Set of 2

2002 -

OSRP: $20

GBTru: -

Paid: $_____

• Can be personalized.

Carry Out Boy

55178

2002 - 2003

OSRP: $17.50

GBTru: $17

Paid: $_____

Mm! Mm! Good!

55179

2002 -

OSRP: $25

GBTru: -

Paid: $_____

• Licensed by the Campbell Soup Co.

Summertime Family Picnic

55180 - Set of 3

2002 -

OSRP: $37.50

GBTru: -

Paid: $_____

Kiddie Parade

55181 - Set of 3

2002 -

OSRP: $30

GBTru: -

Paid: $_____

Merrily Round We Go

55183

2002 -

OSRP: $45

GBTru: -

Paid: $_____

• Animated.
• Battery/adapter operated.

Santa Comes To Town, 2003

55194

2002 - 2003

OSRP: $45

GBTru: $47

Paid: $_____

• Limited to year of production, 2003.
• Ninth in a series.

Fresh Dairy Delivery

55195 - Set of 2

2002 -

OSRP: $25

GBTru: -

Paid: $_____

Ice Cream For Everyone

55196 - Set of 2

2002 -

OSRP: $22.50

GBTru: -

Paid: $_____

Sitting In The Village

55197 - Set of 3

2002 -

OSRP: $25

GBTru: -

Paid: $_____

• Benches are not included.

Animals On The Farm

55199 - Set of 9

2002 -

OSRP: $25

GBTru: -

Paid: $_____

Jonathan The Bear Man

55202

2002 - 2003

OSRP: $12.50

GBTru: $13

Paid: $_____

• Named for a Wyoming artist.

1957 Ambulance

55299

2002 -

OSRP: $20

GBTru: -

Paid: $_____

• Classic Cars Series.

Snowman Sonata And Fence

55302

2002 -

OSRP: *

GBTru: *

* The accessory contained in Harmony House.

56 Gasoline Pump And Sign

55305

2002 -

OSRP: *

GBTru: *

* The accessory contained in Rocky's 56 Filling Station.

Let's Get A New Bike

55314

2002 - 2003

OSRP: *

GBTru: *

* The accessory contained in Wright Bike Shop.

1961 Ford Ranchero

55532

2002 -

OSRP: $20

GBTru: -

Paid: $_____

• Classic Cars Series.
• Licensed by Ford Motor Co.

Main Street Christmas Tree

55205

2003^M - 2003

OSRP: $35

GBTru: $33

Paid: $_____

- Adapter included.
- Limited to year of production.
- Available only at Gold Key dealers.

St. Patrick's Day Parade

55207

2003^M -

OSRP: $20

GBTru: -

Paid: $_____

- Can be personalized.

Work A Little, Play A Little

55208 - Set of 4

2003^M -

OSRP: $25

GBTru: -

Paid: $_____

- Includes two sets of figures dressed for four seasons.

I'm Home!

55209

2003^M -

OSRP: $13.50

GBTru: -

Paid: $_____

Kisses - 25 Cents

55215- Set of 2

2003^M -

OSRP: $25

GBTru: -

Paid: $_____

- Valentine's Day design.
- Special lighting effects.

Welcoming Christmas To Town

55320

2003^M - 2003

OSRP: *

GBTru: *

* The accessory contained in Home For The Holidays Express.

Joyful Greetings

55325

2003^M -

OSRP: *

GBTru: *

- Easter Series.
* The accessory contained in Happy Easter Church.

Easter Egg Hunt

55326 - Set of 3

2003^M -

OSRP: $50

GBTru: -

Paid: $_____

- Easter Series.
- Includes adapter.

Dressed In Our Easter Best

55327 - Set of 2

2003M -

OSRP: $25

GBTru: -

Paid: $_____

• Easter Series.

1956 Pumper

55533

2003M -

OSRP: $25

GBTru: -

Paid: $_____

• Classic Cars.

Personalized School Bus

55534

2003M -

OSRP: $20

GBTru: -

Paid: $_____

• Classic Cars.

No Girls Allowed

55217

2003 -

OSRP: $20

GBTru: -

Paid: $_____

We're Going By Train!

55218 - Set of 2

2003 -

OSRP: $25

GBTru: -

Paid: $_____

Santa Comes To Town, 2004

55222

2003 -

OSRP: $50

GBTru: -

Paid: $_____

• Limited to year of production, 2004.
• Tenth in a series.

Brand New Shoes!

55224 - Set of 2

2003 -

OSRP: $17.50

GBTru: -

Paid: $_____

News Flash!

55225

2003 -

OSRP: $17.50

GBTru: -

Paid: $_____

Listening To A Summer Concert

55227 - Set of 2

2003 -

OSRP: $20

GBTru: -

Paid: $_____

A Day At The Beach

55228

2003 -

OSRP: $25

GBTru: -

Paid: $_____

Billboard Surprise

55229

2003 -

OSRP: $22.50

GBTru: -

Paid: $_____

Here Comes The Birdie!

55230

2003 -

OSRP: $17.50

GBTru: -

Paid: $_____

More Decorations?

55231 - Set of 2

2003 -

OSRP: $17.50

GBTru: -

Paid: $_____

• Chrsitmas Lane Series.

Pleasing The Palate!

55232

2003 -

OSRP: $20

GBTru: -

Paid: $_____

Christmas Is Coming

55233

2003 -

OSRP: $25

GBTru: -

Paid: $_____

Neighborhood Poinsettia Salesman

55235 - Set of 2

2003 -

OSRP: $22.50

GBTru: -

Paid: $_____

Wood Carvings For Sale

55333

2003 -

OSRP: *

GBTru: *

* The accessory contained in Woody's Woodland Crafts.

Village Musicians

55338

2003 -

OSRP: *

GBTru: *

* The accessory contained in Roosevelt Park Band Shell.

The Pillsbury Doughboy™

55342

2003 -

OSRP: *

GBTru: *

* The accessory contained in Pillsbury Doughboy Bake Shop.
• Licensed by The Pillsbury Company.

1955 Ford Thunderbird

55535

2003 -

OSRP: $20

GBTru: -

Paid: $_____

• Classic Cars Series.
• Licensed by Ford Motor Co.

1957 Cadillac Eldorado Brougham

55536

2003 -

OSRP: $20

GBTru: -

Paid: $_____

• Classic Cars Series.
• Licensed by General Motors.

Use the following space(s) to update your guide when the midyear introductions are announced.

Photos of the midyear introductions will be included in the July-August issue of *the Village Chronicle* magazine.

_____

_____

____ - ____

OSRP: $_____

GBTru: -

Paid: $_____

_____

_____

____ - ____

OSRP: $_____

GBTru: -

Paid: $_____

Haunted Mansion (Green Roof)   54935

Dates	OSRP	GBTru	Paid
1998ᴹ - 2000ᴹ	$110	$360	$_____

- This is the SV version.
- Images on screen created by carousel inside building.
- Includes AC adapter.

(Black Roof)   34050

Dates	OSRP	GBTru	Paid
1998ᴹ - 1999	$110	$1225	$_____

- This is the giftware version and came in a black box.
- Images on screen created by carousel inside building.
- Includes AC adapter.

Grimsly Manor   55004

Dates	OSRP	GBTru	Paid
1999 -	$120	-	$_____

- Features special effects including horror sounds and lightning supplied by separate unit in box.
- The earliest pieces have a jack-o'-lantern on the porch. Later ones do not. Care must be taken in selecting one with a jack-o'-lantern since some collectors have added it to a piece that originally did not have one.
- Four bats hang from eaves, rocker is on porch, and a tree is attached in back. Matte finish.
- The box can separate even while in the sleeve so the box must be carried by the bottom.

Creepy Creek Carriage House   55055

Dates	OSRP	GBTru	Paid
2000 - 2003	$75	$85	$_____

- Bat mobile is separate in box.

Hauntsburg House   55058

Dates	OSRP	GBTru	Paid
2000 - 2002	$95	$100	$_____

- Grass platform is separate in box.
- Be careful removing from box; the tree is easily broken.

Haunted Barn

55060

Dates	OSRP	GBTru	Paid
2001^M - 2001	$75	$125	$_____

- Halloween Discover Department 56 design. Limited to year of production.
- Set of 4 includes Barn, "Scarecrow Jack" accessory, fence, and tree.

The Spooky Schooner

55087

Dates	OSRP	GBTru	Paid
2001 - 2002	$80	$90	$_____

- Limited to year of production, 2002.
- Has sound effects and green light.

Shipwreck Lighthouse

55088

Dates	OSRP	GBTru	Paid
2001 - 2003	$110	$120	$_____

- Features animated ghost that glows in the dark.

Haunted Fun House Gift Set

55094

Dates	OSRP	GBTru	Paid
2002^M - 2002	$75	$85	$_____

- Limited to year of production.
- Several features are animated.
- Set of 4 includes the Fun House, "Dressed Up For Fun" accessory, tree, and leaves.

Spooky Farmhouse 55315

Dates	OSRP	GBTru	Paid
2002 -	$55	-	$_____

Helga's House Of Fortunes 55316

Dates	OSRP	GBTru	Paid
2002 -	$95	-	$_____

• Tells fortunes.

Ghostly Carousel 55317

Dates	OSRP	GBTru	Paid
2002 -	$130	-	$_____

• Animated with sounds.

Black Cat Diner 55319

Dates	OSRP	GBTru	Paid
2002 - 2003	$75	$85	$_____

• Holiday Program.
• Limited to year of production.
• Set of 4 includes the Diner, "You Go First!" accessory, 10" tree, and leaves.

Haunted Windmill 55345

Dates	OSRP	GBTru	Paid
2003 -	$95	-	$_____

• Working windmill.
• Makes horror sounds

1031 Trick-Or-Treat Drive 55343

Dates	OSRP	GBTru	Paid
2003 -	$75	-	$_____

• Limited to year of production.
• Set of 8 includes the house, "Just Treats, No Tricks, Please" accessory, and Halloween decorations.

Castle Blackstone 55346

Dates	OSRP	GBTru	Paid
2003 -	$125	-	$_____

• Makes horror sounds.

Witch Way? Flight School 55347

Dates	OSRP	GBTru	Paid
2003 -	$75	-	$_____

• Limited to year of production.
• Set of 7 includes the School, "Practice Makes Perfect" accessory, and Halloween decorations.

Dates	OSRP	GBTru	Paid
____ - ____	$____	-	$____

Trick Or Treat Kids

54937 - Set of 3

1998^M -

OSRP: $33

GBTru: -

Paid: $_____

Costumes For Sale

54973 - Set of 2

1998 - 2002

OSRP: $60

GBTru: $65

Paid: $_____

• Pumpkin lights are battery/adapter operated.

Preparing For Halloween

54982 - Set of 2

1999^M - 2002

OSRP: $40

GBTru: $42

Paid: $_____

Treats for The Kids

55016 - Set of 3

1999 - 2002

OSRP: $33

GBTru: $33

Paid: $_____

Lighting The Jack-O'-Lanterns

55117 - Set of 3

2000 - 2003

OSRP: $32.50

GBTru: $30

Paid: $_____

• Battery/adapter operated.

Scarecrow Jack

55060

2001^M - 2001

OSRP: *

GBTru: *

* This accessory is contained in the Haunted Barn Gift Set.

Halloween Hayride

55148

2001 -

OSRP: $45

GBTru: -

Paid: $_____

Captain Black Bart's Ghost

55149

2001 - 2002

OSRP: $18

GBTru: $18

Paid: $_____

Haunted Tree House

55150

2001 -

OSRP: $45

GBTru: -

Paid: $_____

Dressed Up For Fun

55094

2002^M - 2002

OSRP: *

GBTru: *

* The accessory contained in Haunted Fun House Gift Set.

Bobbing For Apples

55185

2002 -

OSRP: $22.50

GBTru: -

Paid: $_____

Halloween Kids

55186 - Set of 3

2002 -

OSRP: $27.50

GBTru: -

Paid: $_____

Halloween Dance

55189

2002 -

OSRP: $85

GBTru: -

Paid: $_____

• Musical and animated.

Strangers Beware

55192

2002 -

OSRP: $17.50

GBTru: -

Paid: $_____

Campbell's® Trick-Or-Treat

55198

2002 - 2003

OSRP: $17.50

GBTru: $18

Paid: $_____

• Licensed by The Campbell Soup Co.

Gathering Pumpkins

55200

2002 -

OSRP: $30

GBTru: -

Paid: $_____

110

Costume Parade

55201

2002 - 2003

OSRP: $50

GBTru: $50

Paid: $_____

• Limited to year of production.
• Musical and animated.

Building The Scarecrow

55203

2002 - 2003

OSRP: $32.50

GBTru: $34

Paid: $_____

• Limited to year of production.

You Go First!

55319

2002 - 2003

OSRP: *

GBTru: *

* The accessory contained in Black Cat Diner.

Lighting Up Halloween

55238

2003 -

OSRP: $27.50

GBTru: -

Paid: $_____

• Lights up; battery operated.

A Gravely Haunting - 2004

55240 - Set of 2

2003 -

OSRP: $22.50

GBTru: -

Paid: $_____

• Limited to year of production, 2004.

Canine Trick-Or-Treaters

55241 - Set of 2

2003 -

OSRP: $20

GBTru: -

Paid: $_____

Pick Your Own Pumpkin

55244

2003 -

OSRP: $30

GBTru: -

Paid: $_____

Haunted Harvest

55245

2003 -

OSRP: $17.50

GBTru: -

Paid: $_____

Creative Carvings

55246

2003 -

OSRP: $32.50

GBTru: -

Paid: $_____

• Battery/adapter operated.

Forever On Guard

55248

2003 -

OSRP: $17.50

GBTru: -

Paid: $_____

• Battery/adapter operated.

Just Treats, No Tricks, Please

55343

2003 -

OSRP: *

GBTru: *

* The accessory contained in 1031 Trick-Or-Treat Drive.

Practice Makes Perfect

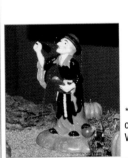

55347

2003 -

OSRP: *

GBTru: *

* The accessory contained in Witch Way? Flight School.

Use the following space(s) to update your guide when the midyear introductions are announced.

Photos of the midyear introductions will be included in the July-August issue of *the Village Chronicle* magazine.

_____

____ - ____

OSRP: $_____

GBTru: -

Paid: $_____

_____

____ - ____

OSRP: $_____

GBTru: -

Paid: $_____

_____

____ - ____

OSRP: $_____

GBTru: -

Paid: $_____

Sounds Collection

City Sounds Vol. 2

Choose either Volume 1 or Volume 2

Vol. 1 Village Sounds

Add to your collecting enjoyment

ELECTRICAL

Place & Plug is a system that allows you to customize the location of your lights when creating a display. Gone are the messy "rats nest" of wires and the time and effort required to hide those unsightly long cords. This is just so simple!

Place & Plug 25' Multi-Outlet Cord 21.00
Connect up to 100 outlets and mantle stems to this cord. It includes 6 outlets to get you started.

Place & Plug 12' Multi-Outlet Cord 15.95
Connect up to 100 outlets and mantle stems to this cord. It includes 4 outlets to get you started.

Place & Plug Outlet Packs (4 outlets per pack) 8.95
Place these outlets anywhere along the lengths of the 25' and/or 12' multi-outlet cords. Just snap them in place and add the mantle stems, and you're done.

Place & Plug 6" Mantle Stems (6 stems/pack) 12.95
Use these 6" stems to light buildings that are close to the multi-outlet cord. Each stem attaches to an outlet.

Place & Plug 12" Mantle Stems (5 stems/pack) 12.95
Use these 12" stems to light buildings that are between 6" and 12" from the cord. Each stem attaches to an outlet.

BOOKS

Village Display Tips 21.95
This book provides hundreds of helpful ideas to incorporate into your displays; topics include finding room to display, creating mountains and water, hiding cords, adding animation, developing backgrounds, and much, much more.

Village Display Tips II 21.95
This book takes display-making even further with more ideas, more techniques, and more color photos of collectors' tips and methods. It's perfect for the novice and experienced display-maker.

The Little Landscaper - Set of 8 .... 39.95
This set of eight booklets is the answer for those collectors looking to add unique and creative dimensions to their scenes; buy one or buy them all; they're easy to follow and fun to do.

#1 - **Little House on the Styrofoam!** 5.95
#2 - **Waterways, Our Way!** 5.95
#3 - **It's All in De Tail** 5.95
#4 - **It's the Very Dickens' of a Village** 5.95
#5 - **Go a Little Higher, Get a Lot Wetter!** 5.95
#6 - **Snow, Laughter, and Magic** 5.95
#7 - **We Have a Lot of Catching Up to Do** 5.95
#8 - **The Halloween Village** 5.95

Dickens' Village Series

This English village owes a great deal of its popularity to the author after whom it was named. Six of his novels are portrayed in at least one building within the collection, although technically the Satis Manor from Great Expectations is part of the Literary Classics® Series. But references to David Copperfield, Nicholas Nickleby, Oliver Twist, The Old Curiosity Shop, and—most especially—A Christmas Carol have been among the most popular pieces in the village. Some have even been reissued in updated forms following their retirement. Furthermore, the pieces in the Charles Dickens' Signature Series™ depict buildings from the life of the novelist.

But there is much more to this collection than just the entertaining stories of one prolific author. Rural countryside pieces with thatched roofs and small town shops dominated for many years, while more recent buildings seem to reflect an urban London from the past. Maritime pieces pay tribute to England's history as a nation of seafarers. There are beautiful churches, formidable castles and palaces, and—before they were designated as Historical Landmark Series™ pieces—representations of some of the nation's most famous structures.

Several accessories are characters from Dickens' works, and there are even images of the man himself reading from his works, writing, and raising a flag. In addition to figures and small non-lit structures, there are exquisite coaches, a variety of mongers, the Twelve Days of Dickens' Village characters, and links to rail lines that crossed the country. The Abington Canal Series and Queens Port pieces prove that it is a diverse country with a diverse history that has been captured brilliantly.

THE ORIGINAL SHOPS OF DICKENS' VILLAGE - Set of 7

Dates	OSRP	GBTru	Paid
1984 - 1988	$175	$900	$ *Gift*

• None of the seven buildings have names on the bottom.

Crowntree Inn   65153

Dates	OSRP	GBTru	Paid
1984 - 1988	$25	$165	$_____

Candle Shop   65153

Dates	OSRP	GBTru	Paid
1984 - 1988	$25	$130	$_____

• Early pieces have gray roofs. Later ones have blue.

Green Grocer   65153

Dates	OSRP	GBTru	Paid
1984 - 1988	$25	$140	$_____

• Though there is snow at the base and above the front window, there is no snow on the roof.

Golden Swan Baker   65153

Dates	OSRP	GBTru	Paid
1984 - 1988	$25	$135	$_____

Bean And Son Smithy Shop   65153

Dates	OSRP	GBTru	Paid
1984 - 1988	$25	$125	$_____

Abel Beesley Butcher

65153

Dates	OSRP	GBTru	Paid
1984 - 1988	$25	$95	$_____

Jones & Co. Brush & Basket Shop

65153

Dates	OSRP	GBTru	Paid
1984 - 1988	$25	$150	$_____

Dickens' Village Church

65161

Dates	OSRP	GBTru	Paid
1985 - 1989	$35	See below	

- There are 5 recognized versions of the Village Church.
- White: Very pale walls and brown cornerstones and roof.
  GBTru: **$250**   Paid: $_____
- Yellow: Yellowish walls with butterscotch stones and roof.
  GBTru: **$150**   Paid: $_____
- Green: Pale green walls with butterscotch stones and roof.
  GBTru: **$190**   Paid: $_____
- Tan: Tan walls with butterscotch stones and roof.
  GBTru: **$130**   Paid: $_____
- Butterscotch: Walls and roof are nearly the same butterscotch color. Only sleeve to read "Village Church." All others read "Shops of Dickens' Village."
  GBTru: **$95**   Paid: $_____

Dickens' Village Mill

65196

Dates	OSRP	GBTru	Paid
1985 - 1986	$35	$4050	$_____

- Limited Edition of 2,500.
- Early pieces have sleeves that read "Dickens' Village Cottage."
- Early release to GCC dealers.

DICKENS' COTTAGES - Set of 3   65188

Dates	OSRP	GBTru	Paid
1985 - 1988	$75	$600	$_____

• None of the three buildings have names on the bottom.
• Early release to GCC dealers.

Thatched Cottage   65188

Dates	OSRP	GBTru	Paid
1985 - 1988	$25	$145	$_____

• Early release to GCC dealers.

Stone Cottage   65188

Dates	OSRP	GBTru	Paid
1985 - 1988	$25	See below	

• The Tan version is considered to be the first shipped.
• The Green version's walls vary from light green to a pea green.
• The chimneys are very fragile.
• Early release to GCC dealers.

	GBTru	Paid
Tan	$325	$_____
Green	$290	$_____

Tudor Cottage   65188

Dates	OSRP	GBTru	Paid
1985 - 1988	$25	$210	$_____

• The chimneys are very fragile and are often crooked.
• Early release to GCC dealers.

Norman Church   65021

Dates	OSRP	GBTru	Paid
1986 - 1987	$40	$2500	$_____

• Limited Edition of 3,500.
• Early Churches are light gray, and they got increasingly darker as production continued.
• Early release to GCC dealers.

CHRISTMAS CAROL COTTAGES - Set of 3 ✓ 65005

as below

Dates	OSRP	GBTru	Paid
1986 - 1995	**$75**	**$95**	$____

• Originally marketed as its own sub-series of Dickens' Village with sleeves and hangtags that read "A Christmas Carol." The early pieces were made in Taiwan, and later ones were made in the Philippines.

Fezziwig's Warehouse ✓ 65005

Dates	OSRP	GBTru	Paid
1986 - 1995	**$25**	**$25**	$____

• Early pieces have panes cut out of the front door. Later ones have a solid front door.

Scrooge & Marley Counting House ✓ 65005

Dates	OSRP	GBTru	Paid
1986 - 1995	**$25**	**$40**	$____

• First of two pieces with this name. Re-issued in 2000.

The Cottage of Bob Cratchit ✓ & Tiny Tim 65005

Dates	OSRP	GBTru	Paid
1986 - 1995	**$25**	**$45**	$____

• Many scholars believe that Dickens modeled his version of this home after his own childhood home on Bayham St. in Camden Town.

Blythe Pond Mill House 65080

Dates	OSRP	GBTru	Paid
1986 - 1990	**$37**	**See below**	

• Early shipments are commonly referred to as the "Correct" version. "Blythe Pond" is correctly inscribed in the bottom of the building.
• This is the rarer of the two versions.
• Later shipments are commonly referred to as the "By The Pond" version. "BY THE POND" is incorrectly inscribed in the bottom of the building.
• The sign above the door is correct on both versions.

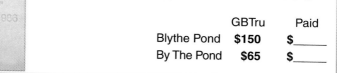

	GBTru	Paid
Blythe Pond	**$150**	$____
By The Pond	**$65**	$____

DICKENS' LANE SHOPS - Set of 3 65072

Dates	OSRP	GBTru	Paid
1986 - 1989	$80	$310	$_____

Thomas Kersey Coffee House   65072

Dates	OSRP	GBTru	Paid
1986 - 1989	$27	$125	$_____

• Bottomstamp reads "Coffee House."

Cottage Toy Shop   65072

Dates	OSRP	GBTru	Paid
1986 - 1989	$27	$120	$_____

• Bottomstamp reads "Toy Shop."

Tuttle's Pub   65072

Dates	OSRP	GBTru	Paid
1986 - 1989	$27	$95	$_____

• Bottomstamp reads "Pub."

Chadbury Station And Train - Set of 4   65285

Dates	OSRP	GBTru	Paid
1986 - 1989	$65	$175	$_____

• The front of the platform on the first version of the station is 9" wide.
• The front of the platform on the second version is 9½" wide.
• Early sleeve reads "Train And Lighted Station." The later sleeve reads "Chadbury Station And Train."

BARLEY BREE - Set of 2   59005

Dates	OSRP	GBTru	Paid
1987 - 1989	$60	$225	$_____

- Though the pieces of this set were originally priced at $30 each, they are boxed together. It is extremely rare for them to be sold separately on the secondary market.
- Early pieces have dark roofs. Later ones have lighter roofs.

The Old Curiosity Shop ✓   59056

Dates	OSRP	GBTru	Paid
1987 - 1999	$32	$35	$_____

- Designed after the Old Curiosity Shop on Portsmouth Street in London.
- First of two pieces with this name. Re-issued in 2000.

Kenilworth Castle   59161

Dates	OSRP	GBTru	Paid
1987 - 1988	$70	$485	$_____

- Bottom reads "Castle."
- Early pieces are approx. 9" tall, later ones approx. 8½".
- It's not unusual for this piece to have concave walls. One with straight walls is considered more valuable.

Brick Abbey   65498

Dates	OSRP	GBTru	Paid
1987 - 1989	$33	$210	$_____

- Many pieces have spires that lean inward. One with straight spires is considered more valuable.

Chesterton Manor House   65684

Dates	OSRP	GBTru	Paid
1987 - 1988	$45	$825	$_____

- Limited Edition of 7,500.
- Both the bottomstamp and box read "Manor."
- Early release to GCC dealers.

Counting House & Silas Thimbleton Barrister

59021

Dates	OSRP	GBTru	Paid
1988 - 1990	$32	$65	$_____

- Early pieces have lamps with natural porcelain panes. Later ones have lamps with panes painted yellow.
- Box reads "Silas Thimbleton Barrister." Bottomstamp reads "Counting House."

C. Fletcher Public House

59048

Dates	OSRP	GBTru	Paid
1988 - 1989	$35	$325	$_____

- Limited Edition of 12,500.
- Box and bottomstamp read "Public House."
- There are some proofs available, though they are rare.
- Early release to GCC dealers.

COBBLESTONE SHOPS - Set of 3

59242

Dates	OSRP	GBTru	Paid
1988 - 1990	$95	$250	$_____

The Wool Shop

59242

Dates	OSRP	GBTru	Paid
1988 - 1990	$32	$140	$_____

Booter And Cobbler

59242

Dates	OSRP	GBTru	Paid
1988 - 1990	$32	$70	$_____

- Some sleeves picture T. Wells Fruit & Spice Shop though they read "Booter & Cobbler" as they should.
- Some others picture Booter & Cobbler as they should and read "T. Wells Fruit & Spice Shop."

T. Wells Fruit & Spice Shop

59242

Dates	OSRP	GBTru	Paid
1988 - 1990	$32	$60	$_____

- Some sleeves picture Booter & Cobbler though they read "T. Wells Fruit & Spice Shop" as they should.
- Some others picture T. Wells Fruit & Spice Shop as they should and read "Booter & Cobbler."

MERCHANT SHOPS - Set of 5 ✓
as below

59269

Dates	OSRP	GBTru	Paid
1988 - 1993	$150	$150	$_____

Poulterer ✓

59269

Dates	OSRP	GBTru	Paid
1988 - 1993	$32.50	$40	$_____

Geo. Weeton Watchmaker ✓

59269

Dates	OSRP	GBTru	Paid
1988 - 1993	$32.50	$30	$_____

The Mermaid Fish Shoppe ✓

59269

Dates	OSRP	GBTru	Paid
1988 - 1993	$32.50	$40	$_____

White Horse Bakery ✓

59269

Dates	OSRP	GBTru	Paid
1988 - 1993	$32.50	$35	$_____

Walpole Tailors ✓

59269

Dates	OSRP	GBTru	Paid
1988 - 1993	$32.50	$30	$_____

NICHOLAS NICKLEBY - Set of 2 ✓   59250

Dates	OSRP	GBTru	Paid
1988 - 1991	$72	$95	$_____

Set with the "K" version of Nicholas Nickleby Cottage: $110 $_____

Nicholas Nickleby Cottage ✓   59250

Dates	OSRP	GBTru	Paid
1988 - 1991	$36	$50	$_____

• Early pieces have a bottomstamp that reads "Nickolas Nickleby."   **GBTru: $75** $_____

Wackford Squeers Boarding School ✓   59250

Dates	OSRP	GBTru	Paid
1988 - 1991	$36	$60	$_____

• Dickens based his version of the school on the Bowes Academy that once stood in Yorkshire.
• The majority of these have a sagging roof.

Ivy Glen Church ✓   59277

Dates	OSRP	GBTru	Paid
1988 - 1991	$35	$55	$_____

Victoria Station ▷   55743

Dates	OSRP	GBTru	Paid
1989 - 1998	$100	$110	$_____

• Inspired by the famous station in London.
• Early release to Showcase and NALED dealers.

Knottinghill Church ✓   55824

Dates	OSRP	GBTru	Paid
1989 - 1995	$50	$50	$_____

DAVID COPPERFIELD - Set of 3 ✓   55506

Dates	OSRP	GBTru	Paid
1989 - 1992	**$125**	**$130**	$_____

**Set with the Tan version of
Peggotty's Seaside Cottage:** | | $160 | $_____

• Early release to Showcase dealers.

Mr. Wickfield Solicitor ✓   55506

Dates	OSRP	GBTru	Paid
1989 - 1992	**$42.50**	**$55**	$_____

• Dickens based his version of this house on one that stands at 71 St. Dunstan's St. in Canterbury, England.
• Early release to Showcase dealers.

Betsy Trotwood's Cottage ✓   55506

Dates	OSRP	GBTru	Paid
1989 - 1992	**$42.50**	**$45**	$_____

• Dickens based his version of this cottage on one owned by Mary Strong in Broadstairs, England. It is now a Dickens museum.
• Early release to Showcase dealers.

Peggotty's Seaside Cottage ✓   55506

Dates	OSRP	GBTru	Paid
1989 - 1992	**$42.50**	**See below**	

• The Tan version was the earlier of the two. Its hull is not painted. Department 56 stated that the green paint it intended to use would not adhere to the porcelain.
• The problem was resolved by using a different green paint.
• This was an early release to Showcase dealers.
• Dickens based his version of the cottage on an actual boat-turned dwelling at the canal at Gravesend.

	GBTru	Paid
Tan	**$85**	$_____
Green	**$55**	$_____

Cobles Police Station ✓ ?   55832

Dates	OSRP	GBTru	Paid
1989 - 1991	**$37.50**	**$95**	$_____

Theatre Royal ✓ 55840

Dates	OSRP	GBTru	Paid
1989 - 1992	$45	$65	$_____

• Inspired by the Theatre Royal in Rochester, England where Dickens saw his first Shakespearean play.

Ruth Marion Scotch Woolens #6837 55859

Dates	OSRP	GBTru	Paid
1989 - 1990	$65	$245	$_?___

• Limited Edition of 17,500.
• Proofs have "Proof" stamped on the bottom and on the sleeve instead of a number. **$170** $_____
• Early release to GCC dealers.

Green Gate Cottage #20806 55867

Dates	OSRP	GBTru	Paid
1989 - 1990	$65	$170	$_?___

• Limited Edition of 22,500.
• Proofs have "Proof" stamped on the bottom and on the sleeve instead of a number. **$150** $_____
• Early release to Showcase Dealers.

The Flat Of Ebenezer Scrooge ✓ 55875

Dates	OSRP	GBTru	Paid
1989 - 2001	$37.50	**See below**	

• Version 1:
• Window panes on the second and third floor are painted yellow. The fourth floor's far left shutter is slightly open.
• Gray trim is darker than on subsequent editions.
• Early release to NALED dealers.

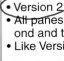

• Version 2:
• All panes have been cut out of the windows on the second and third floors.
• Like Version 1, this was made in Taiwan.

• Version 3:
• Window panes are yellow. The far left shutter on the 4th floor is closed. Made in Philippines and China.
• Christmas Carol Series.
• Ebenezer Scrooge's House introduced in 2001.

	GBTru	Paid
Version 1	$75	$_____
Version 2	$45	$_____
Version 3	$40	$_____

Bishops Oast House ✓   55670

Dates	OSRP	GBTru	Paid
1990 - 1992	$45	$55	$_____

- "Bishops" refers to a surname, not a religious figure.
- Oast houses dot the Kent countryside. Many have been converted into private homes.

KING'S ROAD - Set of 2 ✓   55689

as below

Dates	OSRP	GBTru	Paid
1990 - 1996	$72	$65	$_____

Tutbury Printer ✓   55690

Dates	OSRP	GBTru	Paid
1990 - 1996	$36	$40	$_____

C. H. Watt Physician ✓   55691

Dates	OSRP	GBTru	Paid
1990 - 1996	$36	$40	$_____

Fagin's Hide-A-Way ✓   55522

Dates	OSRP	GBTru	Paid
1991 - 1995	$68	$65	$_____

- Dickens based his Fagin's Hide-A-Way and its characters in Oliver Twist on the people who frequented the series of underground passages in London.

Ashbury Inn ✓   55557

Dates	OSRP	GBTru	Paid
1991 - 1995	$55	$60	$_____

OLIVER TWIST - Set of 2 ✓
As below

55530

Dates	OSRP	GBTru	Paid
1991 - 1993	$75	$65	$_____

Brownlow House ✓

55530

Dates	OSRP	GBTru	Paid
1991 - 1993	$37.50	$45	$_____

• Early samples have charcoal gray roof and trim.
• Dickens based his version of this house on the one at 39 Craven Street in London.

Maylie Cottage ✓

55530

Dates	OSRP	GBTru	Paid
1991 - 1993	$37.50	$40	$_____

Nephew Fred's Flat ✓

55573

Dates	OSRP	GBTru	Paid
1991 - 1994	$35	$65	$_____

• Christmas Carol Series.
• Early pieces were manufactured in Taiwan and are darker than the later ones from China.
• Later version, Fred Holiwell's House, introduced in 2001.

Crown & Cricket Inn

57509

Dates	OSRP	GBTru	Paid
1991 - 1992	$100	$110	$ 100

• Limited to year of production.
• The first of the Charles Dickens' Signature Series.
• Early pieces have light trim, later ones darker gray trim.

Old Michaelchurch ✓

55620

Dates	OSRP	GBTru	Paid
1992 - 1996	$42	$50	$_____

• Early release to Showcase and GCC dealers.

The Pied Bull Inn

57517

Dates	OSRP	GBTru	Paid
1992 - 1993	$100	$105	$ 100

- Limited to year of production.
- Charles Dickens' Signature Series.
- Sign is separate in box.

Hembleton Pewterer

58009

Dates	OSRP	GBTru	Paid
1992 - 1995	$72	$70	$_____

- The right side of the early pieces is composed of two small additions. On the later ones it is one large addition.

King's Road Post Office

58017

Dates	OSRP	GBTru	Paid
1992 - 1998	$45	$45	$_____

- Flag is separate in box.

Boarding & Lodging School - #18

58092

Dates	OSRP	GBTru	Paid
1992 - 1993	$48	$85	$_____

- Limited to year of production. See also 1994 release.
- This Signature Series piece commemorates the 150th anniversary of the publishing of *A Christmas Carol*.
- Early release to Showcase dealers and buying groups.

Dedlock Arms

57525

Dates	OSRP	GBTru	Paid
1993 - 1994	$100	$95	$ 100

- Limited to year of production.
- Charles Dickens' Signature Series.
- Dickens based his version of this tavern from *Bleak House* on the Sondes Arms in Rockingham, England.

Kingsford's Brew House

58114

Dates	OSRP	GBTru	Paid
1993 - 1996	$45	$55	$_____

- Sign is separate in box.

PUMP LANE SHOPPES - Set of 3

58084

Dates	OSRP	GBTru	Paid
1993 - 1996	$112	$115	$_____

Bumpstead Nye Cloaks & Canes

58085

Dates	OSRP	GBTru	Paid
1993 - 1996	$37.50	$40	$_____

Lomas Ltd. Molasses

58086

Dates	OSRP	GBTru	Paid
1993 - 1996	$37.50	$45	$_____

W. M. Wheat Cakes & Puddings

58087

Dates	OSRP	GBTru	Paid
1993 - 1996	$37.50	$45	$_____

• The name on the front of the building reads "WM," the abbreviation of William.

Great Denton Mill

58122

Dates	OSRP	GBTru	Paid
1993 - 1997	$50	$55	$_____

Whittlesbourne Church

58211

Dates	OSRP	GBTru	Paid
1994^M - 1998	$85	$80	$_____

Giggelswick Mutton & Ham

58220

Dates	OSRP	GBTru	Paid
1994^M - 1997	$48	$50	$_____

Boarding & Lodging School - #43

58106

Dates	OSRP	GBTru	Paid
1994 - 1998	$48	$55	$_____

- This School with 43 as its address is similar to the 1992 limited edition that has 18 as its address. Putting the addresses together forms 1843, the year *A Christmas Carol* was published.

PORTOBELLO ROAD
THATCHED COTTAGES - Set of 3

58246

Dates	OSRP	GBTru	Paid
1994 - 1997	$120	$115	$_____

Mr. & Mrs. Pickle

58247

Dates	OSRP	GBTru	Paid
1994 - 1997	$40	$40	$_____

Cobb Cottage

58248

Dates	OSRP	GBTru	Paid
1994 - 1997	$40	$45	$_____

Browning Cottage

58249

Dates	OSRP	GBTru	Paid
1994 - 1997	$40	$50	$_____

Sir John Falstaff Inn ✓ 57533

Dates	OSRP	GBTru	Paid
1994 - 1995	$100	$90	$ _100_

- Limited to year of production.
- Charles Dickens' Signature Series.
- Inspired by the inn across from Dickens' last home, Gad's Hill Place.

Hather Harness 58238

Dates	OSRP	GBTru	Paid
1994 - 1997	$48	$45	$_____

Dickens' Village Start A Tradition Set 58327

Dates	OSRP	GBTru	Paid
1995^M - 1996	$85	$90	$_____

- First available at the 1995 Homes for the Holidays event.
- During that event and the 1996 Homes for the Holidays event, it was specially priced at $65.

- Set of 13 includes the "Town Square Shops"— **Faversham Lamps & Oil** (top) and **Morston Steak And Kidney Pie** (bottom)—the 3 piece accessory "Town Square Carolers," 6 trees, Cobblestone Road, and a bag of snow.

The Maltings 58335

Dates	OSRP	GBTru	Paid
1995^M - 1998	$50	$50	$_____

Dudden Cross Church 58343

Dates	OSRP	GBTru	Paid
1995^M - 1997	$45	$50	$_____

- Early pieces have a bell that hangs in actual cutout in bell tower. Later ones have bell as part of porcelain.

The Grapes Inn ✓ ~~done to have~~   57534

Dates	OSRP	GBTru	Paid
1995 - 1996	$120	$95	$ ~~100~~

- Limited to year of production.
- Charles Dickens' Signature Series.
- Dickens based the Porters in *Our Mutual Friend* on this inn located in the Limehouse section of London.

J. D. Nichols Toy Shop   58328

Dates	OSRP	GBTru	Paid
1995 - 1998	$48	$55	$_____

- Sign is separate in box.

Dursley Manor   58329

Dates	OSRP	GBTru	Paid
1995 - 1999	$50	$60	$_____

Blenham Street Bank   58330

Dates	OSRP	GBTru	Paid
1995 - 1998	$60	$60	$_____

WRENBURY SHOPS - Set of 3   58331

Dates	OSRP	GBTru	Paid
1995 - 1997/98	$100	$120	$_____

Wrenbury Baker   58332

Dates	OSRP	GBTru	Paid
1995 - 1997	$35	$40	$_____

- Sign is separate in box.

The Chop Shop   58333

Dates	OSRP	GBTru	Paid
1995 - 1997	$35	$45	$_____

• Sign is separate in box.

T. Puddlewick Spectacle Shop   58334

Dates	OSRP	GBTru	Paid
1995 - 1998	$35	$45	$_____

• Sign is separate in box.

Ramsford Palace   58336

Dates	OSRP	GBTru	Paid
1996^M - 1996	$175	$235	$_____

• Limited Edition of 27,500.
• Inspired by the Castle Howard in York, England.
• Set of 17 includes the Palace, the 2 piece accessory "Palace Guards," gate, fountain, 8 wall hedges, and 4 corner topiaries.

Butter Tub Farmhouse   58337

Dates	OSRP	GBTru	Paid
1996^M - 1999	$40	$55	$_____

• Butter Tub refers to the Buttertub Pass in Yorkshire, England where pools known as buttertubs form in potholes.

Butter Tub Barn   58338

Dates	OSRP	GBTru	Paid
1996^M - 1999	$48	$55	$_____

• Butter Tub refers to the Buttertub Pass in Yorkshire, England where pools known as buttertubs form in potholes.

The Christmas Carol Cottage 58339

Dates	OSRP	GBTru	Paid
1996ᴹ - 2000	$60	$55	$_____

- Christmas Carol Revisited Series.
- Uses Magic Smoke to create smoking effect rising from the chimney.
- Sign is separate in box.

Gad's Hill Place 57535

Dates	OSRP	GBTru	Paid
1996 - 1997	$98	$90	$ 100

- Limited to year of production.
- Inspired by Dickens' last home, Gad's Hill Place.
- Sign is separate in box.
- Charles Dickens' Signature Series.

Nettie Quinn Puppets & Marionettes 58344

Dates	OSRP	GBTru	Paid
1996 - 2001	$50	$55	$_____

- This is the first Heritage Village Collection design to feature multiple weathervanes, and they are very fragile.
- Sign and 2 marionettes are separate in box.

Mulberrie Court Brownstones 58345

Dates	OSRP	GBTru	Paid
1996 - 1999	$90	$90	$_____

- This piece is frequently adopted into Christmas In The City by collectors.
- Includes 7 sisal bushes to be placed around building.

The Olde Camden Town Church 58346

Dates	OSRP	GBTru	Paid
1996 - 1999	$55	$60	$_____

- Dickens may have based his version of the Church on St. Stephen's Church in Camden, England.
- Christmas Carol Revisited Series.

The Melancholy Tavern 58347

Dates	OSRP	GBTru	Paid
1996 - 1999	$45	$45	$_____

- Dickens may have based his version of the Tavern on the Baker's Chop Shop that once stood in London.
- First of two pieces with this name. Re-issued in 2003.
- Christmas Carol Revisited Series. Sign is separate in box.

Quilly's Antiques 58348

Dates	OSRP	GBTru	Paid
1996 - 1999	$46	$50	$_____

Dickens' Village Start A Tradition Set 58322

Dates	OSRP	GBTru	Paid
1997ᴹ - 1998	$100	$90	$_____

- First available during the November 1997 Homes for the Holidays event. The price was reduced to $65 during the event.

- Set of 13 includes **Sudbury Church** (top), **Old East Rectory** (bottom), a 3 piece accessory "The Spirit Of Giving," 6 sisal trees, Cobblestone Road, and a bag of snow.

J. Lytes Coal Merchant 58323

Dates	OSRP	GBTru	Paid
1997ᴹ - 1999	$50	$55	$_____

- Early pieces have bottomstamps that read "Dickens' **Vallage** Series."

Tower Of London 58500

Dates	OSRP	GBTru	Paid
1997ᴹ - 1997	$165	$215	$_____

- Limited to year of production.
- The first Historical Landmark Series design. See this series in the Small Collection section.
- This, the White Tower, is one of the many towers that comprise the Tower of London, famous for housing a prison as well as the Crown Jewels. Legend says six ravens must be at the tower to preserve the monarchy.
- The actual Tower of London is located along the Thames River in London.
- Set of 5 includes the Tower, a gate with tower, the raven master, a sign, and a wall with ravens.

Barmby Moor Cottage

58324

Dates	OSRP	GBTru	Paid
1997ᴹ - 2000	$48	$45	$_____

• Barmby Moor is a village located east of York, England.

Manchester Square

58301

Dates	OSRP	GBTru	Paid
1997 - 2000	$250	$235	$_____

• Early pieces have bottomstamps that read "Dickens' Village **Seires**."
• Set of 25 includes **Custom House** (top), **Frogmore Chemist** (center), **G. Choir's Weights & Scales** (bottom), **Lydby Trunk & Satchel Shop** (below), the 7 piece accessory "Manchester Square Accessory Set," 12 trees, Cobblestone Road, and a bag of snow.
• Frogmore's sign and G. Choir's scales are separate in box.
• Man's walking stick is fragile.

East Indies Trading Co.

58302

Dates	OSRP	GBTru	Paid
1997 - 1999	$65	$70	$_____

• Similar to the Canadian Trading Co., but with a change of colors.

Canadian Trading Co.

58306

Dates	OSRP	GBTru	Paid
1997 - 1998	$65	$100	$_____

• Similar to the East Indies Trading Co., but with a slight change of colors.
• Available only in Canada.
• Sign is separate in box.

Leacock Poulterer

58303

Dates	OSRP	GBTru	Paid
1997 - 1999	**$48**	**$50**	$_____

• Christmas Carol Revisited Series.

Crooked Fence Cottage

58304

Dates	OSRP	GBTru	Paid
1997 - 2000	**$60**	**$65**	$_____

• Early pieces have bottomstamps that read "Dickens' Village **Seires**."
• Bird cage is separate in box.
• The tree branches in front are very fragile.

Ashwick Lane Hose & Ladder

58305

Dates	OSRP	GBTru	Paid
1997 -	**$54**	-	$_____

• 2 ladders are separate in box.
• This design was also the primary piece in a special GCC gift set in 2000.

The Old Globe Theatre

58501

Dates	OSRP	GBTru	Paid
1997 - 1998	**$175**	**$150**	$_____

• Limited to year of production.
• The second Historical Landmark Series design. See this series in the Small Collection section.
• First samples of the building were made as two pieces. For production it is one piece.
• Some early pieces have "The City Globe" stamped on the bottom.
• The Globe Theatre, located along the Thames River in London, was demolished in 1644 and was rebuilt in 1996 near the original site.
• Set of 4 includes the Theatre, two trumpeters, and a sign.

Thomas Mudge Timepieces

58307

Dates	OSRP	GBTru	Paid
1998ᴹ - 2000	**$60**	**$65**	$_____

• Clock is separate in box.
• Lamppost is fragile.

Seton Morris Spice Merchant Gift Set   58308

Dates	OSRP	GBTru	Paid
1998ᴹ - 1998	$65	$70	$_____

- Limited to year of production.
- First available during the November 1998 Homes for the Holidays event.
- Set of 10 includes the shop, a 3 piece accessory "Christmas Apples," 4 sisal trees, Cobblestone Road, and a bag of snow.

Kensington Palace   58309

Dates	OSRP	GBTru	Paid
1998ᴹ - 1998	$195	$165	$_____

- Limited to year of production.
- Introduced during the 1998 International Collectible Expo, this special edition of the famous London royal residence was first available during the November 1998 Homes for the Holidays event.
- A portion of the proceeds benefited the Ronald McDonald Houses across the U.S. and Canada.
- Early pieces had boxes that read "Princess of Whales." When discovered, stickers that read "Princess of Wales" were placed over the mistake.
- Set includes the Palace, palace gates, a statue of William III, a flag of Great Britain, 4 sisal trees, 4 sisal hedges, adhesive adornments, and Cobblestone Road.

Tattyeave Knoll   58311

Dates	OSRP	GBTru	Paid
1998ᴹ - 1999	$55	$60	$_____

Heathmoor Castle   58313

Dates	OSRP	GBTru	Paid
1998 - 1999	$90	$110	$_____

- Limited to year of production.
- 2 pennants are separate in box.
- 1 lion on each of the two center turrets is supposed to appear as if it is broken.

Teaman & Crupp China Shop   58314

Dates	OSRP	GBTru	Paid
1998 - 2003	$64	$65	$_____

• Sign is separate in box.

Lynton Point Tower   58315

Dates	OSRP	GBTru	Paid
1998 - 2001	$80	$80	$_____

• 2 small attachments are separate in box.
• Oars at boat are fragile.

North Eastern Sea Fisheries Ltd.   58316

Dates	OSRP	GBTru	Paid
1998 - 1999	$70	$75	$_____

The Horse And Hounds Pub   58340

Dates	OSRP	GBTru	Paid
1998 -	$70	-	$_____

• Two signs are separate in box.

Great Expectations Satis Manor   58310

Dates	OSRP	GBTru	Paid
1998 - 2001	$110	$85	$_____

• The first Literary Classics design. See this series in the Small Collection section.
• Charles Dickens used Restoration House in Rochester, England as the model for his Satis Manor.
• Set of 4 plus book includes the Manor and the accessory "Miss Havisham, Estella, and Pip."

Big Ben

58341

Dates	OSRP	GBTru	Paid
1998 - 2003	**$95**	**$95**	$_____

- The fourth Historical Landmark Series design. See this series in the Small Collection section.
- It is a replica of London's Big Ben along the Thames River.
- Set of 2 includes Big Ben with working clock and sign.

Chancery Corner

58352

Dates	OSRP	GBTru	Paid
1999ᴹ - 1999	**$65**	**$75**	$_____

- Limited to year of production.
- This was the first Dickens' Village design to include a three-dimensional scene in the house.
- First available during the 1999 Discover Department 56 event.
- Set of 8 includes the house, 2 sisal trees, 2 fence sections with gate, walkway, birdbath, and snow.

Dudley Docker

58353

Dates	OSRP	GBTru	Paid
1999ᴹ - 2000	**$70**	**$75**	$_____

Old Queensbridge Station

58443

Dates	OSRP	GBTru	Paid
1999 - 2002	**$100**	**$100**	$_____

- 6 hanging plants and a clock are separate in box.
- Do not handle by the metal canopies.
- Set of 2 includes the Station and a platform.

Margrove Orangery
58440

Dates	OSRP	GBTru	Paid
1999 - 2001	$98	$95	$_____

Aldeburgh Music Box Shop
58441

Dates	OSRP	GBTru	Paid
1999 - 2000	$60	$70	$_____

- Dream House Sweepstakes Grand Prize winner assisted in the design.
- Music box plays "Chopin's "Fantaisie-Impromptu."
- Named after a seaside town in England.

Aldeburgh Music Box Shop Gift Set
58442

Dates	OSRP	GBTru	Paid
1999 - 2000	$85	$90	$_____

- Limited Edition of 35,000.
- First available during the Spring 2000 Discover Department 56 event.
- Music box plays "Heindenroselin."
- Set of 3 includes Shop, "The Mother's Gift" accessory, walkway with pediments, floral hedges and topiaries, and 2 hanging baskets.
- Sign is separate in box for this and the design above.

McShane Cottage
58444

Dates	OSRP	GBTru	Paid
1999 - 2001	$55	$55	$_____

- Set of 2 includes the Cottage and a duck house.

Staghorn Lodge
58445

Dates	OSRP	GBTru	Paid
1999 - 2002	$72	$75	$_____

- Early pieces have brown antlers above the front door or antlers that were simply painted on. Later ones have gold antlers.

Leed's Oyster House

58446

Dates	OSRP	GBTru	Paid
1999 - 2001	**$68**	**$65**	$____

• The positions of the holes for the signs are reversed from the ones shown on the sleeve. This requires that the location of the signs be switched.

The China Trader

58447

Dates	OSRP	GBTru	Paid
1999 - 2000	**$72**	**$80**	$____

The Spider Box Locks

58448

Dates	OSRP	GBTru	Paid
1999 - 2001	**$60**	**$60**	$____

• Sign and key are separate in box.

Wingham Lane Parrot Seller

58449

Dates	OSRP	GBTru	Paid
1999 - 2001	**$68**	**$70**	$____

• Sign and 5 bird cages are separate in box.
• This shop derives its name from the Wingham Bird Park located near Canterbury, England.

The Old Royal Observatory
Gold Dome Edition

58451

Dates	OSRP	GBTru	Paid
1999 - 2000	**Promo**	**$320**	$____

• Limited to 5,500, Department 56 sent one to its valued retailers as a thank you for their support.
• The fifth Historical Landmark Series design. See this series in the Small Collection section.

The Old Royal Observatory

58453

Dates	OSRP	GBTru	Paid
1999 - 2000	**$95**	**$100**	$____

• Limited Edition of 35,000.
• The fifth Historical Landmark Series design. See this series in the Small Collection section.
• Set of 2 includes Observatory and sign.

Fezziwig's Ballroom Animated Gift Set 58470

Dates	OSRP	GBTru	Paid
2000ᴹ - 2000	$75	$115	$_____

- First available during the 2000 Discover Dept. 56 event.
- The silver bell honors Department 56's 25th anniversary.
- The dancers inside the building spin on a revolving turntable.
- Set of 6 includes the warehouse, the accessory "Scrooge At Fezziwig's Ball," 3 sisal trees, and a bag of snow.
- Christmas Carol Series.

St. Martin-In-The-Fields Church 58471

Dates	OSRP	GBTru	Paid
2000ᴹ - 2002	$96	$105	$_____

- Inspired by the famous church in London's Trafalgar Sq.
- The Roman numerals on the portico of Department 56's version read 1716 instead of 1726.
- Ornamental top for spire is separate in box.

Ashwick Lane Gift Set 05700

Dates	OSRP	GBTru	Paid
2000ᴹ - 2000	$65	$70	$_____

- Gold accents have been added to the hinges and rail posts of the 1997 version of this building.
- This set is an exclusive for GCC dealers.
- Set of 10 includes the fire house, a 3 piece accessory "At The Firehouse" that has a brass plaque that can be personalized, 4 trees, Cobblestone Road, and a bag of snow.

Crowntree Freckleton Windmill 58472

Dates	OSRP	GBTru	Paid
2000 - 2001	$80	$110	$_____

- 25th Anniversary Limited Edition of 30,000.
- Abington Canal Series.
- Windmill is animated.
- The open door and fence are very fragile.

Abington Lockside Inn

58473

Dates	OSRP	GBTru	Paid
2000 - 2003	$68	$60	$_____

• Abington Canal Series.

Abington Lockkeeper's Residence

58474

Dates	OSRP	GBTru	Paid
2000 - 2002	$58	$60	$_____

• Abington Canal Series.
• Bell is separate in box.

Lilycott Garden Conservatory

58475

Dates	OSRP	GBTru	Paid
2000 - 2001	$65	$75	$_____

• Discover Department 56 Spring Event Piece.
• Set of 5 includes building, "Sweet Roses" accessory, and 3 topiary trees.
• Fountain is separate in box.

Hedgerow Garden Cottage

58476

Dates	OSRP	GBTru	Paid
2000 - 2002	$57	$60	$_____

Burwickglen Golf Clubhouse

58477

Dates	OSRP	GBTru	Paid
2000 - 2002	$96	$95	$_____

• Sign, 9 pennants, and "pin" are separate in box.

Glendun Cocoa Works

58478

Dates	OSRP	GBTru	Paid
2000 - 2003	$80	$85	$_____

• Lantern is separate in box.
• Smokestack and ironwork brace are fragile.

Rockingham School

58479

Dates	OSRP	GBTru	Paid
2000 - 2002	$85	$80	$_____

• Sign is separate in box.
• Spires and small stacks are fragile.

Royal Stock Exchange

58480

Dates	OSRP	GBTru	Paid
2000 - 2001	$110	$110	$_____

• Urns are fragile.

Royal Staffordshire Porcelains

58481

Dates	OSRP	GBTru	Paid
2000 - 2002	$65	$65	$_____

• Sign is separate in box.

The Old Curiosity Shop

58482

Dates	OSRP	GBTru	Paid
2000 -	$50	-	$_____

• This is the updated version of the same piece originally issued in 1987.
• Do not handle by hitching posts.

Scrooge & Marley Counting House

58483

Dates	OSRP	GBTru	Paid
2000 -	$80	-	$_____

• This is the updated version of the same piece originally issued in 1986.
• Sign is separate in box.
• Christmas Carol Series.

Sherlock Holmes - 221B Baker Street   58601

Dates	OSRP	GBTru	Paid
2000 - 2003	$90	$100	$_____

- This is the fifth Literary Classics piece. See this series in the Small Collection section.
- Inspired by Arthur Conan Doyle's famous works, this is Department 56's interpretation of the home of England's greatest fictional detective.
- Set of 3 plus book includes the house and 2 piece accessory "Elementary My Dear Watson."

Brightsmith & Sons, Queens Jewellers   58484

Dates	OSRP	GBTru	Paid
2001ᴹ - 2001	$75	$250	$_____

- Special Swarovski crystals are featured on the building.
- Only available at Dept. 56 25th Anniversary celebration.
- Sign separate in box.

Somerset Valley Church   58485

Dates	OSRP	GBTru	Paid
2001ᴹ - 2001	$75	$85	$_____

- First available during the 2001 Holiday Discover Department 56 event.
- Church bell can be set to chime hourly.
- Set of 9 includes the Church, the accessory "Christmas Eve Celebration," 3 sisal trees, 2 fieldstone wall sections, and a bag of snow.

Cratchit's Corner   58486

Dates	OSRP	GBTru	Paid
2001ᴹ -	$80	-	$_____

- Christmas Carol Series.

Dickens' Village

Mrs. Brimm's Tea Room Gift Set

58487

Dates	OSRP	GBTru	Paid
2001 - 2002	$65	$75	$_____

- First available during the Mother's Day Spring Program.
- Set of 4 includes building, sign that can be personalized, tree, and accessory "High Tea."
- Hanging sign and 2 hanging plants are separate in box.
- 5% of proceeds goes to fight against breast cancer.

Dickens' Gad's Hill Chalet

58488

Dates	OSRP	GBTru	Paid
2001 - 2003	$65	$70	$_____

- Set of 2 includes Chalet and "Dickens Writing" accessory.

"Bidwell Windmill" #2

58489

Dates	OSRP	GBTru	Paid
2001 - 2003	$80	$80	$_____

- Abington Canal Series.
- Windmill is animated.

Ebenezer Scrooge's House

58490

Dates	OSRP	GBTru	Paid
2001 -	$85	-	$_____

- Christmas Carol Series.
- Hanging sack is separate in the box.
- This is an updated version of The Flat of Ebenezer Scrooge (1989).

Fred Holiwell's House

58492

Dates	OSRP	GBTru	Paid
2001 -	$62	-	$_____

- Christmas Carol Series.
- This is an updated version of Nephew Fred's Flat (1991).

Sheffield Manor

58493

Dates	OSRP	GBTru	Paid
2001 - 2002	$130	$150	$_____

- Limited to year of production, 2002.

The Slone Hotel

58494

Dates	OSRP	GBTru	Paid
2001 - 2003	$90	$85	$_____

- Set of 2 includes includes Hotel and "Doorman" accessory.
- Spire is separate in the box.
- Awning supports are very fragile.

Bayly's Blacksmith

58495

Dates	OSRP	GBTru	Paid
2001 -	$70	-	$_____

- Sign is separate in the box.

St. Ives Lock House

58496

Dates	OSRP	GBTru	Paid
2001 - 2003	$75	$75	$_____

- Abington Canal series.
- The ladder is extremely fragile.

Piccadilly Gallery

58498

Dates	OSRP	GBTru	Paid
2001 - 2002	**$75**	**$70**	$_____

• Lamps are fragile.

Thornbury Chapel

58502

Dates	OSRP	GBTru	Paid
2001 - 2003	**$60**	**$60**	$_____

Christmas At Codington Cottage

05925

Dates	OSRP	GBTru	Paid
2002ᴹ - 2002	**$75**	**$85**	$_____

• Department store exclusive.
• Limited to year of production.
• The "Winter Frolic" accessory is animated.
• The railing and water pump are very fragile.
• Set of 7 includes the Cottage, "Winter Frolic" accessory, 3 Natural Evergreens, a Bare Branch Tree, and snow.
• A similar design, Codington Cottage with a different accessory and no trees or snow, was released as a regular issue in 2002.

1 Royal Tree Court

58506

Dates	OSRP	GBTru	Paid
2002ᴹ - 2002	**$75**	**$75**	$_____

• Holiday 2002 Special Edition.
• Limited to year of production.
• Animated.
• Set of 8 includes the house, "Bearing Gifts" accessory, 2 riverstone walls, 2 frosted topiaries, a Bare Branch Tree, and snow.
• Spires are fragile.

Norfolk Biffins Bakery

58491

Dates	OSRP	GBTru	Paid
2002ᴹ -	$65	-	$_____

• Christmas Carol Series.

Hop Castle Folly

58633

Dates	OSRP	GBTru	Paid
2002ᴹ - 2002	$65	$130	$_____

• Club 56 dealer exclusive.
• Limited to 5,600 numbered pieces.
• Inspired by an actual building in northern England.
• Set of 2 includes the building and "Lord Of The Follies" accessory.
• Weathervane is separate in the box.
• Certificate of authenticity is included in the box.

Regent Street Coffeehouse

58507

Dates	OSRP	GBTru	Paid
2002 -	$70	-	$_____

Antiquarian Bookseller

58508

Dates	OSRP	GBTru	Paid
2002 -	$57	-	$_____

Mordecai Mould Undertaker

58509

Dates	OSRP	GBTru	Paid
2002 -	$70	-	$_____

• All Hallow's Eve design.
• Named for the undertaker in Dickens' "Life And Adventures Of Martin Chuzzlewit."

Collyweston Post Office

58510

Dates	OSRP	GBTru	Paid
2002 - 2003	$50	$45	$_____

The Leather Bottle

58511

Dates	OSRP	GBTru	Paid
2002 - 2003	$65	$60	$_____

- Abington Canal Series.
- Charles Dickens frequented a pub named The Leather Bottle.

Belle's House

58512

Dates	OSRP	GBTru	Paid
2002 -	$55	-	$_____

- Christmas Carol Series.
- A special 20th Anniversary edition of this design was issued in 2004.

The Daily News

58513

Dates	OSRP	GBTru	Paid
2002 -	$75	-	$_____

- Set of 2 includes the building and "The First Edition" accessory.
- Named after the newspaper where Charles Dickens was the editior.

Westminster Abbey

58517

Dates	OSRP	GBTru	Paid
2002 -	$95	-	$_____

- This is a replica of one of England's most famous landmarks.
- Historical information is printed on the back of facade.

Codington Cottage

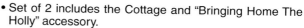

58514

Dates	OSRP	GBTru	Paid
2002 - 2003	**$65**	**$65**	$_____

- Set of 2 includes the Cottage and "Bringing Home The Holly" accessory.
- A similar design, Christmas At Codington Cottage with a different accessory, trees, and snow, was released as a department store exclusive in 2002.

Shakespeare's Birthplace

58515

Dates	OSRP	GBTru	Paid
2002 - 2003	**$85**	**$85**	$_____

- Limited to 25,000 numbered pieces.
- Inspired by the author's birthplace in Stratford-Upon-Avon.
- Set of 4 includes the building and "All The World's A Stage" accessory.

Sweetbriar Cottage

58518

Dates	OSRP	GBTru	Paid
2002 - 2003	**$65**	**$65**	$_____

- Spring Gift Set.
- Set of 3 includes the Cottage, "Rose Garden Beauty" accessory, and a spring tree.

London Skating Club

58700

Dates	OSRP	GBTru	Paid
2003ᴹ - 2003	$75	-	$_____

- Holiday Gift Set.
- Set of 5 includes "Victorian Skaters" accessory, birch tree, and snow.
- Skaters move around rink.

Gunnersbury Park Folly

58702

Dates	OSRP	GBTru	Paid
2003ᴹ - 2003	$65	$80	$_____

- Club 56 dealer exclusive. Limited to 5,600 pieces.

Melancholy Tavern

58703

Dates	OSRP	GBTru	Paid
2003ᴹ -	$65	-	$_____

- This is the updated version of the piece originally issued in 1996.

Green's Park Nosegays

58704

Dates	OSRP	GBTru	Paid
2003 -	$65	-	$_____

- Spring Gift Set.
- Set of 2 includes the building and "For You, My Lady" accessory.

Tower Bridge Of London

58705

Dates	OSRP	GBTru	Paid
2003 -	$165	-	$_____

- Historical Landmark Series. Numbered ltd. edition of 20,000.
- Dickens' Village 20th Anniversary Series. Includes pin.
- It is a replica of London's Tower Bridge.
- Set of 4.

Theatre Of The Macabre

58706

Dates	OSRP	GBTru	Paid
2003 -	$65	-	$_____

- All Hallow's Eve Series.

All Saints Church

58707

Dates	OSRP	GBTru	Paid
2003 -	$70	-	$_____

- All Hallow's Eve Series.

Notting Hill Water Tower

58708

Dates	OSRP	GBTru	Paid
2003 -	$55	-	$_____

Williams Gas Works

58709

Dates	OSRP	GBTru	Paid
2003 -	$70	-	$_____

Dickens' Birthplace

58710

Dates	OSRP	GBTru	Paid
2003 -	$50	-	$_____

- Limited to year of production. Includes lantern and plaque.
- Dickens' Village 20th Anniversary Series. Includes pin.
- It is a replica of the house in which Dickens was born in Portsmouth, England.

Stump Hill Gatehouse 58711

Dates	OSRP	GBTru	Paid
2003 -	$50	-	$_____

Hospital For Sick Children At Ormond Street 58712

Dates	OSRP	GBTru	Paid
2003 -	$65	-	$_____

- Limited to year of production.
- Dickens' Village 20th Anniversary Series. Includes pin.
- This was inspired by the hospital in London.

Naval Academy, Queens Port 58713

Dates	OSRP	GBTru	Paid
2003 -	$75	-	$_____

Lighthouse, Queens Port 58714

Dates	OSRP	GBTru	Paid
2003 -	$70	-	$_____

Belle's House - Special Edition

Dates	OSRP	GBTru	Paid
2004 - 2004	n/a-	$_____	

- Numbered limited of 500 pieces.
- This edition differs from the original (2002) in that it has a Dickens' Village 20th Anniversary stamp on the bottom, has an intricate bay window, and features Belle looking out an upper window at Scrooge.
- A number limited of 500 pieces, the first 250 were distributed when Department 56 randomly drew names from its *celebrations* magazine subscription list. The other 250 had not been distributed at the time of this printing.

Use the following space(s) to update your guide when the midyear introductions are announced.

Photos of the midyear introductions will be included in the July-August issue of *the Village Chronicle* magazine.

	Dates	OSRP	GBTru	Paid
	___ - ___	$___	-	$___

	Dates	OSRP	GBTru	Paid
	___ - ___	$___	-	$___

	Dates	OSRP	GBTru	Paid
	___ - ___	$___	-	$___

	Dates	OSRP	GBTru	Paid
	___ - ___	$___	-	$___

	Dates	OSRP	GBTru	Paid
	___ - ___	$___	-	$___

Dickens' Village

National Council of 56 Clubs

NCC
22 Samoset Road
Orleans, MA 02653
(540) 659-6804
www.ncc56.com

NCC pins

Why Join an NCC Club?

❖ Make friends with nice people who understand your addiction.

❖ Learn the latest news about D56 products and your villages.

❖ Obtain the NCC exclusive pieces, when available, such as "Jack's Umbrella Shop" (set of 2) and the "Under the NCC Umbrella" accessories.

❖ Discuss the many techniques for making mountains or water.

❖ Discover the subtle nuances of lighting methods.

❖ Find out about special deals, closeouts and sales.

❖ Win door, game and contest prizes.

❖ Take excursions to yard sales, gatherings, house tours.

❖ Learn more about your village and display techniques from seasoned collectors.

❖ Contribute to a good cause (most NCC clubs support local charities.)

❖ Glean information and ideas from other clubs and collectors in the US and Canada through the NCC Bulletin.

❖ Have others help you search for missing pieces.

❖ Meet new collector friends from outside your area in the NCC hospitality rooms at gatherings.

How to Find a Club

❖ Ask your local dealer

❖ Visit the National Council of 56 Clubs' Web site at www.ncc56.com

❖ Inquire at Internet chat sites (AOL, Yahoo, etc.)

❖ Watch for special feature articles on collectors and check the events column in your local newspaper

❖ Introduce yourself to fellow shoppers

❖ Attend village gatherings and collectable shows (The NCC often staffs information tables.)

❖ Start your own club. (Contact the NCC for the "Handbook for Clubs," better known as the "Start A Club" guide.)

Produced as an NCC exclusive lighted house and 2002 lapel pin

The National Council of 56 Clubs is an independent umbrella organization for Department 56 collector clubs in the United States and Canada. The NCC is operated by volunteers dedicated to the goal of "clubs helping clubs help collectors."

Carolers (White Post Version)   (Black Post Version)

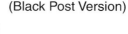

65269 - Set of 3

1984 - 1990

OSRP: $10

GBTru: $65

Paid: $_____

• Made for a short time, the white post set includes a viola that is very light with dark brown trim.

65269 - Set of 3

GBTru: $30

Paid: $_____

• Early pieces of the black post set have a viola that is one color and made in Taiwan. The second viola has dark trim and was made in the Philippines.

Village Train

65277 - Set of 3

1985 - 1985

OSRP: $12

GBTru: $245

Paid: $_____

• Also called the "Brighton Train" due to the name on the side of the middle car.

Christmas Carol Figures

65013 - Set of 3

1986 - 1990

OSRP: $12.50

GBTru: $55

Paid: $_____

• A Christmas Carol Series. Sleeve shows Tiny Tim with crutch, but there isn't one in the figurine.

Farm People & Animals

59013 - Set of 5

1987 - 1989

OSRP: $24

GBTru: $70

Paid: $_____

• Early pieces had box that read "Heritage Village Farm Set."

Blacksmith

59340 - Set of 3

1987 - 1990

OSRP: $20

GBTru: $55

Paid: $_____

Silo & Hay Shed

59501 - Set of 2

1987 - 1989

OSRP: $18

GBTru: $100

Paid: $_____

• Early versions have roofs with rust, gold, and brown stripes. Later ones are brown.

Dickens' Village Sign

65692

1987 - 1993

OSRP: $6

GBTru: $10

Paid: $_____

• Bottomstamp reads "Handcrafted by Jiean Fung Porcelains, Taiwan."
• The early signs have a dark background.

Ox Sled (Tan Pants)

59510

1987 - 1989

OSRP: $20

GBTru: $130

Paid: $_____

• The driver has tan pants and is seated on a green cushion.

(Blue Pants Version)

GBTru: $60

Paid: $_____

• The driver has blue pants and is seated on a black cushion.

(Blue Pants/Mold Change Version)

GBTru: $70

Paid: $_____

• Blue pants, black cushion, and the snow under the oxen is not attached to hind legs.

Dover Coach (Version 1)

65900

1987 - 1990

OSRP: $18

GBTru: $55

Paid: $_____

• The coachman is clean shaven, and the wheels are very crude. Made in Taiwan.
• Box reads "Horse With Coach."

(Version 2)

GBTru: $50

Paid: $_____

• The coachman has a mustache; the wheels are more round. Made in Taiwan.

(Version 3)

GBTru: $40

Paid: $_____

• The coachman has a mustache, and the wheels are round. Made in Sri Lanka.

Shopkeepers

59668 - Set of 4

1987 - 1988

OSRP: $15

GBTru: $25

Paid: $_____

• One of only two accessories to have "snow" sprinkled on them.

City Workers ✓

59676 - Set of 4

1987 - 1988

OSRP: $15

GBTru: $30

Paid: $_____

• One of only two acc. to have "snow" sprinkled on them.
• Some boxes read "City People"; some have no name.

Village Well & Holy Cross

65471 - Set of 2

1987 - 1989

OSRP: $13

GBTru: $85

Paid: $_____

• Early versions have blue water, dark birds. Later ones have colorless water, light birds.

Childe Pond And Skaters

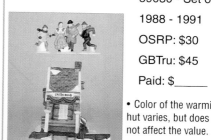

59030 - Set of 4

1988 - 1991

OSRP: $30

GBTru: $45

Paid: $_____

• Color of the warming hut varies, but does not affect the value.

Fezziwig And Friends

59285 - Set of 3

1988 - 1990

OSRP: $12.50

GBTru: $40

Paid: $_____

• Christmas Carol Series.

Nicholas Nickleby Characters ✓

59293 - Set of 4

1988 - 1991

OSRP: $20

GBTru: $25

Paid: $_____

• Sleeves have misspelling— "Nicholas Nickelby."

David Copperfield Characters

55514 - Set of 5

1989 - 1992

OSRP: $32.50

GBTru: $35

Paid: $_____

Lamplighter With Lamp ✓

55778 - Set of 2

1989 -

OSRP: $9

GBTru: -

Paid: $_____

Royal Coach ✓

55786

1989 - 1992

OSRP: $55

GBTru: $60

Paid: $_____

• Early release to NALED dealers.

Constables

55794 - Set of 3

1989 - 1991

OSRP: $17.50

GBTru: $45

Paid: $_____

Violet Vendor/Carolers/Chestnut Vendor ✓

55808 - Set of 3
1989 - 1992
OSRP: $23
GBTru: $32
Paid: $_____

King's Road Cab

55816
1989 - 1998
OSRP: $30
GBTru: $32
Paid: $_____

Christmas Carol Christmas Morning Figures ✓

55883 - Set of 3
1989 - 2002
OSRP: $18
GBTru: $20
Paid: $_____

• Christmas Carol Series.
• Early release to NALED dealers.

Christmas Carol Christmas Spirits Figures

55891 - Set of 4
1989 - 2001
OSRP: $27.50
GBTru: $33
Paid: $_____

• Christmas Carol Series.

Town Crier & Chimney Sweep ✓

3

55697 - Set of 2
1990 - 2001ᴹ
OSRP: $15
GBTru: $18
Paid: $_____

Carolers On The Doorstep ✓

(2) 55700 - Set of 4
1990 - 1993
OSRP: $25
GBTru: $28
Paid: $_____

Holiday Travelers ✓

55719 - Set of 3
1990 - 1999
OSRP: $22.50
GBTru: $28
Paid: $_____

The Flying Scot Train

55735 - Set of 4
1990 - 1998
OSRP: $48
GBTru: $45
Paid: $_____

Victoria Station Train Platform ✓

55751

1990 - 1999

OSRP: $20

GBTru: $22

Paid: $_____

• Porcelain and metal.
• Reads "Platform 1" on one side; "Platform 2" on the other.

Oliver Twist Characters ✓

(2)

55549 - Set of 3

1991 - 1993

OSRP: $35

GBTru: $30

Paid: $_____

Bringing Home The Yule Log

55581 - Set of 3

1991 - 1998

OSRP: $27.50

GBTru: $25

Paid: $_____

Poultry Market ✓

55590 - Set of 3

1991 - 1995

OSRP: $30

GBTru: $36

Paid: $_____

• Early samples have patches on the left hand side of the drape.
• 3 geese are separate in box.

Come Into The Inn

55603 - Set of 3

1991 - 1994

OSRP: $22

GBTru: $24

Paid: $_____

Holiday Coach ✓

55611

1991 - 1998

OSRP: $68

GBTru: $70

Paid: $_____

• Early pieces have gold chains, and later ones have silver chains.

Gate House ✓ Gift

(2)

55301

1992 - 1992

OSRP: $22.50

GBTru: $28

Paid: $_____

• Brick varies from gray to blue.
• Event piece for 1992 dealer Open Houses.

The Old Puppeteer ✓

(2)

58025 - Set of 3

1992 - 1995

OSRP: $32

GBTru: $36

Paid: $_____

• 2 marionettes are separate in box and can easily be lost.

The Bird Seller ✓

58033 - Set of 3
1992 - 1995
OSRP: $25
GBTru: $27
Paid: $_____

Village Street Peddlers ✓

(2)

58041 - Set of 2
1992 - 1994
OSRP: $16
GBTru: $20
Paid: $_____

English Post Box ✓

58050
1992 - 2000
OSRP: $4.50
GBTru: $8
Paid: $_____

• Metal.

Lionhead Bridge ✓

(2)

58645
1992 - 1997
OSRP: $22
GBTru: $25
Paid: $_____

Chelsea Market Fruit Monger & ✓ Cart

58130 - Set of 2
1993 - 1997
OSRP: $25
GBTru: $26
Paid: $_____

• Lantern and staff are separate in box.

Chelsea Market Fish Monger & ✓ Cart

58149 - Set of 2
1993 - 1997
OSRP: $25
GBTru: $25
Paid: $_____

• Lantern and staff are separate in box.

Chelsea Market Flower Monger & ✓ Cart

(2)

58157 - Set of 2
1993 - 2000
OSRP: $27.50
GBTru: $30
Paid: $_____

• A similar design was produced for Lord & Taylor. See the Special Design section.

Chelsea Lane Shoppers ✓

58165 - Set of 4
1993 - 1999
OSRP: $30
GBTru: $33
Paid: $_____

Vision Of A Christmas Past ✓

58173 - Set of 3
1993 - 1996
OSRP: $27.50
GBTru: $28
Paid: $_____

• Christmas Carol Series.

C. Bradford, Wheelwright & Son

58181 - Set of 2
1993 - 1996
OSRP: $24
GBTru: $25
Paid: $_____

Bringing Fleeces To The Mill ✓

58190 - Set of 2
1993 - 1998
OSRP: $35
GBTru: $38
Paid: $_____

Dashing Through The Snow

58203
1993 - 2002
OSRP: $32.50
GBTru: $36
Paid: $_____

Winter Sleighride

58254
1994 - 2001
OSRP: $18
GBTru: $24
Paid: $_____

• In early samples, the handle is attached to the sleigh with wires that curl before entering the sleigh.

Chelsea Market Mistletoe Monger & Cart ✓

58262 - Set of 2
1994 - 1998
OSRP: $25
GBTru: $26
Paid: $_____

• Lantern and staff are separate in box.

Chelsea Market Curiosities ✓ Monger & Cart

58270 - Set of 2
1994 - 1998
OSRP: $27.50
GBTru: $30
Paid: $_____

• Violin is separate in box.

Portobello Road Peddlers

58289 - Set of 3
1994 - 1998
OSRP: $27.50
GBTru: $30
Paid: $_____

Thatchers

58297 - Set of 3

1994 - 1997

OSRP: $35

GBTru: $35

Paid: $_____

• Frequently displayed with Cobb Cottage which has its roof undergoing repair.

A Peaceful Glow On Christmas Eve

58300 - Set of 3

1994 - 2003

OSRP: $30

GBTru: $26

Paid: $_____

Christmas Carol Holiday Trimming Set

58319 - Set of 21

1994 - 1997

OSRP: $65

GBTru: $65

Paid: $_____

• Christmas Carol Series.

Postern

98710

1994 - 1994

OSRP: $17.50

GBTru: $18

Paid: $_____

• Special imprint on bottom commemo-rates the village's 10th anniversary.

A Partridge In A Pear Tree - #I

58351

1995 - 1999

OSRP: $35

GBTru: $42

Paid: $_____

• 12 Days of Dickens' Village Series.
• 3 sets of bells are separate in box.

Two Turtle Doves - #II

58360 - Set of 4

1995 - 1999

OSRP: $32.50

GBTru: $42

Paid: $_____

• 12 Days of Dickens' Village Series.

Three French Hens - #III

58378 - Set of 3

1995 - 1999

OSRP: $32.50

GBTru: $42

Paid: $_____

• 12 Days of Dickens' Village Series.

Four Calling Birds - #IV

58379 - Set of 2

1995 - 1999

OSRP: $32.50

GBTru: $40

Paid: $_____

• 12 Days of Dickens' Village Series.

Five Golden Rings - #V

58381 - Set of 2

1995 - 1999

OSRP: $27.50

GBTru: $38

Paid: $_____

• 12 Days of Dickens' Village Series.

Six Geese A-Laying - #VI

58382 - Set of 2

1995 - 1999

OSRP: $30

GBTru: $38

Paid: $_____

• 12 Days of Dickens' Village Series.

Brixton Road Watchman ✔

58390 - Set of 2

1995 - 1999

OSRP: $25

GBTru: $28

Paid: $_____

• Man's walking stick is fragile.

Tallyho!

58391 - Set of 5

1995 - 1998

OSRP: $50

GBTru: $50

Paid: $_____

Chelsea Market Hat Monger & Cart

58392 - Set of 2

1995 - 2000

OSRP: $27.50

GBTru: $30

Paid: $_____

• Lantern and staff are separate in box.

Ye Olde Lamplighter Dickens' Village Sign

58393

1995 - 2001^M

OSRP: $20

GBTru: $25

Paid: $_____

Cobbler & Clock Peddler

58394 - Set of 2

1995 - 1997

OSRP: $25

GBTru: $25

Paid: $_____

• Though designed for Dickens', many collectors believe it more appropriate for Alpine.

Town Square Carolers

58327 - Set of 3

1995 - 1996

OSRP: *

GBTru: *

* Accessory contained in the Dickens' Village Start A Tradition Set.

Palace Guards

58336 - Set of 2

1996^M - 1996

OSRP: *

GBTru: *

* Accessory contained in the Ramsford Palace Set.

Tending The New Calves

58395 - Set of 3

1996^M - 1999

OSRP: $30

GBTru: $33

Paid: $_____

Caroling With The Cratchit Family

58396 - Set of 3

1996^M -

OSRP: $37.50

GBTru: -

Paid: $_____

• Christmas Carol Revisited Series.

Yeomen Of The Guard

58397 - Set of 5

1996^M - 1997

OSRP: $30

GBTru: $45

Paid: $_____

• Lances and swords are fragile.

Seven Swans A-Swimming - #VII

58383 - Set of 4

1996 - 2000

OSRP: $27.50

GBTru: $35

Paid: $_____

• 12 Days of Dickens' Village Series.

Eight Maids A-Milking - #VIII

58384 - Set of 2

1996 - 2000

OSRP: $25

GBTru: $30

Paid: $_____

• 12 Days of Dickens' Village Series.

The Fezziwig Delivery Wagon

58400

1996 -

OSRP: $32.50

GBTru: -

Paid: $_____

• Christmas Carol Revisited Series.
• Similar design made for Lord & Taylor. See Special Design section.

Red Christmas Sulky

58401
1996 - 2001
OSRP: $30
GBTru: $30
Paid: $_____

Gingerbread Vendor

58402 - Set of 2
1996 - 2001
OSRP: $22.50
GBTru: $25
Paid: $_____

A Christmas Carol Reading By Charles Dickens

58403 - Set of 4
1996 - 2001
OSRP: $45
GBTru: $45
Paid: $_____

• Christmas Carol Revisited Series.
• Sign is separate in box.

A Christmas Carol Reading By Charles Dickens

58404 - Set of 7
1996 - 1997
OSRP: $75
GBTru: $80
Paid: $_____

• Limited to 42,500.
• Christmas Carol Revisited Series.
• 4 lanterns and 2 signs separate in box.

Delivering Coal For The Hearth

58326 - Set of 2
1997ᴹ - 1999
OSRP: $32.50
GBTru: $30
Paid: $_____

• Early pieces have maroon wheels and buckets attached. Later ones have red wheels and buckets on hooks.

Nine Ladies Dancing - #IX

58385 - Set of 3
1997 - 2000
OSRP: $30
GBTru: $38
Paid: $_____

• 12 Days of Dickens' Village Series.

Ten Pipers Piping - #X

58386 - Set of 3
1997 - 2000
OSRP: $30
GBTru: $38
Paid: $_____

• 12 Days of Dickens' Village Series.

Ashley Pond Skating Party

58405 - Set of 6
1997 - 1999
OSRP: $70
GBTru: $70
Paid: $_____

• One side of hanging sign reads "Ashley Pond," the other "Ashley Road Pond."

The Fire Brigade Of London Town

58406 - Set of 5

1997 -

OSRP: $70

GBTru: -

Paid: $_____

Father Christmas's Journey

58407 - Set of 2

1997 - 2001

OSRP: $30

GBTru: $35

Paid: $_____

• A similar design was produced for North Pole City. See the Special Design section.

Christmas Pudding Costermonger

58408 - Set of 3

1997 - 2001^M

OSRP: $32.50

GBTru: $33

Paid: $_____

• Lantern is separate in box.

The Spirit Of Giving

58322 - Set of 3

1997 - 1998

OSRP: *

GBTru: *

* Accessory contained in the Dickens' Village Start A Tradition Set.

Manchester Square Accessory Set

58301 - Set of 7

1997 - 2000

OSRP: *

GBTru: *

* Accessory contained in the Manchester Square Set.
• Man's walking stick is fragile.

Christmas Apples

58308 - Set of 3

1998^M - 1998

OSRP: *

GBTru: *

* Accessory contained in the Seton Morris Spice Merchant Set.

Miss Havisham, Estella, And Pip

58310 - Set of 3

1998 - 2001

OSRP: *

GBTru: *

* Accessory contained in the Great Expectations Set.

Here We Come A-Wassailing

58410 - Set of 5

1998 - 2001^M

OSRP: $45

GBTru: $48

Paid: $_____

Sitting In Camden Park

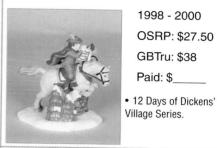

58411 - Set of 4

1998 -

OSRP: $35

GBTru: -

Paid: $_____

Eleven Lords A-Leaping - #XI

58413

1998 - 2000

OSRP: $27.50

GBTru: $38

Paid: $_____

• 12 Days of Dickens' Village Series.

Until We Meet Again

58414 - Set of 2

1998 - 2001

OSRP: $27.50

GBTru: $30

Paid: $_____

Child's Play

58415 - Set of 2

1998 - 2001ᴹ

OSRP: $25

GBTru: $27

Paid: $_____

Tending The Cold Frame

58416 - Set of 3

1998 - 1999

OSRP: $32.50

GBTru: $40

Paid: $_____

• A similar design was also produced for Bachman's. See the Special Design section.

Ale Mates

58417 - Set of 2

1998 -

OSRP: $25

GBTru: -

Paid: $_____

Twelve Drummers Drumming - #XII

58387

1999ᴹ - 2000

OSRP: $65

GBTru: $110

Paid: $_____

• 12 Days of Dickens' Village Series.

A Good Day's Catch

58420 - Set of 2

1999ᴹ - 2000

OSRP: $27.50

GBTru: $30

Paid: $_____

The Mother's Gift

58442

1999 - 2000

OSRP: *

GBTru: *

* Accessory contained in the Aldeburgh Music Box Shop Gift Set.

The Queen's Parliamentary Coach

58454

1999 - 2000

OSRP: $60

GBTru: $65

Paid: $_____

• Limited to year of production.

Members Of Parliament

58455 - Set of 2

1999 - 2000

OSRP: $19

GBTru: $20

Paid: $_____

• Paper in man's hand is real.

King's Road Market Cross

58456

1999 - 2000

OSRP: $25

GBTru: $30

Paid: $_____

• Dream House Sweep-stakes Deluxe Prize winner assisted in the design.

Meeting Family At The Railroad Station

58457 - Set of 4

1999 - 2001^M

OSRP: $32.50

GBTru: $33

Paid: $_____

Master Gardeners

58458 - Set of 2

1999 - 2001^M

OSRP: $30

GBTru: $32

Paid: $_____

Under The Bumbershoot

58460

1999 - 2002

OSRP: $20

GBTru: $22

Paid: $_____

• Similar designs were produced for the NCC. See the Special Design section.

A Treasure From The Sea

58461 - Set of 2

1999 - 2001^M

OSRP: $22.50

GBTru: $24

Paid: $_____

Fine Asian Antiques

58462 - Set of 2

1999 - 2001ᴹ

OSRP: $27.50

GBTru: $28

Paid: $_____

Busy Railway Station

58464 - Set of 3

1999 - 2001ᴹ

OSRP: $27.50

GBTru: $28

Paid: $_____

• Red and green lights are battery/adapter operated.

Locomotive Shed & Water Tower

58465

1999 - 2001

OSRP: $32.50

GBTru: $35

Paid: $_____

Queensbridge Railroad Yard Acc.

58466 - Set of 3

1999 - 2001ᴹ

OSRP: $37.50

GBTru: $38

Paid: $_____

12 Days Of Dickens' Village Sign

58467

1999 - 2000

OSRP: $20

GBTru: $35

Paid: $_____

• 12 Days of Dickens' Village Series.

Scrooge At Fezziwig's Ball

58470

2000ᴹ - 2000

OSRP: *

GBTru: *

* Accessory contained in the Fezziwig's Ballroom Gift Set.

Holiday Quintet

58520 - Set of 6

2000ᴹ -

OSRP: $37.50

GBTru: -

Paid: $_____

• Lamppost is battery/adapter operated.
• Bow and baton are fragile.

At The Fire House

05700 - Set of 3

2000ᴹ - 2000

OSRP: *

GBTru: *

* Accessory contained in the GCC Ashwick Lane Gift Set.

Sweet Roses

58475 - Set of 5

2000 - 2001

OSRP: *

GBTru: *

* Accessory contained in the Lilycott Garden Conservatory Gift Set.

Abington Locks

58521 - Set of 2

2000 - 2003

OSRP: $48

GBTru: $45

Paid: $_____

• Abington Canal Series.

Abington Canal Boat

58522 - Set of 2

2000 - 2002

OSRP: $35

GBTru: $35

Paid: $_____

• Abington Canal Series.

Gourmet Chocolates Delivery Wagon

58523

2000 - 2003

OSRP: $45

GBTru: $45

Paid: $_____

Hedgerow Dovecote

58524 - Set of 2

2000 - 2002

OSRP: $32.50

GBTru: $33

Paid: $_____

Par For The Course

58525 - Set of 3

2000 - 2002

OSRP: $27.50

GBTru: $28

Paid: $_____

Following The Leader

58526 - Set of 2

2000 - 2002

OSRP: $32.50

GBTru: $30

Paid: $_____

Master Potter

58527

2000 - 2002

OSRP: $18

GBTru: $22

Paid: $_____

Sliding Down Cornhill With Bob Cratchit

58528

2000 -

OSRP: $25

GBTru: -

Paid: $_____

• Christmas Carol Series.

Polo Players

58529 - Set of 2

2000 - 2002

OSRP: $40

GBTru: $44

Paid: $_____

These Are For You

58530 - Set of 2

2000 - 2002

OSRP: $25

GBTru: $25

Paid: $_____

Horses At The Lampguard

58531 - Set of 3

2000 -

OSRP: $45

GBTru: -

Paid: $_____

Keeping The Streets Clean

58532 - Set of 2

2000 - 2002

OSRP: $18

GBTru: $22

Paid: $_____

Merry Go Roundabout

58533

2000 -

OSRP: $32.50

GBTru: -

Paid: $_____

Sherlock Holmes-The Hansom Cab

58534

2000 - 2003

OSRP: $35

GBTru: $38

Paid: $_____

Abington Canal

58535 - Set of 2

2000 - 2003

OSRP: $30

GBTru: $33

Paid: $_____

• Abington Canal Series.

Abington Bridge

58536

2000 - 2003

OSRP: $37.50

GBTru: $38

Paid: $_____

• Abington Canal Series.

Elementary My Dear Watson

58601

2000 - 2003

OSRP: *

GBTru: *

* Accessory contained in Sherlock Holmes - 221B Baker Street set.

Christmas Eve Celebration

58485

2001^M - 2001

OSRP: *

GBTru: *

* Accessory contained in the Somerset Valley Church Gift Set.

Bob Cratchit And Tiny Tim

58537

2001^M -

OSRP: $15

GBTru: -

Paid: $_____

• Christmas Carol Series.

Ghost Of Christmas Present Visits Scrooge

58538

2001^M - 2001

OSRP: $15

GBTru: $22

Paid: $_____

• Christmas Carol Series.

High Tea

58487

2001 - 2002

OSRP: *

GBTru: *

* The accessory contained in Mrs. Brimm's Tea Room Gift Set.

Dickens Writing

58488

2001 - 2003

OSRP: *

GBTru: *

* The accessory contained in the Dickens' Gad's Hill Chalet.

Doorman

58494

2001 - 2003

OSRP: *

GBTru: *

* The accessory contained in The Slone Hotel.

The Big Prize Turkey

58539 - Set of 2

2001 -

OSRP: $27.50

GBTru: -

Paid: $_____

• Christmas Carol Series.

Cobbler's Corner Stand

58540 - Set of 2

2001 -

OSRP: $27.50

GBTru: -

Paid: $_____

Blacksmith To The Rescue

58541

2001 -

OSRP: $22.50

GBTru: -

Paid: $_____

• Originally was named "Shoeing The Horse."

A Christmas Carol Visit

58542 - Set of 4

2001 -

OSRP: $27.50

GBTru: -

Paid: $_____

• Christmas Carol Series.

Taking Grain To The Mill

58545

2001 - 2003

OSRP: $20

GBTru: $22

Paid: $_____

• Abington Canal Series.

A Family Tradition

58546 - Set of 2

2001 - 2002

OSRP: $20

GBTru: $22

Paid: $_____

Lock Keeper

58547

2001 - 2003

OSRP: $12.50

GBTru: $15

Paid: $_____

• Abington Canal Series.

Chimney Sweep & Son

58548

2001 -

OSRP: $18.50

GBTru: -

Paid: $_____

An Elegant Ride

58549

2001 -

OSRP: $30

GBTru: -

Paid: $_____

Street Merchants

58550 - Set of 3

2001 -

OSRP: $17.50

GBTru: -

Paid: $_____

Formal Gardens

58551

2001 - 2003

OSRP: $65

GBTru: $65

Paid: $_____

Holiday Joy

58552

2001 - 2003

OSRP: $32.50

GBTru: $40

Paid: $_____

• Battery/ adapter operated.

Dickens' Raising The Flag

58555

2001 - 2003

OSRP: $15

GBTru: $18

Paid: $_____

• Includes British and Canadian flags.

Winter Frolic

05925

2002^M - 2002

OSRP: *

GBTru: *

* The accessory contained in Christmas At Codington Cottage.

Bearing Gifts

58506

2002^M - 2002

OSRP: *

GBTru: *

* The accessory contained in 1 Royal Tree Court.

Lord Of The Follies

58633

2002^M - 2002

OSRP: *

GBTru: *

* The accessory contained in Hop Castle Folly.

Chestnut Vendor

58557

2002^M -

OSRP: $32.50

GBTru: -

Paid: $_____

• Battery/ adapter operated.

The First Edition

58513

2002 -

OSRP: *

GBTru: *

* The accessory contained in The Daily News.

Bringing Home The Holly

58514

2002 - 2003

OSRP: *

GBTru: *

* The accessory contained in Codington Cottage.

All The World's A Stage

58515

2002 - 2003

OSRP: *

GBTru: *

* The accessory contained in Shakespeare's Birthplace.

Rose Garden Beauty

58518

2002 - 2003

OSRP: *

GBTru: *

* The accessory contained in Sweetbriar Cottage.

A Gentleman and Lady

58559

2002 -

OSRP: $15

GBTru: -

Paid: $_____

London Newspaper Stand

58560 - Set of 2

2002 -

OSRP: $25

GBTru: -

Paid: $_____

Jack-Of-The-Lantern

58561

2002 -

OSRP: $25

GBTru: -

Paid: $_____

• All Hallow's Eve design.

Last Mail Call Of The Day

58562

2002 -

OSRP: $10

GBTru: -

Paid: $_____

Love or Money?

58563

2002 -

OSRP: $15

GBTru: -

Paid: $_____

• Christmas Carol
Series.

Temple Bar

58564

2002 - 2003

OSRP: $60

GBTru: $55

Paid: $_____

• Historical Landmark
Series.

Covered Bridge At The Manor

58565

2002 -

OSRP: $45

GBTru: -

Paid: $_____

The Charitable Vicar

58566 - Set of 2

2002 -

OSRP: $25

GBTru: -

Paid: $_____

A Rare Find

58567

2002 -

OSRP: $15

GBTru: -

Paid: $_____

• Battery/ adapter
operated.

A Christmas Beginning

58568

2002 -

OSRP: $17.50

GBTru: -

Paid: $_____

Omnibus

58569

2002 -

OSRP: $55

GBTru: -

Paid: $_____

The Coffee-Stall

58571 - Set of 2

2003^M -

OSRP: $27.50

GBTru: -

Paid: $_____

Victorian Skaters

58700 - Set of 3

2003^M -

OSRP: *

GBTru: *

* The accessory contained in London Skating Club.

The Halfpenny Showman

58572

2003 -

OSRP: $17.50

GBTru: -

Paid: $_____

The Strange Case Of Dr. Jekyll & Mr. Hyde

58573

2003 -

OSRP: $15

GBTru: -

Paid: $_____

• All Hallow's Eve Series.
• Inspired by Robert Louis Stevenson's novel.

Horse Drawn Hearse

58574

2003 -

OSRP: $35

GBTru: -

Paid: $_____

• All Hallow's Eve Series.

Christmas Morning Parade

58575 - Set of 2

2003 -

OSRP: $17.50

GBTru: -

Paid: $_____

London Gas Worker

58576

2003 -

OSRP: $15

GBTru: -

Paid: $_____

Dickens Learns To Read

58577

2003 -

OSRP: $12.50

GBTru: -

Paid: $_____

• Dickens' Village 20th Anniversary Series.

A Story For The Children

58578

2003 -

OSRP: $12.50

GBTru: -

Paid: $_____

• Dickens' Village 20th Anniversary Series.

Ready For Duty, Queens Port

58579

2003 -

OSRP: $15

GBTru: -

Paid: $_____

Bringing Christmas Cheer, Queens Port

58580

2003 -

OSRP: $20

GBTru: -

Paid: $_____

A Busy Day In Town

58581 - Set of 3

2003 -

OSRP: $25

GBTru: -

Paid: $_____

• Dickens' Village 20th Anniversary Series.

A Basket Full Of Blooms

58583

2003 -

OSRP: $16.50

GBTru: -

Paid: $_____

For You, My Lady

58704

2003 -

OSRP: *

GBTru: *

* The accessory contained in Green's Park Nosegays.

Scrooge

2004 -

OSRP: *

GBTru: *

* The accessory contained in Belle's House - Special Edition

_____

_____

____ - ____

OSRP: $_____

GBTru: -

Paid: $_____

New England Village® Series

In its diversity, there is also its charm. The northeastern corner of the country contains the six states jointly known as New England. Blazing colors of autumn grace the pages of innumerable calendars, but nature's glory is only part of New England's fame. It is not an overlooked part, though, for Autumn Birches and Maples enhance many displays, and the accompanying activity of Tapping the Maples is another highlight. Some of the recent village pieces lack snow, further enabling collectors to create year round scenes.

Agriculture once dominated the area, and multiple barns, farmhouses, and livestock depict that segment of the region's past. Even cranberry bogs are represented. Equally a part of the area's history and economy was the maritime industry. The Atlantic's waters provided livelihood to Lobster Trappers, boat builders, and fish canneries. Its rugged coast accounts for the several lighthouses that have been captured in miniature. An expanding Seaside Series enables collectors to truly develop this aspect of New England life.

The rushing streams generated power for the start of America's industrial age, a period captured in the imposing Smythe Woolen Mill. Many New England towns grew up around these economic centers. If the mills were one symbol of the area in the 1800s, another was certainly its churches. Vivid scenes of fall foliage often include the stately white steeple of a local church. Church bazaars were a highlight for these small towns, loosely connected by rail stations, but strongly unified by the work ethic and patriotic spirit such as that demonstrated by Paul Revere.

NEW ENGLAND VILLAGE- Set of 7   65307

Dates	OSRP	GBTru	Paid
1986 - 1989	$170	$950	$_____

• None of the seven buildings have names on the bottom.

Apothecary   65307

Dates	OSRP	GBTru	Paid
1986 - 1989	$25	$105	$_____

General Store   65307

Dates	OSRP	GBTru	Paid
1986 - 1989	$25	$230	$_____

• Do not handle by porch posts; they are very fragile.

Nathaniel Bingham Fabrics   65307

Dates	OSRP	GBTru	Paid
1986 - 1989	$25	$120	$_____

Livery Stable & Boot Shop   65307

Dates	OSRP	GBTru	Paid
1986 - 1989	$25	$110	$_____

Brick Town Hall   65307

Dates	OSRP	GBTru	Paid
1986 - 1989	$25	$120	$_____

Steeple Church (Version 1)   65307

Dates	OSRP	GBTru	Paid
1986 - 1989	**$25**	**$130**	$_____

- Front tree is attached with porcelain slip.
- Sleeve is open on sides.

(Version 2)

		GBTru	Paid
		$85	$_____

- Front tree is attached with glue.
- Sleeve is open at top and bottom.
- This design was re-issued in 1989 with item # 65390.

Red Schoolhouse   65307

Dates	OSRP	GBTru	Paid
1986 - 1989	**$25**	**$230**	$_____

Jacob Adams Farmhouse & Barn   65382

Dates	OSRP	GBTru	Paid
1986 - 1989	**$65**	**$350**	$_____

- Early pieces have sleeves that read "New England Village Farm." Later ones read "Jacob Adams Farmhouse and Barn."

- Because the animals were simply in tissue and placed in the box with no separate compartments, they are often damaged.
- Set of 5 includes Farmhouse, Barn, 2 cows, and a horse.
- Do not handle house by columns.

Craggy Cove Lighthouse   59307

Dates	OSRP	GBTru	Paid
1987 - 1994	**$35**	**$55**	$_____

- Early pieces have a drain hole at the bottom of the tower. Later ones do not. Not only does the hole help collectors decide how early their piece was manufactured, but it also allows them to insert a "beacon."

Weston Train Station 59315

Dates	OSRP	GBTru	Paid
1987 - 1989	$42	$205	$_____

• This station looks very much like the now-dilapidated station in the Boston, MA suburb of Weston.

Smythe Woolen Mill 65439

Dates	OSRP	GBTru	Paid
1987 - 1988	$42	$890	$_____

• Limited Edition of 7,500.

Timber Knoll Log Cabin 65447

Dates	OSRP	GBTru	Paid
1987 - 1990	$28	$135	$_____

• Bottomstamp reads "Log Cabin."
• Do not handle by columns.

Old North Church 59323

Dates	OSRP	GBTru	Paid
1988 - 1998	$40	$45	$_____

• Inspired by the historic landmark in Boston, Christ Church, where sexton Robert Newman hung lanterns in its steeple to warn colonists in Charlestown that the British were on their way to Lexington and Concord.

CHERRY LANE SHOPS - Set of 3 59390

Dates	OSRP	GBTru	Paid
1988 - 1990	$80	$265	$_____

Ben's Barbershop 59390

Dates	OSRP	GBTru	Paid
1988 - 1990	$27	$95	$_____

Otis Hayes Butcher Shop　　　　　　　59390

Dates	OSRP	GBTru	Paid
1988 - 1990	$27	$75	$_____

• Do not handle by columns.

Anne Shaw Toys　　　　　　　　　　59390

Dates	OSRP	GBTru	Paid
1988 - 1990	$27	$115	$_____

Ada's Bed And Boarding House　　　59404
(Version 1)

Dates	OSRP	GBTru	Paid
1988 - 1991	$36	$150	$_____

• Rear Steps: Part of the building's mold.
• 2nd Floor Windows: Alternating yellow panes.
• Color: Lemon yellow.
• Samples are pink/wine.　　**GBTru: $475**　Paid: $_____

(Version 2)

	GBTru	Paid
	$110	$_____

• Rear Steps: Part of the building's mold.
• 2nd Floor Windows: Alternating yellow panes.
• Color: Pale yellow.

(Version 3)

	GBTru	Paid
	$75	$_____

• Rear Steps: Separate attachment.
• 2nd Floor Windows: Top halves solid, bottom halves cut out.
• Color: Pale yellow.
• This version also has less snow on the roof and at base.

Steeple Church (Version 3)　　　　　65390

Dates	OSRP	GBTru	Paid
1989 - 1990	$30	$75	$_____

• Front tree is attached with porcelain slip.
• Notice the different item number from original 1986 piece.

Berkshire House (Williamsburg Blue)   59420

Dates	OSRP	GBTru	Paid
1989 - 1991	$40	$110	$_____

- This version has pale shutters and porch rail spindles.
- Be careful when removing this piece from the box as it is very easy to break off the porch railing.
- Samples are forest green.   **GBTru: $90**   Paid: $_____

(Teal Version)

	GBTru	Paid
	$75	$_____

- This version has yellow shutters and porch rail spindles.
- Be careful when removing this piece from the box as it is very easy to break off the porch railing.

Jannes Mullet Amish Farm House   59439

Dates	OSRP	GBTru	Paid
1989 - 1992	$32	$65	$_____

Jannes Mullet Amish Barn   59447

Dates	OSRP	GBTru	Paid
1989 - 1992	$48	$70	$_____

Shingle Creek House   59463

Dates	OSRP	GBTru	Paid
1990 - 1994	$37.50	$40	$_____

- Early release to Showcase and NALED dealers.

Captain's Cottage   59471

Dates	OSRP	GBTru	Paid
1990 - 1996	$40	$50	$_____

- Do not handle by columns.

SLEEPY HOLLOW - Set of 3   59544

Dates	OSRP	GBTru	Paid
1990 - 1993	$96	$150	$_____

• This set was inspired by Washington Irving's classic, *The Legend of Sleepy Hollow*. The story takes place along the Hudson River in North Tarrytown, NY.

Sleepy Hollow School   59544

Dates	OSRP	GBTru	Paid
1990 - 1993	$32	$75	$_____

• A bell hangs in the tower.

Van Tassel Manor   59544

Dates	OSRP	GBTru	Paid
1990 - 1993	$32	$45	$_____

Ichabod Crane's Cottage   59544

Dates	OSRP	GBTru	Paid
1990 - 1993	$32	$45	$_____

Sleepy Hollow Church   59552

Dates	OSRP	GBTru	Paid
1990 - 1993	$36	$65	$_____

McGrebe-Cutters & Sleighs   56405

Dates	OSRP	GBTru	Paid
1991 - 1995	$45	$50	$_____

Bluebird Seed And Bulb

56421

Dates	OSRP	GBTru	Paid
1992 - 1996	$48	$50	$_____

Yankee Jud Bell Casting

56430

Dates	OSRP	GBTru	Paid
1992 - 1995	$44	$45	$_____

Stoney Brook Town Hall

56448

Dates	OSRP	GBTru	Paid
1992 - 1995	$42	$50	$_____

A. BIELER FARM - Set of 2

56480

Dates	OSRP	GBTru	Paid
1993 - 1996	$92	$100	$_____

Pennsylvania Dutch Farmhouse

56481

Dates	OSRP	GBTru	Paid
1993 - 1996	$42	$55	$_____

Pennsylvania Dutch Barn

56482

Dates	OSRP	GBTru	Paid
1993 - 1996	$50	$55	$_____

Blue Star Ice Co.

56472

Dates	OSRP	GBTru	Paid
1993 - 1997	$45	$55	$_____

• Acrylic ice blocks easily come unglued.

Arlington Falls Church

56510

Dates	OSRP	GBTru	Paid
1994ᴹ - 1997	$40	$50	$_____

• Do not handle by columns.

Cape Keag Fish Cannery

56529

Dates	OSRP	GBTru	Paid
1994 - 1998	$48	$50	$_____

Pigeonhead Lighthouse

56537

Dates	OSRP	GBTru	Paid
1994 - 1998	$50	$60	$_____

• Posts near beacon and at front of building are extremely fragile.

BREWSTER BAY COTTAGES - Set of 2

56570

Dates	OSRP	GBTru	Paid
1995ᴹ - 1997	$90	$100	$_____

Jeremiah Brewster House

56568

Dates	OSRP	GBTru	Paid
1995ᴹ - 1997	$45	$50	$_____

• Early pieces have sleeves that read "Thomas T. Julian House." Later ones have stickers with the correct name placed over the mistake.

Thomas T. Julian House

56569

Dates	OSRP	GBTru	Paid
1995^M - 1997	$45	$50	$_____

• Early pieces have sleeves that read "Jeremiah Brewster House." Later ones have stickers with the correct name placed over the mistake.
• Do not handle by columns.

Chowder House

56571

Dates	OSRP	GBTru	Paid
1995 - 1998	$40	$50	$_____

• Sign is separate in box.

Woodbridge Post Office

56572

Dates	OSRP	GBTru	Paid
1995 - 1998	$40	$45	$_____

Pierce Boat Works

56573

Dates	OSRP	GBTru	Paid
1995 - 2000	$55	$60	$_____

Apple Valley School

56172

Dates	OSRP	GBTru	Paid
1996^M -	$35	-	$_____

J. Hudson Stoveworks

56574

Dates	OSRP	GBTru	Paid
1996 - 1998	$60	$60	$_____

• Black metal kettle is separate in box.

Navigational Charts & Maps 56575

Dates	OSRP	GBTru	Paid
1996 - 1999	$48	$60	$_____

• Several attachments are very fragile.

Bobwhite Cottage 56576

Dates	OSRP	GBTru	Paid
1996 - 2001	$50	$60	$_____

• A bobwhite is a small quail native to North America.
• Spires are fragile.

Van Guilder's Ornamental Ironworks 56577

Dates	OSRP	GBTru	Paid
1997ᴹ - 1999	$50	$50	$_____

• This is the first New England Village design with multiple weathervanes.

East Willet Pottery 56578

Dates	OSRP	GBTru	Paid
1997 - 1999	$45	$50	$_____

• Do not handle by columns.

Steen's Maple House 56579

Dates	OSRP	GBTru	Paid
1997 - 2001	$60	$60	$_____

• Uses Magic Smoke to create smoking effect rising from the chimney.
• Buckets are separate in box.

Semple's Smokehouse 56580

Dates	OSRP	GBTru	Paid
1997 - 1999	$45	$55	$_____

The Emily Louise

56581

Dates	OSRP	GBTru	Paid
1998^M - 2000	$70	$75	$_____

- The wreath is "free-floating" and is easily damaged.
- 2 flags are separate in box.
- Set of 2 includes the ship and a dock.

Franklin Hook & Ladder Co.

56601

Dates	OSRP	GBTru	Paid
1998 - 2000	$55	$60	$_____

Moggin Falls General Store

56602

Dates	OSRP	GBTru	Paid
1998 -	$60	-	$_____

- Picture on sleeve is reversed.
- Flag and 2 signs are separate in box.

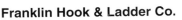

Deacon's Way Chapel

56604

Dates	OSRP	GBTru	Paid
1998 - 2000	$68	$70	$_____

Harper's Farm

56605

Dates	OSRP	GBTru	Paid
1998 - 2000	$65	$70	$_____

- Weathervane and 2 spires are separate in box.

Little Women - The March Residence
56606

Dates	OSRP	GBTru	Paid
1999ᴹ - 2000	$90	$100	$____

- Second in the Literary Classic Series. See this series in the Small Collection section.
- Louisa May Alcott based the March Residence on the Orchard House in Concord, MA where she grew up.
- Set of 4 plus book includes the Residence and the accessory "A Letter From Papa" which depicts Marmie, Jo, Amy, Beth, and Meg.
- The water pump's handle is very fragile.

Hale & Hardy House
56610

Dates	OSRP	GBTru	Paid
1999 - 2001	$60	$65	$____

- 2 signs are separate in box.

Trinity Ledge
56611

Dates	OSRP	GBTru	Paid
1999 - 2002	$85	$85	$____

- The three pinafore flags attached signal U - S - A.
- Includes U.S. and Canadian flags.

Harper's Farmhouse
56612

Dates	OSRP	GBTru	Paid
1999 -	$57	-	$____

- Dream House Sweepstakes Grand Prize winner assisted in the design.
- 3 lightning rods are separate in box.

P. L. Wheeler's Bicycle Shop
56613

Dates	OSRP	GBTru	Paid
1999 - 2002	$57	$60	$____

- This is one of the first New England pieces not to have snow.
- Sign and weathervane are packaged separately.

Platt's Candles & Wax

56614

Dates	OSRP	GBTru	Paid
1999 - 2001	$60	$55	$____

• Candelabra and weathervane are separate in box.

Susquehanna Station

56624

Dates	OSRP	GBTru	Paid
2000ᴹ - 2002	$60	$55	$____

• Set of 2 includes the Station and signal with coal car.

Mountain View Cabin

56625

Dates	OSRP	GBTru	Paid
2000 - 2001	$55	$150	$____

• 25th Anniversary Limited Edition of 10,000.

Verna Mae's Boutique Gift Set

56626

Dates	OSRP	GBTru	Paid
2000 - 2001	$65	$70	$____

• Discover Department 56 Spring Event Piece.
• Set of 3 includes building, "New Spring Finery" accessory, and flowering tree.
• Sign is separate in box.

The Cranberry House
56627

Dates	OSRP	GBTru	Paid
2000 - 2002	$60	$60	$_____

• Weathervane and 3 utensils are separate in the box.

Wm. Walton Fine Clocks & Pocket Pieces
56628

Dates	OSRP	GBTru	Paid
2000 - 2002	$60	$60	$_____

• Clock and 2 lanterns are separate in the box.
• Hitching post is fragile.

Laurel Hill Church
56629

Dates	OSRP	GBTru	Paid
2000 - 2003	$68	$70	$_____

• This is the first church to include a cemetery.
• Do not handle by fence when removing from box.
• Gravestones are fragile.

Revere Silver Works
56632

Dates	OSRP	GBTru	Paid
2001ᴹ - 2002	$60	$60	$_____

• Set of 2 includes shop and "Creating Silver Keepsakes."
• Pitcher ornament is included separately in the box.

Breakers Point Lighthouse
56636

Dates	OSRP	GBTru	Paid
2001 -	$85	-	$_____

• Seaside Series.
• Weathervane is separate in the box.

Springfield Studio Gift Set

56634

Dates	OSRP	GBTru	Paid
2001 - 2002	$65	$70	$_____

• First available during the Mother's Day Spring program.
• Set of 5 includes Studio, 2 piece accessory "Spring Portrait," sign, and tree.
• Hanging plant is separate in the box.
• 5% of proceeds goes to fight against breast cancer.

Captain Kensey's House

56651

Dates	OSRP	GBTru	Paid
2001 - 2003	$55	$65	$_____

• Seaside Series.

Whale Tale Pub & Inn

56652

Dates	OSRP	GBTru	Paid
2001 - 2003	$62	$65	$_____

• Seaside Series.
• Sign is separate in the box.

Otter Creek Sawmill

56653

Dates	OSRP	GBTru	Paid
2001 - 2003	$70	$65	$_____

• Mountain Lake Lodge Series.

Whitehill Round Barn

56654

Dates	OSRP	GBTru	Paid
2001 -	$65	-	$_____

• Four weathervanes are separate in the box.

Chapman's Cider House

56655

Dates	OSRP	GBTru	Paid
2002^M -	$65	-	$____

• Named in honor of Johnny Appleseed.
• Sign is separate in the box.
• Do not handle by porch posts.

Salt Bay Lobster Co.

56658

Dates	OSRP	GBTru	Paid
2002 -	$57	-	$____

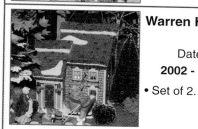

Warren Homestead And Walden Cottage

56659

Dates	OSRP	GBTru	Paid
2002 -	$85	-	$____

• Set of 2.

Hutchison Grain Elevator

56660

Dates	OSRP	GBTru	Paid
2002 -	$55	-	$____

Castle Glassworks

56661

Dates	OSRP	GBTru	Paid
2002 - 2003	$75	$60	$____

• Limited to 15,000 numbered pieces.

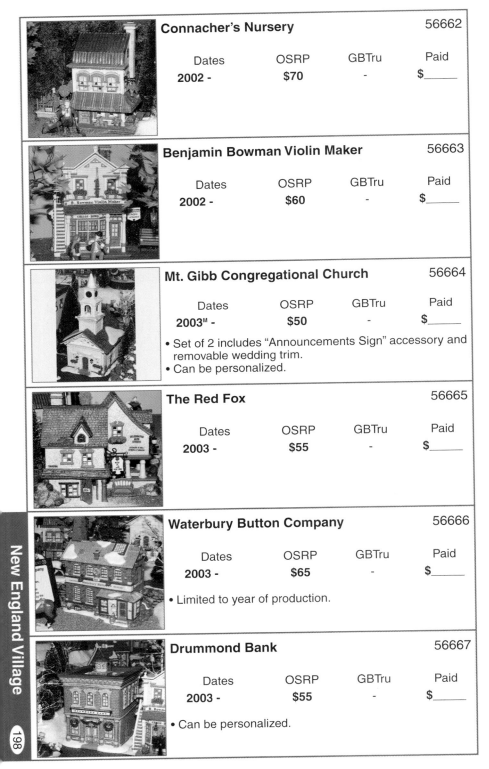

Connacher's Nursery 56662

Dates	OSRP	GBTru	Paid
2002 -	$70	-	$____

Benjamin Bowman Violin Maker 56663

Dates	OSRP	GBTru	Paid
2002 -	$60	-	$____

Mt. Gibb Congregational Church 56664

Dates	OSRP	GBTru	Paid
2003ᴹ -	$50	-	$____

- Set of 2 includes "Announcements Sign" accessory and removable wedding trim.
- Can be personalized.

The Red Fox 56665

Dates	OSRP	GBTru	Paid
2003 -	$55	-	$____

Waterbury Button Company 56666

Dates	OSRP	GBTru	Paid
2003 -	$65	-	$____

- Limited to year of production.

Drummond Bank 56667

Dates	OSRP	GBTru	Paid
2003 -	$55	-	$____

- Can be personalized.

Use the space(s) below to update your guide when the midyear introductions are announced.

Photos of the midyear introductions will be included in the July-August issue of *the Village Chronicle* magazine.

	Dates	OSRP	GBTru	Paid
	____ - ____	$____	-	$____

	Dates	OSRP	GBTru	Paid
	____ - ____	$____	-	$____

	Dates	OSRP	GBTru	Paid
	____ - ____	$____	-	$____

	Dates	OSRP	GBTru	Paid
	____ - ____	$____	-	$____

	Dates	OSRP	GBTru	Paid
	____ - ____	$____	-	$____

Notes:

Covered Wooden Bridge

65315

1986 - 1990

OSRP: $10

GBTru: $25

Paid: $_____

• The sleeve reads "Covered Bridge."

New England Winter Set

65323 - Set of 5

1986 - 1990

OSRP: $18

GBTru: $30

Paid: $_____

• Sleeves on early pieces read "Winter Village Accessories."

New England Village Sign

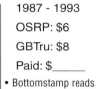

65706

1987 - 1993

OSRP: $6

GBTru: $8

Paid: $_____

• Bottomstamp reads "Handcrafted by Jiean Fung Porcelains, Taiwan."
• Early signs have more detail and richer colors.

Maple Sugaring Shed

65897 - Set of 3

1987 - 1989

OSRP: $19

GBTru: $120

Paid: $_____

• Smokestack and pegs in trees are very fragile.

Village Harvest People

59412 - Set of 4

1988 - 1991

OSRP: $27.50

GBTru: $35

Paid: $_____

• The sleeves read "Harvest Time."

Woodcutter And Son

59862 - Set of 2

1988 - 1990

OSRP: $10

GBTru: $35

Paid: $_____

Red Covered Bridge ✓

59870

1988 - 1994

OSRP: $15

GBTru: $20

Paid: $_____

Farm Animals

59455 - Set of 4

1989 - 1991

OSRP: $15

GBTru: $30

Paid: $_____

• Another item with the same name was produced in 1995.

Amish Family (With Mustache)   (Without Mustache)

59480 - Set of 3

1990 - 1992

OSRP: $20

GBTru: $45

Paid: $_____

GBTru: $28

Paid: $_____

• Father has mustache which is against Amish customs.
• Early release: NALED and Showcase dealers.

• Re-issued with father without mustache.

Amish Buggy

59498

1990 - 1992

OSRP: $22

GBTru: $45

Paid: $_____

Sleepy Hollow Characters

59560 - Set of 3

1990 - 1992

OSRP: $27.50

GBTru: $30

Paid: $_____

• From characters in Washington Irving's "Legend of Sleepy Hollow."

Skating Party

55239 - Set of 3

1991 - 2001

OSRP: $27.50

GBTru: $28

Paid: $_____

Market Day

56413 - Set of 3

1991 - 1993

OSRP: $35

GBTru: $30

Paid: $_____

Harvest Seed Cart

56456 - Set of 3

1992 - 1995

OSRP: $27.50

GBTru: $30

Paid: $_____

Town Tinker

56464 - Set of 2

1992 - 1995

OSRP: $24

GBTru: $25

Paid: $_____

• Pots and pans are separate in box, and are easily lost.

Knife Grinder

56499 - Set of 2

1993 - 1996

OSRP: $22.50

GBTru: $25

Paid: $_____

• A pair of ice skates is separate in box.

Blue Star Ice Harvesters

56502 - Set of 2

1993 - 1997

OSRP: $27.50

GBTru: $28

Paid: $_____

• Porcelain and acrylic.
• Acrylic ice blocks easily come unglued.

Over The River And Through The Woods

56545

1994 - 1998

OSRP: $35

GBTru: $35

Paid: $_____

The Old Man And The Sea

56553 - Set of 3

1994 - 1998

OSRP: $25

GBTru: $30

Paid: $_____

Two Rivers Bridge

56561

1994 - 1997

OSRP: $35

GBTru: $38

Paid: $_____

• Porcelain and resin.

Farm Animals

56588 - Set of 8

1995 -

OSRP: $32.50

GBTru: -

Paid: $_____

• Another item with the same name was produced in 1989.
• Also has 8 hay bales.

Lobster Trappers

56589 - Set of 4

1995 - 2000

OSRP: $35

GBTru: $38

Paid: $_____

• 3 "cooked" lobsters are separate in box.
• Lobster in man's hand often breaks off.

Lumberjacks

56590 - Set of 2

1995 - 1998

OSRP: $30

GBTru: $35

Paid: $_____

• Porcelain and wood.

New England Village Acc.

203

Harvest Pumpkin Wagon

56591

1995 - 1999

OSRP: $45

GBTru: $50

Paid: $_____

• Similar designs were produced for Heinz and Bachman's. See the Special Design section.

Fresh Paint New England Village Sign

56592

1995 - 2001ᴹ

OSRP: $20

GBTru: $24

Paid: $_____

A New Potbellied Stove For Christmas

56593 - Set of 2

1996 - 1998

OSRP: $35

GBTru: $37

Paid: $_____

Christmas Bazaar Handmade Quilts

56594 - Set of 2

1996 - 1999

OSRP: $25

GBTru: $25

Paid: $_____

Christmas Bazaar Woolens & Preserves

56595 - Set of 2

1996 - 1999

OSRP: $25

GBTru: $28

Paid: $_____

• Early shipments read "Jame & Jellies" on the sign.

Christmas Bazaar Flapjacks & Hot Cider

56596 - Set of 2

1997 - 1999

OSRP: $27.50

GBTru: $28

Paid: $_____

Christmas Bazaar Toy Vendor & Cart

56597 - Set of 2

1997 - 1999

OSRP: $27.50

GBTru: $28

Paid: $_____

Christmas Bazaar Sign

56598 - Set of 2

1997 - 1999

OSRP: $16

GBTru: $20

Paid: $_____

Tapping The Maples

56599 - Set of 7

1997 - 2001ᴹ

OSRP: $85

GBTru: $80

Paid: $_____

Sea Captain & His Mates

56587 - Set of 4

1998ᴹ - 2000

OSRP: $32.50

GBTru: $35

Paid: $_____

Load Up The Wagon

56630 - Set of 2

1998 - 2002

OSRP: $40

GBTru: $40

Paid: $_____

• Actual wood is used for the logs.

Under The Mistletoe

56631

1998 - 2001

OSRP: $16.50

GBTru: $18

Paid: $_____

Fly-casting In The Brook

56633

1998 - 2002

OSRP: $15

GBTru: $18

Paid: $_____

• Caution: Wire is very fragile.

Volunteer Firefighters

56635 - Set of 2

1998 - 2000

OSRP: $37.50

GBTru: $40

Paid: $_____

Farmer's Market

56637 - Set of 2

1998 - 2003

OSRP: $55

GBTru: $60

Paid: $_____

An Artist's Touch

56638

1998 - 2001ᴹ

OSRP: $17

GBTru: $18

Paid: $_____

• "Canvas" is porcelain with a decal, and easel is metal.

A Letter From Papa

56606 - Set of 3

1999ᴹ - 2000

OSRP: *

GBTru: *

* Accessory contained in Little Women - The March Residence.

It's Almost Thanksgiving

56639 - Set of 4

1999ᴹ -

OSRP: $60

GBTru: -

Paid: $_____

• Porcelain and resin.

Pennyfarthing Pedaling

56615

1999 - 2003

OSRP: $13.50

GBTru: $12

Paid: $_____

Doctor's House Call

56616 - Set of 2

1999 - 2001

OSRP: $27.50

GBTru: $25

Paid: $_____

The Sailors' Knot

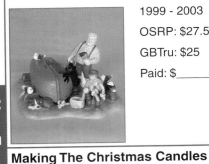

56617

1999 - 2003

OSRP: $27.50

GBTru: $25

Paid: $_____

The Woodworker

56619

1999 - 2003

OSRP: $35

GBTru: $33

Paid: $_____

• The Dream House Sweepstakes Deluxe Prize winner assisted in the design.

Making The Christmas Candles

56620 - Set of 2

1999 - 2002

OSRP: $25

GBTru: $24

Paid: $_____

Let's Go One More Time

56621 - Set of 3

1999 - 2001

OSRP: $30

GBTru: $27

Paid: $_____

Dairy Delivery Sleigh

56622
1999 -
OSRP: $37.50
GBTru: -
Paid: $_____

Mill Creek Crossing

56623
1999 - 2003
OSRP: $32.50
GBTru: $25
Paid: $_____

Postal Pick-up

56641
2000^M - 2001^M
OSRP: $14
GBTru: $18
Paid: $_____

New Spring Finery

56626
2000 - 2001
OSRP: *
GBTru: *

* Accessory contained in the Verna Mae's Boutique Gift Set.

A Day At The Cabin

56642 - Set of 2
2000 - 2003
OSRP: $25
GBTru: $25
Paid: $_____

Gathering Cranberries

56644
2000 - 2002
OSRP: $30
GBTru: $30
Paid: $_____

The Perfect Tree

56645
2000 -
OSRP: $20
GBTru: -
Paid: $_____

Here Comes Sinter Klaus

56646
2000 - 2002
OSRP: $17
GBTru: $18
Paid: $_____

Best Of The Harvest

56647 - Set of 2

2000 - 2002

OSRP: $25

GBTru: $25

Paid: $_____

Creating Silver Keepsakes

56632

2001^M - 2002

OSRP: *

GBTru: *

* Accessory contained in Revere Silver Works.

Silver For Sale

56650 - Set of 2

2001^M - 2002

OSRP: $20

GBTru: $22

Paid: $_____

Spring Portrait

56634

2001 - 2002

OSRP: *

GBTru: *

* The accessory contained in Springfield Studio Gift Set.

On The Boardwalk

56680 - Set of 3

2001 -

OSRP: $27.50

GBTru: -

Paid: $_____

• Seaside Series.

Boardwalk Sunday Stroll

56681 - Set of 2

2001 -

OSRP: $20

GBTru: -

Paid: $_____

• Seaside Series.

Lumberjack

56682

2001 -

OSRP: $27.50

GBTru: -

Paid: $_____

Milking The Cow

56683

2001 -

OSRP: $20

GBTru: -

Paid: $_____

Running The Apple Press

56684

2001 -

OSRP: $24

GBTru: -

Paid: $_____

New England Raising The Flag

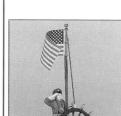

56687

2001 -

OSRP: $15

GBTru: -

Paid: $_____

Loading The Grain

56688 - Set of 2

2002 -

OSRP: $37.50

GBTru: -

Paid: $_____

Glassworks Craftsman

56689

2002 - 2003

OSRP: $15

GBTru: $18

Paid: $_____

Admiring Nature's Beauty

56690

2002 -

OSRP: $15

GBTru: -

Paid: $_____

Maestro And His Protégé

56691

2002 -

OSRP: $18

GBTru: -

Paid: $_____

Salty's Live Bait Shack

56692 - Set of 2

2002 -

OSRP: $35

GBTru: -

Paid: $_____

Today's Catch

56693

2002 -

OSRP: $17.50

GBTru: -

Paid: $_____

Delivering The Christmas Spirit

56694

2002 -

OSRP: $20

GBTru: -

Paid: $_____

New England Town Tree

56695

2002 -

OSRP: $25

GBTru: -

Paid: $_____

Good Day, Reverend

56697 - Set of 2

2003^M -

OSRP: $18.50

GBTru: -

Paid: $_____

Masonry Bake Oven

56698

2003 -

OSRP: $16.50

GBTru: -

Paid: $_____

Dancing An Irish Jig

57102 - Set of 2

2003 -

OSRP: $20

GBTru: -

Paid: $_____

A Penny Saved Is A Penny Earned

57103

2003 -

OSRP: $12.50

GBTru: -

Paid: $_____

Family Sleigh Ride

57105

2003 -

OSRP: $30

GBTru: -

Paid: $_____

The Hitching Post

57106

2003 -

OSRP: $18

GBTru: -

Paid: $_____

Pitching Horseshoes

57107
2003 -
OSRP: $15
GBTru: -
Paid: $_____

Use the following space(s) to update your guide when the midyear introductions are announced.

Photos of the midyear introductions will be included in the July-August issue of *the Village Chronicle* magazine.

_____
_____
____ - ____
OSRP: $_____
GBTru: -
Paid: $_____

_____
_____
____ - ____
OSRP: $_____
GBTru: -
Paid: $_____

_____
_____
____ - ____
OSRP: $_____
GBTru: -
Paid: $_____

_____
_____
____ - ____
OSRP: $_____
GBTru: -
Paid: $_____

_____
_____
____ - ____
OSRP: $_____
GBTru: -
Paid: $_____

_____
_____
____ - ____
OSRP: $_____
GBTru: -
Paid: $_____

Notes:

Alpine Village Series®

The hills truly are "alive with the sounds of music" since Department 56 reached a licensing agreement with the parent organization of the famed musical. Since the von Trapp Villa and Wedding Church are larger than most early pieces, both the buildings and characters have added a new dimension to the mountainous European community. Collectors have also acquired their long-awaited castle, and displays have taken on a new look. Nor is this the first time that a change has occurred. After a decade of small, mostly pastel colors, buildings grew larger and brighter.

For many years this was a quaint, intimate community. After its initial five buildings, it grew at a very slow pace; in fact, it is the only village that has ever gone an entire year (1989) without an addition. That intimacy is one of the appeals that have attracted many collectors to the village. It is composed primarily of rustic buildings that can be perched precariously on the sides of mountains or in secluded valleys.

The musical sounds echoing through those valleys come not from one but two music boxes. "Something Good" accompanies the dancers in the musical gazebo. But the true classic is the "Silent Night" Music Box that plays the beloved classic that was composed at the Church of St. Nikolaus in Oberndorf, Austria, also depicted in the village.

Many Alpine advocates base their love for the village on their personal heritage; others are attracted by the beauty and simplicity of the series. It is interesting that several of the names on buildings appear in German while others are printed in English. Regardless of the language, Alpine Village is wunderwschön…beautiful.

ALPINE VILLAGE - Set of 5   65404

Dates	OSRP	GBTru	Paid
1986 - 1996/97	$125	$150	$_____

- None of the buildings in this set have names on their bottoms or their sleeves.
- Early release to NALED dealers.

Besson Bierkeller   65405

Dates	OSRP	GBTru	Paid
1986 - 1996	$25	$35	$_____

- English translation: Beer Cellar.
- Early release to NALED dealers.

Gasthof Eisl   65406

Dates	OSRP	GBTru	Paid
1986 - 1996	$25	$35	$_____

- English translation: Guest House.
- Early release to NALED dealers.

Apotheke   65407

Dates	OSRP	GBTru	Paid
1986 - 1997	$25	$35	$_____

- English translation: Apothecary.
- Early release to NALED dealers.

E. Staubr Backer   65408

Dates	OSRP	GBTru	Paid
1986 - 1997	$25	$35	$_____

- English translation: Bakery.
- Early release to NALED dealers.

Milch-Kase   65409

Dates	OSRP	GBTru	Paid
1986 - 1996	$25	$35	$_____

- English translation: Milk-Cheese.
- Early release to NALED dealers.

Josef Engel Farmhouse

59528

Dates	OSRP	GBTru	Paid
1987 - 1989	$33	$735	$_____

Alpine Church (White Trim)

65412

Dates	OSRP	GBTru	Paid
1987 - 1991	$32	$260	$_____

• This version was available in the early shipments and is the rarer of the two versions.

(Tan Trim)

GBTru	Paid
$150	$_____

• This version was available in later shipments.

Grist Mill

59536

Dates	OSRP	GBTru	Paid
1988 - 1997	$42	$50	$_____

Bahnhof

56154

Dates	OSRP	GBTru	Paid
1990 - 1993	$42	$75	$_____

• English translation: Train Station.
• The early pieces had gilded trim. The later ones had a yellow-mustard trim.

St. Nikolaus Kirche

56170

Dates	OSRP	GBTru	Paid
1991 - 1999	$37.50	$45	$_____

• Designed after Church of St. Nikolaus in Oberndorf, Austria, the home of the Christmas hymn "Silent Night."

ALPINE SHOPS - Set of 2

56189

Dates	OSRP	GBTru	Paid
1992 - 1997/98	$75	$75	$_____

Metterniche Wurst

56190

Dates	OSRP	GBTru	Paid
1992 - 1997	$37.50	$40	$_____

• English translation: Sausage Shop.

Kukuck Uhren

56191

Dates	OSRP	GBTru	Paid
1992 - 1998	$37.50	$40	$_____

• English translation: Clock Shop.

Sport Laden

56120

Dates	OSRP	GBTru	Paid
1993 - 1998	$50	$50	$_____

• English translation: Sports Shop.

Konditorei Schokolade

56146

Dates	OSRP	GBTru	Paid
1994 - 1998	$37.50	$45	$_____

• English translation: Bakery & Chocolate Shop.
• The bottomstamp and the sleeve read "Bakery & Chocolate Shop."

Kamm Haus

56171

Dates	OSRP	GBTru	Paid
1995 - 1999	$42	$50	$_____

• English translation: House On The Crest.

Danube Music Publisher   56173

Dates	OSRP	GBTru	Paid
1996 - 2000	**$55**	**$55**	$_____

• The German translation of the building's name, Donau Musik Verlag, is found above its front door.
• A sign is separate in the box.

Bernhardiner Hundchen   56174

Dates	OSRP	GBTru	Paid
1997ᴹ - 2000	**$50**	**$60**	$_____

• English translation: St. Bernard Kennel.

Spielzeug Laden   56192

Dates	OSRP	GBTru	Paid
1997 - 2000	**$65**	**$65**	$_____

• English translation: Toy Shop.
• Sign, doll, and 2 jack-in-the-boxes are separate in box.

Federbetten Und Steppdecken   56176

Dates	OSRP	GBTru	Paid
1998ᴹ - 2001	**$48**	**$55**	$_____

• English translation: Featherbeds And Quilts.
• A sign is separate in the box.

The Sound Of Music® von Trapp Villa   56178

Dates	OSRP	GBTru	Paid
1998 - 2002	**$130**	**$135**	$_____

• Inspired by the stately mansion where Maria, the Captain, and their children lived in the *Sound Of Music*®.
• 2 lanterns are separate in the box.
• Set of 5 includes Villa, the von Trapps, and a gate.
• Licensed by R&H Org., Argyle & Fox.

Heidi's Grandfather's House

56177

Dates	OSRP	GBTru	Paid
1998 - 2001	$64	$65	$_____

- Inspired by Johanna Spyri's classic novel.
- Antlers are separate in the box.

Glockenspiel

56210

Dates	OSRP	GBTru	Paid
1999 - 2003	$80	$90	$_____

- Music box plays "Emperor Waltz."

The Sound Of Music® Wedding Church

56211

Dates	OSRP	GBTru	Paid
1999 - 2002	$60	$65	$_____

- Inspired by the church where Maria and the Captain got married in the *Sound Of Music*®.
- A star-shaped spire is separate in the box.
- Licensed by R&H Org., Argyle & Fox.

Hofburg Castle

56216

Dates	OSRP	GBTru	Paid
2000ᴹ - 2002	$68	$75	$_____

- 3 flags are separate in the box.

Nussknacker Werkstatt

56217

Dates	OSRP	GBTru	Paid
2000 - 2001	$60	$180	$_____

- English translation: Nutcracker Workshop.
- 25th Anniversary Limited Edition of 5,600.
- Sign and tin soldier are separate in the box.

Altstädter Bierstube

56218

Dates	OSRP	GBTru	Paid
2000 -	$65	-	$_____

- English translation: Altstadter Beerhouse.
- 2 signs are separate in the box.

Schwarzwalder Kuckucksuhren

56220

Dates	OSRP	GBTru	Paid
2001ᴹ - 2003	$65	$65	$_____

• English translation: Cuckoo Clock Shop.

Getreidemühle Zwettl

56221

Dates	OSRP	GBTru	Paid
2001 -	$85	-	$_____

• English translation: Grain Mill.
• Animated.

Käsehändler Schmitt

56222

Dates	OSRP	GBTru	Paid
2001 - 2003	$55	$50	$_____

• English translation: Cheese Shop.
• Sign is separate in the box.

Nikolausfiguren

56223

Dates	OSRP	GBTru	Paid
2002ᴹ -	$65	-	$_____

• English translation: Nicholas Figurines.
• Sign and 3 hanging ornaments are separate in the box.

Bauernhof Drescher

56229

Dates	OSRP	GBTru	Paid
2002 -	$95	-	$_____

• English translation: Barn and Farmhouse.
• Set of 2.

Rathaus Neudorf   56230

Dates	OSRP	GBTru	Paid
2002 -	**$65**	-	$____

• English translation: Town Hall.

Jägerutte - Hunting Cabin   56231

Dates	OSRP	GBTru	Paid
2003ᴹ -	**$65**	-	$____

Alpen Akademie der Musik   56232

Dates	OSRP	GBTru	Paid
2003 -	**$65**	-	$____

Use the space(s) below to update your guide when the midyear introductions are announced.

Photos of the midyear introductions will be included in the July-August issue of *the Village Chronicle* magazine.

	Dates	OSRP	GBTru	Paid
	____ - ____	$____	-	$____

	Dates	OSRP	GBTru	Paid
	____ - ____	$____	-	$____

Alpine Villagers

65420 - Set of 3

1986 - 1992

OSRP: $13

GBTru: $22

Paid: $_____

• Figures became thinner in later years of production.

Alpine Village Sign

65714

1987 - 1993

OSRP: $6

GBTru: $10

Paid: $_____

• Bottomstamp reads "Handcrafted by Jiean Fung Porcelains, Taiwan."
• Early signs have more detail and richer colors.

The Toy Peddler

56162 - Set of 3

1990 - 1998

OSRP: $22

GBTru: $24

Paid: $_____

Buying Bakers Bread

56197 - Set of 2

1992 - 1995

OSRP: $20

GBTru: $22

Paid: $_____

Climb Every Mountain

56138 - Set of 4

1993 - 2001^M

OSRP: $27.50

GBTru: $30

Paid: $_____

Polka Fest

56073 - Set of 3

1994 - 1999

OSRP: $30

GBTru: $33

Paid: $_____

"Silent Night" Music Box

56180

1995 - 1999

OSRP: $32.50

GBTru: $36

Paid: $_____

• Based on the Silent Night Memorial Chapel in Oberndorf, Austria.
• First HV music box.

Alpenhorn Player Alpine Village Sign

56182

1995 - 2001^M

OSRP: $20

GBTru: $20

Paid: $_____

Nutcracker Vendor & Cart

56183
1996 - 2002
OSRP: $20
GBTru: $24
Paid: $_____

A New Batch Of Christmas Friends

56175 - Set of 3
1997ᴹ - 2000
OSRP: $27.50
GBTru: $30
Paid: $_____

Heidi & Her Goats

56201 - Set of 4
1997 - 2001ᴹ
OSRP: $30
GBTru: $27
Paid: $_____

Trekking In The Snow

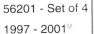

56202 - Set of 3
1998 - 2002
OSRP: $27.50
GBTru: $28
Paid: $_____

St. Nicholas

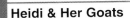

56203
1998 -
OSRP: $12
GBTru: -
Paid: $_____

The Sound Of Music® Gazebo

56212
1999 - 2002
OSRP: $40
GBTru: $36
Paid: $_____

• Plays "Something Good."
• R & H Org., Argyle & Fox.

Sisters Of The Abbey

56213 - Set of 2
1999 -
OSRP: $20
GBTru: -
Paid: $_____

Leading The Bavarian Cow

56214
1999 - 2002
OSRP: $20
GBTru: $24
Paid: $_____

Alpine Villagers

56215 - Set of 5

1999 -

OSRP: $32.50

GBTru: -

Paid: $_____

Here Comes The Bride

56300

2000ᴹ - 2002

OSRP: $18

GBTru: $20

Paid: $_____

At The October Fest

56302 - Set of 3

2000 -

OSRP: $27.50

GBTru: -

Paid: $_____

Cuckoo Clock Vendor & Cart

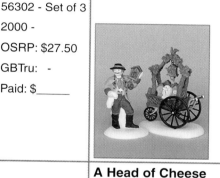

56303 - Set of 2

2001ᴹ -

OSRP: $20

GBTru: -

Paid: $_____

Home From The Mill

56304

2001 - 2003

OSRP: $20

GBTru: $18

Paid: $_____

A Head of Cheese

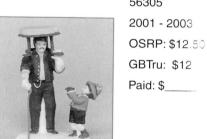

56305

2001 - 2003

OSRP: $12.50

GBTru: $12

Paid: $_____

The Finishing Touch

56306

2002ᴹ -

OSRP: $20

GBTru: -

Paid: $_____

Back From The Fields

56309

2002 -

OSRP: $17.50

GBTru: -

Paid: $_____

Tap The First Barrel

56310

2002 -

OSRP: $17.50

GBTru: -

Paid: $_____

The Bierfest Judge

56311 - Set of 2

2002 -

OSRP: $25

GBTru: -

Paid: $_____

Going Hunting

56312

2003^M -

OSRP: $15

GBTru: -

Paid: $_____

Mozart Monument

56313

2003 -

OSRP: $15

GBTru: -

Paid: $_____

Use the following space(s) to update your guide when the midyear introductions are announced.

Photos of the midyear introductions will be included in the July-August issue of *the Village Chronicle* magazine.

_____

_____

____ - ____

OSRP: $_____

GBTru: -

Paid: $_____

_____

_____

____ - ____

OSRP: $_____

GBTru: -

Paid: $_____

_____

_____

____ - ____

OSRP: $_____

GBTru: -

Paid: $_____

Christmas In The City® Series

Few places are as magical at the holiday season as a city with its bright lights, glittering decorations, and the sounds of Christmas. The normally hectic pace accelerates, but not in a frantic way. Many collectors recall this period vividly. Noses pressed against department store windows, we marveled at the trains, dolls, and stuffed animals that peered back at us. We looked in awe at the colorful town tree.

All of those memories are recaptured in miniature as Department 56 recalls scenes from the middle of the last century. Skaters in Rockefeller Center, trains carrying shoppers through Grand Central Station, the majesty of the Empire State Building, and celebrations of another new year under the Times Tower bring us back to an earlier age in New York. Or your City can be any urban area of that era. Boston, Chicago, and New York baseball stadiums may help you to define your metropolis. It features houses of worship, theaters, and restaurants. There are large stores and small shops. We have government buildings as well as hospital, police, and fire services. Culture can be found in the museum, art academy, and educational institutions. Recently a maritime portion has expanded the City's landscape.

Local neighborhoods with family businesses and ethnic shops contrast with the heart of "downtown." Townhouses and apartment buildings house local residents while hotels host tourists and businessmen. Merchants, shoppers, and visitors all add to the hustle and bustle on busy city streets. There are food vendors, school children, and street musicians on crowded corners. Vehicles fill city streets. It is a wonderful place to be at a wonderful time.

CHRISTMAS IN THE CITY - Set of 3   65129

Dates	OSRP	GBTru	Paid
1987 - 1990	$112	$475	$_____

• All 3 pieces have "Christmas In The City" inscribed on the bottoms. Individual names do not appear.

Bakery   65129

Dates	OSRP	GBTru	Paid
1987 - 1990	$37.50	$105	$100

• Early pieces are light. Later ones are darker.
• Has 2 large and 2 small window grates.
• The chimneys are fragile.

Tower Restaurant   65129

Dates	OSRP	GBTru	Paid
1987 - 1990	$37.50	$195	$100

• Sleeve reads "Tower Cafe." Bottom has no name.
• Early pieces are very dark. Later ones are lighter.
• Has 11 window grates.

Toy Shop And Pet Store   65129

Dates	OSRP	GBTru	Paid
1987 - 1990	$37.50	$190	$75

• Early pieces are very dark. Later ones are lighter.
• Has 6 window grates.
• The chimneys are fragile.

Sutton Place Brownstones   59617

Dates	OSRP	GBTru	Paid
1987 - 1989	$80	$675	$_____

• Bottom is inscribed with "Sutton Place Rowhouse."
• Earliest pieces have grates at attic windows.
• It's not unusual for this piece to have concave walls. One with straight walls is considered more valuable.

The Cathedral   59625

Dates	OSRP	GBTru	Paid
1987 - 1990	$60	$250	$60

• Early pieces are smaller (10½" high), darker, and have snow on the steps. Later ones are larger (11½" high), lighter, and have no snow on the steps.

Palace Theatre

59633

Dates	OSRP	GBTru	Paid
1987 - 1989	$45	$610	$ _45_

- Early pieces have gilded trim and more snow on roof. Later ones have yellow/mustard trim.
- It's not unusual for this piece to have concave walls. One with straight walls is considered more valuable. _?_

Chocolate Shoppe

59684

Dates	OSRP	GBTru	Paid
1988 - 1991	$40	$110	$ _90_

- Early pieces are dark. Later ones are lighter.
- Has 2 window grates on second story.
- The roof of the attached bookstore is often not level.

City Hall

59692

Dates	OSRP	GBTru	Paid
1988 - 1991	$65	$135	$ _65_

- Do not handle by the tower.
- The City Hall "Proof" is smaller than the regular City Hall edition. It came in a box with no sleeve or lightcord.

Proof GBTru = $110 $_____

Hank's Market

59706

Dates	OSRP	GBTru	Paid
1988 - 1992	$40	$75	$ _47_

- This is also referred to as the "Corner Grocer."
- Early samples have the vertical "Grocery" sign attached to the pillar to the right of the door and no 59¢ sign in the lettuce bin.

Variety Store And Barber Shop

59722

Dates	OSRP	GBTru	Paid
1988 - 1990	$45	$120	$ _100_

- The design was inspired by a store in Stillwater, MN.
- The mold was also used for the Bachman's Hometown Series Drugstore. See the Special Design section.
- Sleeve reads "Variety Store & Barbershop."

Ritz Hotel

59730

Dates	OSRP	GBTru	Paid
1989 - 1994	$55	$65	$ _55_

- Early pieces have yellow/mustard accents. Later ones have gilded accents and are smaller.
- Columns are easily broken.

Dorothy's Dress Shop
59749

Dates	OSRP	GBTru	Paid
1989 - 1990	$70	$295	$ _450_

• Limited Edition of 12,500.

Gift

5607 Park Avenue Townhouse
59773

Dates	OSRP	GBTru	Paid
1989 - 1992	$48	$75	$ _48_

• Early pieces have gilded trim at the top edge of the roof. Later ones have yellow/mustard trim.

5609 Park Avenue Townhouse
59781

Dates	OSRP	GBTru	Paid
1989 - 1992	$48	$75	$ _48_

• Early pieces have gilded trim at the top edge of the roof. Later ones have yellow/mustard trim.

Red Brick Fire Station
55360

Dates	OSRP	GBTru	Paid
1990 - 1995	$55	$75	$ _55_

• Cornerstones vary from gray to light blue.

Wong's In Chinatown
55379

Dates	OSRP	GBTru	Paid
1990 - 1994	$55	$75	$ _55_

• Early pieces have red top windows. Later ones have gilded windows.
• Includes fire escape and ladder packaged separately in the box.

Hollydale's Department Store
55344

Dates	OSRP	GBTru	Paid
1991 - 1997	$75	$85	$ _75_

• Early pieces are from Taiwan then China and have holly on first floor canopies only. Later ones are from China and then the Philippines and have holly on all canopies.
• Includes 4 porcelain topiaries and 6 metal flags in box.

"Little Italy" Ristorante   55387

Dates	OSRP	GBTru	Paid
1991 - 1995	$50	$75	$ 50

• Chimney on pizzeria oven can easily be broken when inserting in box.

All Saints Corner Church   55425

Dates	OSRP	GBTru	Paid
1991 - 1998	$96	$105	$ 96

• The spires and the steeple are very fragile.

Arts Academy   55433

Dates	OSRP	GBTru	Paid
1991 - 1993	$45	$70	$ 45

The Doctor's Office   55441

Dates	OSRP	GBTru	Paid
1991 - 1994	$60	$70	$ 60

• Includes fire escape and ladder separately in the box.

Cathedral Church Of St. Mark   55492

Dates	OSRP	GBTru	Paid
1991 - 1992	$120	$1150	$___

• Limited Edition of 3,024 instead of the intended 17,500 due to production problems.
• Commonly referred to as St. Mark's Church.
• Early release to GCC, the only dealers to receive them.
• This design was originally intended for Dickens' Village.
• This building is very susceptible to firing cracks and other flaws. When purchasing one, you should examine it very closely, being certain to insert a light in it while in a darkened room.

UPTOWN SHOPPES - Set of 3　　55310

Dates	OSRP	GBTru	Paid
1992 - 1996	$150	$165	$_____

Haberdashery　　55311

Dates	OSRP	GBTru	Paid
1992 - 1996	$40	$50	$ 40

• Has 1 window grate.

Music Emporium　　55312

Dates	OSRP	GBTru	Paid
1992 - 1996	$54	$65	$ 55

• Music on the side of the building was inspired by a similar idea on the side of a music store in Minneapolis, MN.

City Clockworks　　55313

Dates	OSRP	GBTru	Paid
1992 - 1996	$56	$65	$ 60

• Clock is easily broken, especially when removing or inserting building in box.

Town Tree　　55654

Dates	OSRP	GBTru	Paid
1993 -	$45	-	$_____

• Set of 5 includes Tree and 4 porcelain benches.

WEST VILLAGE SHOPS - Set of 2　　58807

Dates	OSRP	GBTru	Paid
1993 - 1996	$90	$90	$_____

Potter's Tea Seller

58808

Dates	OSRP	GBTru	Paid
1993 - 1996	$45	$50	$_____

Spring St. Coffee House

58809

Dates	OSRP	GBTru	Paid
1993 - 1996	$45	$50	$_____

• Sign is separate in the box.

Brokerage House

58815

Dates	OSRP	GBTru	Paid
1994 - 1997	$48	$65	$_____

• "18" is the price of Dept. 56's initial stock offering at $18.
• "Price & Price" is in honor of Judith Price—Dept. 56's Ms. Lit Town—and her husband.
• "1960" is in honor of the year they were married.

First Metropolitan Bank

58823

Dates	OSRP	GBTru	Paid
1994 - 1997	$60	$70	$_____

• Do not handle by columns.

Heritage Museum Of Art

58831

Dates	OSRP	GBTru	Paid
1994 - 1998	$96	$100	$_____

• Includes 2 red banners packaged separately in the box.
• Gold flags are easily broken when removing this piece from its box.
• Do not handle by columns.

Ivy Terrace Apartments

58874

Dates	OSRP	GBTru	Paid
1995ᴹ - 1997	$60	$70	$_____

• Includes a sisal garden on the penthouse terrace.

Holy Name Church

58875

Dates	OSRP	GBTru	Paid
1995 - 2003	**$96**	**$100**	$_____

- Inspired by the Cathedral of the Immaculate Conception in Kansas City, MO.
- Gold cross packaged separately in the box.

Brighton School

58876

Dates	OSRP	GBTru	Paid
1995 - 1998	**$52**	**$70**	$_____

- The flag on top of roof is easily broken, especially when removing the piece from its box.

BROWNSTONES ON THE SQUARE - Set of 2

58877

Dates	OSRP	GBTru	Paid
1995 - 1998/2000	**$90**	**$90**	$_____

Beekman House

58878

Dates	OSRP	GBTru	Paid
1995 - 2000	**$45**	**$50**	$_____

- Has 1 window grate.
- Includes fire escape and ladder, as well as a lantern packaged separately in the box.

Pickford Place

58879

Dates	OSRP	GBTru	Paid
1995 - 1998	**$45**	**$50**	$_____

- Has 3 window grates.
- Includes lantern packaged separately in the box.

Washington Street Post Office

58880

Dates	OSRP	GBTru	Paid
1996^M - 1998	**$52**	**$70**	$_____

- Includes two mail boxes packaged separately in the box—one for local mail and one for air mail.

Grand Central Railway Station   58881

Dates	OSRP	GBTru	Paid
1996 - 1999	**$90**	**$110**	$_____

- Inspired by New York City's Grand Central Terminal.
- Includes 2 lanterns packaged separately in the box.
- The spires are easily broken, especially when removing the piece from its box.

Café Caprice French Restaurant   58882

Dates	OSRP	GBTru	Paid
1996 - 2001	**$45**	**$60**	$_____

- The sample pieces have a different color scheme, including striped awnings.

The City Globe   58883

Dates	OSRP	GBTru	Paid
1997ᴹ - 2000	**$65**	**$65**	$_____

- The globe on the top of the building is very fragile and will easily break off.

Hi-De-Ho Nightclub   58884

Dates	OSRP	GBTru	Paid
1997ᴹ - 1999	**$52**	**$60**	$_____

- The club name highlights a Cab Calloway jazz riff.

Johnson's Grocery & Deli   58886

Dates	OSRP	GBTru	Paid
1997 - 2002	**$60**	**$65**	$_____

- Includes sign packaged separately in the box.

The Capitol   58887

Dates	OSRP	GBTru	Paid
1997 - 1998	**$110**	**$120**	$_____

Riverside Row Shops 58888

Dates	OSRP	GBTru	Paid
1997 - 1999	**$52**	**$60**	**$____**

• Includes bank, barber shop, stationery store.

The Grand Movie Theater 58870

Dates	OSRP	GBTru	Paid
1998^M - 1999	**$50**	**$60**	**$____**

Scottie's Toy Shop Exclusive Gift Set 58871

Dates	OSRP	GBTru	Paid
1998^M - 1998	**$65**	**$100**	**$____**

• First available during the 1999 Homes for the Holidays event.
• This was the first Village design to include a three-dimensional scene in a building.
• Set of 10 includes the Toy Shop, the 3-piece accessory "5¢ Pony Rides," 4 sisal trees, Cobblestone Road, and a bag of Fresh Fallen Snow.

Old Trinity Church 58940

Dates	OSRP	GBTru	Paid
1998 - 2000	**$96**	**$110**	**$____**

Precinct 25 Police Station 58941

Dates	OSRP	GBTru	Paid
1998 - 2003	**$56**	**$65**	**$____**

• The globes on the front of the Station are fragile.

The Wedding Gallery 58943

Dates	OSRP	GBTru	Paid
1998 - 2002	$60	$65	$_____

• Includes a brass plaque that can be personalized and affixed to the building.

The University Club 58945

Dates	OSRP	GBTru	Paid
1998 - 2000	$60	$70	$_____

• Includes 3 green flags packaged separately in the box.

The Times Tower 55510

Dates	OSRP	GBTru	Paid
1999^M - 1999	$185	$215	$_____

• Inspired by the Times Tower in Times Square.
• Includes numerals that can be substituted for those atop the building up to the year 2009.

• Set of 3 includes the Tower, the accessory "The New Year's Kiss," and confetti.
• There is also limited edition "party set" of 2000 numbered pieces.
GBTru for LE: $325
• Licensed by Jamestown One Times Square, L.P.

Parkview Hospital 58947

Dates	OSRP	GBTru	Paid
1999^M - 2000	$65	$70	$_____

Wintergarten Café 58948

Dates	OSRP	GBTru	Paid
1999^M - 1999	$60	$70	$_____

• This piece is frequently adopted into Alpine Village by collectors.

5th Avenue Salon
58950

Dates	OSRP	GBTru	Paid
1999 - 2001	$68	$75	$_____

• The two lanterns on the back wall are easily damaged.

The Consulate
58951

Dates	OSRP	GBTru	Paid
1999 - 2000	$95	$110	$_____

• Limited to year of production.
• Main spire is packaged separately in the box.
• Spires are easily damaged when removing from box.
• Set of 2 includes Consulate, flag pole, and 25 flags.

Molly O'Brien's Irish Pub
58952

Dates	OSRP	GBTru	Paid
1999 -	$62	-	$_____

• Includes a lantern as well as a brass plaque that can be personalized. Both are packaged separately in the box.

Lafayette's Bakery
58953

Dates	OSRP	GBTru	Paid
1999 - 2002	$62	$65	$_____

Clark Street Automat
58954

Dates	OSRP	GBTru	Paid
1999 - 2000	$68	$75	$_____

• Includes special bulb that must be inserted on an angle.

Paramount Hotel
58911

Dates	OSRP	GBTru	Paid
2000ᴹ - 2003	$85	$90	$_____

• Lighting includes traditional bulb at base plus flickering lights in ballroom and gold star on top of building.
• Includes separate cord for flickering lights.

Jenny's Corner Book Shop 58912

Dates	OSRP	GBTru	Paid
2000^M -	$65	-	$_____

• Sign, bird cage, and weathervane are separate in the box.

The Majestic Theater 58913

Dates	OSRP	GBTru	Paid
2000 - 2001	$100	$145	$_____

• 25th Anniversary Limited Edition of 15,000.

42nd St. Fire Company 58914

Dates	OSRP	GBTru	Paid
2000 -	$80	-	$_____

• Includes lantern packaged separately in the box.
• Includes separate cord for flashing red lights above the overhead doors.
• The dog on the base is fragile.

Gardengate House 58915

Dates	OSRP	GBTru	Paid
2000 - 2002	$68	$70	$_____

Foster Pharmacy 58916

Dates	OSRP	GBTru	Paid
2000 - 2002	$85	$90	$_____

• Includes 3 lanterns packaged separately in the box.
• The separate sign is very easily broken when inserting or removing.

Mrs. Stover's Bungalow Candies 58917

Dates	OSRP	GBTru	Paid
2000 - 2003	$75	$75	$_____

• Includes sign packaged separately in the box.
• Licensed by Russell Stover Candies, Inc.

Department 56 Studio, 1200 Second Ave. 58918

Dates	OSRP	GBTru	Paid
2001^M - 2001	$100	$255	$_____

- Replica of Architect's and Engineer's Building where Dept. 56 was once located in Minneapolis, MN .
- Special issue for Department 56's silver anniversary.
- Only available at that event. Lantern separate in box.

Baker Bros. Bagel Bakery 58920

Dates	OSRP	GBTru	Paid
2001^M - 2002	$75	$75	$_____

- Includes table with umbrella packaged separately in the box.
- Several attachments can be easily broken when removing from box.

Paradise Travel Company 58921

Dates	OSRP	GBTru	Paid
2001^M - 2002	$75	$75	$_____

- Includes sign packaged separately in the box.

Yankee Stadium 58923

Dates	OSRP	GBTru	Paid
2001^M -	$85	-	$_____

- Legendary Ballparks Series.
- Replica of the facade of Yankee Stadium in New York.
- Includes two flags packaged separately in the box.
- Licensed by Major League Baseball Properties, Inc.

The Monte Carlo 58925

Dates	OSRP	GBTru	Paid
2001 - 2002	$85	$90	$_____

- Numbered limited edition of 15,000.
- Garland and 2 wreaths are separate in the box.

Sterling Jewelers 58926

Dates	OSRP	GBTru	Paid
2001 - 2003	$70	$70	$_____

Architectural Antiques
58927

Dates	OSRP	GBTru	Paid
2001 - 2003	$75	$75	$_____

• Set of 17 includes house and various antiques.

Tavern In The Park Restaurant
58928

Dates	OSRP	GBTru	Paid
2001 -	$75	-	$_____

• Christmas In The Park Series.
• Flag is separate in the box.

Nicholas & Co. Toys Starter Set
58929

Dates	OSRP	GBTru	Paid
2001 - 2003	$65	$70	$_____

• Set of 2 includes building and "Look At All The Toys" accessory.
• Sign is separate in the box.

Cathedral Of St. Paul
58930

Dates	OSRP	GBTru	Paid
2001 -	$150	-	$_____

• Re-issue of the Historical Landmark Series limited edition with copper colored roof. See that edition in the Small Collections section.

Fenway Park
58932

Dates	OSRP	GBTru	Paid
2001 -	$75	-	$_____

• Legendary Ballparks Series.
• Replica of the façade of Fenway Park in Boston.
• Includes flag and banners packaged separately in box.
• Licensed by Major League Baseball Properties, Inc.

Wrigley Field

58933

Dates	OSRP	GBTru	Paid
2001 -	$95	-	$_____

- Legendary Ballparks Series.
- Replica of the façade of Wrigley Field in Chicago.
- Includes three flags packaged separately in the box.
- Licensed by Major League Baseball Properties, Inc.

Radio City Music Hall

58924

Dates	OSRP	GBTru	Paid
2002ᴹ -	$95	-	$_____

- Replica of Radio City Music Hall in New York City.
- A separate cord lights the marquee.
- Licensed by Radio City Trademarks L.L.C.

Parkside Holiday Brownstone

58937

Dates	OSRP	GBTru	Paid
2002ᴹ - 2002	$75	$80	$_____

- Holiday 2002 Special Edition.
- A separate cord lights decorative Christmas lights.
- Set of 4 includes building and "Last String Of Lights" accessory, City Lit Bare Branch Tree with adapter, and snow.
- Lamp and rooftop tree separate in the box.

Chez Monet

58938

Dates	OSRP	GBTru	Paid
2002ᴹ - 2003	$65	$70	$_____

- Intended to be used as a Valentine's Day design.

Hudson Public Library

58942

Dates	OSRP	GBTru	Paid
2002 -	$80	-	$_____

Midtown Barbershop

58944

Dates	OSRP	GBTru	Paid
2002 -	$65	-	$____

• Sign is separate in the box.

East Harbor Fish Co.

58946

Dates	OSRP	GBTru	Paid
2002 -	$85	-	$____

• Two signs and two "lamps" are separate in box.
• Special adapter is included to activate building's bulb and decorative Christmas lights.
• Do not handle by posts.

DeFazio's Pizzeria

58949

Dates	OSRP	GBTru	Paid
2002 -	$65	-	$____

• Set of 2 includes the Pizzeria and "Pizza Pick-Up" accessory.

Seasons Department Store

59201

Dates	OSRP	GBTru	Paid
2002 -	$70	-	$____

Harley-Davidson® City Dealership

59202

Dates	OSRP	GBTru	Paid
2002 -	$85	-	$____

• Sign is separate in box.
• Licensed by Harley-Davidson®.

Ebbets Field

59203

Dates	OSRP	GBTru	Paid
2002 -	$75	-	$_____

- Legendary Ballparks Series.
- Replica of façade of Ebbets Field that stood in Brooklyn.
- Flag separate in box.
- Licensed by Major League Baseball Properties, Inc.

Central Synagogue

59204

Dates	OSRP	GBTru	Paid
2002 - 2003	$110	$110	$_____

- Limited to year of production.
- Historical Landmark Series.
- This is a replica of Central Synagogue in New York City.

1234 Four Seasons Parkway

59205

Dates	OSRP	GBTru	Paid
2003ᴹ -	$75	-	$_____

- Seasonal decorations and flowering trees are separate in box.
- First use of removable snow to winterize buildings.

Church Of The Holy Light

59206

Dates	OSRP	GBTru	Paid
2003ᴹ - 2003	$75	$70	$_____

- Holiday 2003 Special Edition.
- Set of 6 includes the Church, "Christmas Eve Visit" accessory, birch tree, frosted pine tree, and snow.
- Adapter included to light star atop nativity scene.

Katie McCabe's Restaurant & Books

59208

Dates	OSRP	GBTru	Paid
2003ᴹ -	$70	-	$_____

- Fire escape (4 pieces) and sign are separate in box.

Empire State Building
59207

Dates	OSRP	GBTru	Paid
2003^M -	$185	-	$_____

- Historical Landmark Series.
- This is a replica of the Empire State Building in Manhattan.
- At 23 inches, this is the tallest building manufactured by Department 56.
- Features several holiday lighting effects, including different colors in detachable top section.
- Four American flags are separate in box.

Historic Chicago Water Tower
59209

Dates	OSRP	GBTru	Paid
2003 -	$65	-	$_____

- Historical Landmark Series.
- Set of 2 includes Tower and sign.
- This is a replica of the Chicago Water Tower, one of the few buildings to survive the great Chicago fire of 1871.

Blue Line Bus Depot
59210

Dates	OSRP	GBTru	Paid
2003 -	$75	-	$_____

Harrison House
59211

Dates	OSRP	GBTru	Paid
2003 -	$70	-	$_____

- Portions of the proceeds benefit ovarian cancer research.

5th Avenue Shoppes
59212

Dates	OSRP	GBTru	Paid
2003 -	$95	-	$_____

- Includes art gallery, wine cellar, and flower shop.

East Harbor Ferry

59213

Dates	OSRP	GBTru	Paid
2003 -	$85	-	$_____

- Numbered limited edtion of 10,000.
- Set of 3 includes Ferry and "Ferry Ticket Sales" 2 piece accessory.
- Can be personalized.
- American and Canadian flags are separate in box.

Harley-Davidson® Detailing, Parts & Service

59214

Dates	OSRP	GBTru	Paid
2003 -	$85	-	$_____

- Licensed by Harley-Davidson®.

Old Comiskey Park

59215

Dates	OSRP	GBTru	Paid
2003 -	$80	-	$_____

- Legendary Ballparks Series.
- Replica of the façade of Comiskey Park that once stood in Chicago.
- Licensed by Major League Baseball Properties, Inc.

Kelly's Irish Crafts

59216

Dates	OSRP	GBTru	Paid
2003 -	$65	-	$_____

- Set of 2 includes building and "Tin Whistles - 25 Cents" accessory.

Use the space(s) below to update your guide when the midyear introductions are announced.

Photos of the midyear introductions will be included in the July-August issue of *the Village Chronicle* magazine.

	Dates	OSRP	GBTru	Paid
	_____ - _____	$_____	-	$_____

	Dates	OSRP	GBTru	Paid
	_____ - _____	$_____	-	$_____

	Dates	OSRP	GBTru	Paid
	_____ - _____	$_____	-	$_____

	Dates	OSRP	GBTru	Paid
	_____ - _____	$_____	-	$_____

	Dates	OSRP	GBTru	Paid
	_____ - _____	$_____	-	$_____

Notes:

Lighted Tree W/Children & Ladder

65102 - Set of 3

1986 - 1989

OSRP: $35

GBTru: $150

Paid: $_____

• Sleeves from the early shipments read "Christmas In the City" even though the village didn't make its debut for another year.
• Battery operated.
• Many have been sold on the secondary market as defective, but it's usually just a matter of crossed wires. Once they are switched, the unit works nicely.
• The boy on the ladder is often damaged from falling off.

Christmas In The City Sign

59609

1987 - 1993

OSRP: $6

GBTru: $12

Paid: $_____

Automobiles

59641 - Set of 3

1987 - 1996

OSRP: $15

GBTru: $20

Paid: $_____

City People

59650 - Set of 5

1987 - 1990

OSRP: $27.50

GBTru: $45

Paid: $_____

City Newsstand ✓

59714 - Set of 4

1988 - 1991

OSRP: $25

GBTru: $55

Paid: $_____

City Bus & Milk Truck ✓

59838 - Set of 2

1988 - 1991

OSRP: $15

GBTru: $25

Paid: $_____

• Wording on sleeve reads "Transport."

Salvation Army Band ✓

59854 - Set of 6

1988 - 1991

OSRP: $24

GBTru: $65

Paid: $_____

• Conductor's baton is easily damaged.

Boulevard

55166 - Set of 14
1989 - 1992
OSRP: $25
GBTru: $35
Paid: $_____

• Includes 4 sections (2 straight/ 2 curved), 4 trees, 4 hitching posts, and 2 benches.

Mailbox & Fire Hydrant

55174 - Set of 2
1989 - 1990
OSRP: $5
GBTru: $15
Paid: $_____

• Retired after one year due to unauthorized use of red and blue colors of U.S. Postal Service.

Organ Grinder ✓

59579 - Set of 3
1989 - 1991
OSRP: $21
GBTru: $25
Paid: $_____

Popcorn Vendor ✓

59587 - Set of 3
1989 - 1992
OSRP: $22
GBTru: $26
Paid: $_____

River Street Ice House Cart ✓

59595
1989 - 1991
OSRP: $20
GBTru: $45
Paid: $_____

Central Park Carriage ✓

59790
1989 -
OSRP: $30
GBTru: -
Paid: $_____

• Designated as Christmas In The Park Series in 2002.

Mailbox & Fire Hydrant

52140 - Set of 2
1990 - 1998
OSRP: $5
GBTru: $10
Paid: $_____

• Re-issue of Mailbox & Fire Hydrant (1989) after changing to red and green and putting "H.V. Mail" on front.

Busy Sidewalks

55352 - Set of 4
1990 - 1992
OSRP: $28
GBTru: $45
Paid: $_____

'Tis The Season ✓

(2)

55395 ✓

1990 - 1994

OSRP: $12.50

GBTru: $16

Paid: $_____

• Separate metal kettle can easily be lost.

Rest Ye Merry Gentleman ✓

55409

1990 - 2002

OSRP: $12.50

GBTru: $14

Paid: $_____

• Bench is metal.

Utility Accessories ✓

55123 - Set of 8

1991 - 1998

OSRP: $12.50

GBTru: $16

Paid: $_____

• It is not unusual for the stop signs to be discolored.
• Metal.

City Subway Entrance ✓

55417

1991 - 1998

OSRP: $15

GBTru: $20

Paid: $_____

• Metal.

All Around The Town ✓

55450 - Set of 2

1991 - 1993

OSRP: $18

GBTru: $25

Paid: $_____

The Fire Brigade ✓

55468 - Set of 2

1991 - 1995

OSRP: $20

GBTru: $28

Paid: $_____

• Includes plastic fire ladder separate in box.

"City Fire Dept." Fire Truck ✓

55476

1991 - 1995

OSRP: $18

GBTru: $30

Paid: $_____

• Includes plastic fire ladder separate in box.

Caroling Thru The City

55484- Set of 3

1991 - 1998

OSRP: $27.50

GBTru: $28

Paid: $_____

Don't Drop The Presents! ✓

55328 - Set of 2
1992 - 1995
OSRP: $25
GBTru: $27
Paid: $_____

Welcome Home ✓

55336 - Set of 3
1992 - 1995
OSRP: $27.50
GBTru: $28
Paid: $_____

Village Express Van ✓

58653
1992 - 1996
OSRP: $25
GBTru: $30
Paid: $_____

• License plate is abbreviated address of Dept. 56 headquarters, 6435 City West Pkwy.
• See the Special Design section.

Playing In The Snow

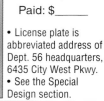

55565 - Set of 3
1993 - 1996
OSRP: $25
GBTru: $30
Paid: $_____

• The branches are easily broken.

Street Musicians

55646 - Set of 3
1993 - 1997
OSRP: $25
GBTru: $26
Paid: $_____

• The violinist's bow is fragile.

Town Tree Trimmers ✓

55662 - Set of 4
1993 - 2001
OSRP: $32.50
GBTru: $40
Paid: $_____

Christmas At The Park

58661 - Set of 3
1993 -
OSRP: $27.50
GBTru: -
Paid: $_____

• Intended for use with the Town Tree.

Chamber Orchestra ✓

58840 - Set of 4
1994 - 1998
OSRP: $37.50
GBTru: $40
Paid: $_____

• The conductor's baton and the musicians' bows and flute are fragile.

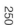

Holiday Field Trip ✓

58858 - Set of 3
1994 - 1998
OSRP: $27.50
GBTru: $35
Paid: $_____

Hot Dog Vendor ✓

58866 - Set of 3
1994 - 1997
OSRP: $27.50
GBTru: $30
Paid: $_____

• Porcelain and metal.

"Yes, Virginia..."

58890 - Set of 2
1995 - 2000
OSRP: $12.50
GBTru: $14
Paid: $_____

One-Man Band & The Dancing Dog

58891 - Set of 2
1995 - 1998
OSRP: $17.50
GBTru: $24
Paid: $_____

Choirboys All-In-A-Row

58892
1995 - 1998
OSRP: $20
GBTru: $24
Paid: $_____

A Key To The City CIC Sign

58893
1995 - 2001ᴹ
OSRP: $20
GBTru: $22
Paid: $_____

• Porcelain and metal.

City Taxi

58894
1996 - 2001
OSRP: $12.50
GBTru: $20
Paid: $_____

• Similar designs were produced for several retailers. See the Special Design section.

The Family Tree

58895
1996 - 2003
OSRP: $18
GBTru: -
Paid: $_____

Going Home For The Holidays

58896 - Set of 3
1996 - 1999
OSRP: $27.50
GBTru: $28
Paid: $_____

Steppin' Out On The Town

58885 - Set of 5
1997^M - 1999
OSRP: $35
GBTru: $35
Paid: $_____

• The gentleman's walking stick is fragile.

Johnson's Grocery Holiday Deliveries

58897
1997 - 2001
OSRP: $18
GBTru: $22
Paid: $_____

• Similar designs were produced for retailers. See the Special Design section.

Spirit Of The Season

58898
1997 - 1999
OSRP: $20
GBTru: $20
Paid: $_____

Let's Go Shopping In The City

58899 - Set of 3
1997 - 1999
OSRP: $35
GBTru: $36
Paid: $_____

Big Smile For The Camera

58900 - Set of 2
1997 - 1999
OSRP: $27.50
GBTru: $32
Paid: $_____

5¢ Pony Rides

58871 - Set of 3
1998^M - 1998
OSRP: *
GBTru: *

* Accessory contained in the Scottie's Toy Shop Gift Set.

Heritage Village Utility Accessories

52776 - Set of 11
1998 - 2001
OSRP: $15
GBTru: $18
Paid: $_____

• The sticker on the right side of the mailbox reads "S.V. Mail."

A Carriage Ride For The Bride

58901

1998 -

OSRP: $40

GBTru: -

Paid: $_____

• The front wheels can separate from the rest of the carriage and cause damage.

To Protect And To Serve

58902 - Set of 3

1998 -

OSRP: $32.50

GBTru: -

Paid: $_____

City Police Car

58903

1998 - 2001^M

OSRP: $16.50

GBTru: $20

Paid: $_____

• Features a battery-operated beacon.

1919 Ford Model-T

58906

1998 - 2000

OSRP: $20

GBTru: $24

Paid: $_____

• Licensed by Ford Motor Co.

Ready For The Road

58907

1998 - 2000

OSRP: $20

GBTru: $24

Paid: $_____

• Licensed by Harley-Davidson.

The New Year's Kiss

55510

1999^M - 1999

OSRP: *

GBTru: *

* Accessory contained in The Times Tower Gift Set.

Bringing Home The Baby

58909 - Set of 2

1999^M - 2000

OSRP: $27.50

GBTru: $32

Paid: $_____

The City Ambulance

58910

1999^M - 2000

OSRP: $15

GBTru: $22

Paid: $_____

Busy City Sidewalks

58955 - Set of 4

1999 -

OSRP: $32.50

GBTru: -

Paid: $_____

Visiting The Nativity

58956 - Set of 3

1999 -

OSRP: $37.50

GBTru: -

Paid: $_____

• Dream House Sweep-stakes Deluxe Prize winner assisted in the design. Also see Nativity Creche in GVA.

Fresh Flowers For Sale

58957 - Set of 2

1999 - 2001

OSRP: $30

GBTru: $32

Paid: $_____

• Dream House Sweep-stakes Deluxe Prize winner assisted in the design.

Excellent Taste

58958 - Set of 2

1999 - 2002

OSRP: $22

GBTru: $22

Paid: $_____

Picking Out The Christmas Tree

58959 - Set of 3

1999 -

OSRP: $37.50

GBTru: -

Paid: $_____

All In Together Girls

58960

1999 - 2001ᴹ

OSRP: $23.50

GBTru: $24

Paid: $_____

Rockefeller Plaza Skating Rink

52504

2000ᴹ - 2003

OSRP: $125

GBTru: $95

Paid: $_____

Hailing A Cab

58961 - Set of 3

2000ᴹ - 2002

OSRP: $27.50

GBTru: $28

Paid: $_____

City Professions - Doctor & Nurse

58962 - Set of 2

2000^M - 2002

OSRP: $17.50

GBTru: $20

Paid: $_____

A Treasured Book

58963 - Set of 3

2000^M - 2003

OSRP: $35

GBTru: $35

Paid: $_____

1935 Duesenberg®

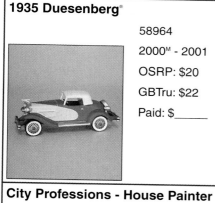

58964

2000^M - 2001

OSRP: $20

GBTru: $22

Paid: $_____

City Professions - Postman & Dairy Delivery Man

58965 - Set of 2

2000^M - 2001^M

OSRP: $17.50

GBTru: $18

Paid: $_____

City Professions - House Painter & Newspaper Boy

58966 - Set of 2

2000^M - 2001^M

OSRP: $17.50

GBTru: $20

Paid: $_____

On To The Show

58967

2000 - 2003

OSRP: $20

GBTru: $20

Paid: $_____

Fire Drill Practice

58968

2000 -

OSRP: $25

GBTru: -

Paid: $_____

1937 Pirsch Pumper Fire Truck

58969

2000 - 2003

OSRP: $25

GBTru: $26

Paid: $_____

The Life Of The Party

58970 - Set of 2

2000 - 2002

OSRP: $30

GBTru: $30

Paid: $_____

• Mask in woman's hand and man's cane are easily broken.

Hot Chocolate For Sale

58971

2000 - 2003

OSRP: $27.50

GBTru: $28

Paid: $_____

Russell Stover® Delivery Truck

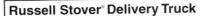

58972

2000 - 2003

OSRP: $20

GBTru: $20

Paid: $_____

• Licensed by Russell Stover Candies, Inc.

Pretzel Cart

58973

2001ᴹ -

OSRP: $22

GBTru: -

Paid: $_____

Midtown News Stand

58974 - Set of 2

2001ᴹ -

OSRP: $32.50

GBTru: -

Paid: $_____

Planning A Winter Vacation

58975

2001ᴹ - 2002

OSRP: $12.50

GBTru: $14

Paid: $_____

Full Count

58977 - Set of 2

2001ᴹ -

OSRP: $25

GBTru: -

Paid: $_____

• Legendary Ballparks Series.
• Licensed by Major League Baseball Prop.

Look At All The Toys

58929

2001 - 2003

OSRP: *

GBTru: *

* The accessory contained in Nicholas & Co. Toys Starter Set.

City Zoological Garden

58978 - Set of 7

2001 - 2003

OSRP: $95

GBTru: $75

Paid: $_____

• Christmas In The Park Series.

Santa In The City

58979

2001 -

OSRP: $25

GBTru: -

Paid: $_____

• Christmas In The Park Series.
• Reindeer's antlers are very fragile.

City Shopping

58980

2001 - 2003

OSRP: $13

GBTru: $13

Paid: $_____

Architectural Treasure

58981

2001 - 2002

OSRP: $12.50

GBTru: $13

Paid: $_____

Hot Roasted Chestnuts

58983 - Set of 2

2001 -

OSRP: $18

GBTru: -

Paid: $_____

Raising The Flag In The City

58986

2001 -

OSRP: $15

GBTru: -

Paid: $_____

Last String Of Lights

58937

2002ᴹ - 2002

OSRP: *

GBTru: *

* The accessory contained in the Parkside Holiday Brownstone.

For Your Sweetheart

58987

2002ᴹ -

OSRP: $22.50

GBTru: -

Paid: $_____

Christmas In The City Acc. (vertical text, left margin)

Serving Irish Ale

58988

2002ᴹ -

OSRP: $20

GBTru: -

Paid: $_____

Peanuts, Pennants & Programs

58989

2002ᴹ -

OSRP: $15

GBTru: -

Paid: $_____

• Legendary Ballparks Series.

Choosing Rights

58990

2002ᴹ - 2003

OSRP: $15

GBTru: $15

Paid: $_____

• Legendary Ballparks Series.

The Radio City Rockettes

58991

2002ᴹ -

OSRP: $12.50

GBTru: -

Paid: $_____

• Originally designed with tall white hats.
• Licensed by Radio City Trademarks L.L.C.

Pizza Pick-Up

58949

2002 -

OSRP: *

GBTru: *

* The accessory contained in DeFazio's Pizzeria.

City Park Gateway

58992 - Set of 2

2002 -

OSRP: $42.50

GBTru: -

Paid: $_____

• Christmas In The Park Series.
• Working clock.

Asleep At The Bus Stop

58993

2002 -

OSRP: $12.50

GBTru: -

Paid: $_____

Presents For The Family

58994

2002 -

OSRP: $12.50

GBTru: -

Paid: $_____

Family Out For A Walk

58995 - Set of 2

2002 -

OSRP: $20

GBTru: -

Paid: $_____

Fresh Fish Today

58996 - Set of 2

2002 -

OSRP: $27.50

GBTru: -

Paid: $_____

America's Finest

58998

2002 -

OSRP: $20

GBTru: -

Paid: $_____

• Licensed by Harley-Davidson.

For The Love Of Books

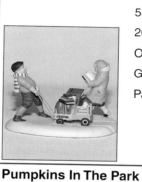

58999

2002 -

OSRP: $18

GBTru: -

Paid: $_____

Keep America Beautiful

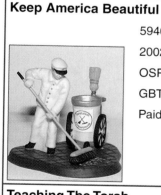

59400

2002 -

OSRP: $13

GBTru: -

Paid: $_____

Pumpkins In The Park

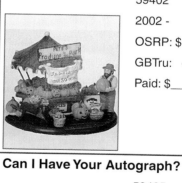

59402

2002 -

OSRP: $40

GBTru: -

Paid: $_____

Teaching The Torah

59403

2002 - 2003

OSRP: $15

GBTru: $15

Paid: $_____

Can I Have Your Autograph?

59405

2002 -

OSRP: $16.50

GBTru: -

Paid: $_____

• Legendary Ballparks Series.

Ebbets Field Scoreboard

59406

2002 -

OSRP: $20

GBTru: -

Paid: $_____

• Legendary Ballparks Series.

How Tall Is It?

59407

2003ᴹ -

OSRP: $15

GBTru: -

Paid: $_____

1930 Harley-Davidson® VL W/Sidecar

59409

2003ᴹ -

OSRP: $22.50

GBTru: -

Paid: $_____

• Licensed by Harley-Davidson.

Milwaukee Or Bust

59410

2003ᴹ -

OSRP: $45

GBTru: -

Paid: $_____

• Licensed by Harley-Davidson.

Christmas Eve Visit

59206

2003ᴹ - 2003

OSRP: *

GBTru: *

• Adapter included
* The accessory contained in Church Of The Holy Light.

Ferry Ticket Sales

59213

2003 -

OSRP: *

GBTru: *

* The accessory contained in East Harbor Ferry.

Tin Whistles - 25 Cents

59216

2003 -

OSRP: *

GBTru: *

* The accessory contained in Kelly's Irish Crafts.

Blue Line Bus

59411

2003 -

OSRP: $20

GBTru: -

Paid: $_____

• Vintage Car Series.

Off To College!

59413

2003 -

OSRP: $17.50

GBTru: -

Paid: $_____

Harley-Davidson® Motorcycle Truck

59414

2003 -

OSRP: $20

GBTru: -

Paid: $_____

• Licensed by Harley-Davidson.

Hot Pretzels

59415

2003 -

OSRP: $25

GBTru: -

Paid: $_____

• Christmas In The Park Series.
• Includes adapter.

1940 V16 Cadillac Coupe

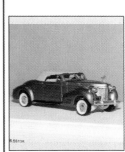

59416

2003 -

OSRP: $20

GBTru: -

Paid: $_____

• Vintage Car Series.
• Licensed by General Motors.

Taxi

59417

2003 -

OSRP: $20

GBTru: -

Paid: $_____

• Vintage Car Series.

Pier 87 Bait & Tackle

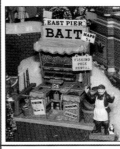

59419 - Set of 2

2003 -

OSRP: $30

GBTru: -

Paid: $_____

Traffic Policeman

59421

2003 -

OSRP: $15

GBTru: -

Paid: $_____

Sidewalk Games

59422 - Set of 3

2003 -

OSRP: $20

GBTru: -

Paid: $_____

City Sledding

59423

2003 -

OSRP: $45

GBTru: -

Paid: $_____

• Includes adapter.

Warming Up

59425 - Set of 2

2003 -

OSRP: $16.50

GBTru: -

Paid: $_____

Use the following space(s) to update your guide when the midyear introductions are announced.

Photos of the midyear introductions will be included in the July-August issue of *the Village Chronicle* magazine.

_____

_____

____ - ____

OSRP: $_____

GBTru: -

Paid: $_____

_____

_____

____ - ____

OSRP: $_____

GBTru: -

Paid: $_____

_____

_____

____ - ____

OSRP: $_____

GBTru: -

Paid: $_____

_____

_____

____ - ____

OSRP: $_____

GBTru: -

Paid: $_____

_____

_____

____ - ____

OSRP: $_____

GBTru: -

Paid: $_____

The Holy Land™ Collection

Formerly a separate collection, Little Town of Bethlehem is now one of the series within the Holy Land Collection. This umbrella collection also includes the Easter series and the Parables From The Holy Land. Furthermore, Department 56 has indicated that this collection will expand to include ancient Egypt, the Roman Empire, and caravan routes to the Far East.

Department 56 originally created its version of the Nativity story in 1987. A self-contained set of 12, including three buildings and the primary characters, was released in porcelain and remained unchanged for a dozen years. In keeping with the tale and life of the time, the buildings were simple stone and brick structures.

In 1999 the set was retired, but within weeks new releases were announced. Collectors could purchase individual buildings and accessories that would complement the original set, or begin their Nativity scene using just the new pieces. The new accessories were crafted in resin, rather than porcelain, enabling the designs to be more detailed.

The new pieces have not only augmented the original series with historical pieces such as Herod's Temple but have also added brilliantly crafted buildings like the Rug Merchant's Colonnade and accessories featuring people and animals in a desert camp and oasis, as well in routine daily activities.

The establishment of different series within the Holy Land will enable collectors to create a vast geographical display, develop seasonal approaches, or form vignettes using only a single series from the entire collection.

Little Town Of
Bethlehem Series

Little Town Of Bethlehem

59757

Dates	OSRP	GBTru	Paid
1987 - 1999	**$150**	**$195**	**$_____**

- The early pieces have a small amount of snow on the manger's right wall. The later ones do not.
- Set of 12 includes manger with Jesus, inn, marketplace, Joseph, Mary, 3 wise men, shepherd with sheep, camel, cow and sheep, a donkey, and cypress trees.
- For the first 4 years of production, a sheep stood next to the cow. From 1991 through 1999, the sheep was not included.

Innkeeper's Caravansary

59795

Dates	OSRP	GBTru	Paid
1999 - 2003	**$70**	**$65**	**$_____**

Gatekeeper's Dwelling

59797

Dates	OSRP	GBTru	Paid
1999 - 2001	**$55**	**$60**	**$_____**

Nativity

59796

Dates	OSRP	GBTru	Paid
1999 -	$55	-	$____

- Set of 2 includes the building and Joseph, Mary, and Jesus accessory.
- This set is also included as part of the Gift Set, Holy Night Nativity, in 2002.

Herod's Temple

59799

Dates	OSRP	GBTru	Paid
2000 - 2001	$150	$180	$____

- 25th Anniversary Limited Edition of 5,600.
- Set of 5 includes Temple, 2 piece accessory "High Priests," gate, and vinyl ancient stone courtyard.

Carpenter's Shop

59801

Dates	OSRP	GBTru	Paid
2000 - 2002	$72	$70	$____

- Set of 3 includes Shop and 2 piece accessory "Carpenter & Son."

Rug Merchant's Colonnade

59802

Dates	OSRP	GBTru	Paid
2000 -	$110	-	$____

• Set of 4 includes Colonnade, 2 piece accessory "Rug Merchant & Wool Spinner," and ladder.

Caravansary Corner

59806

Dates	OSRP	GBTru	Paid
2001 - 2003	$75	$75	$____

• Set of 2 includes building and man.

Caravansary Rooms at the Inn

59807

Dates	OSRP	GBTru	Paid
2001 - 2003	$110	$110	$____

• Set of 3 includes building and two figurines.

Holy Night Nativity

05837

Dates	OSRP	GBTru	Paid
2002ᴹ - 2002	$85	$85	$

- Department store exclusive.
- Limited to year of production.
- Set of 6 is the combination of Nativity, "Wise Men From The East" accessory, and "Palm Trees."

Potter's Shop

59812

Dates	OSRP	GBTru	Paid
2002 -	$65	-	$

- Set of 2 includes building and "Pottery Craftsman" accessory.

The Birth Of Christ Nativity Set

59816

Dates	OSRP	GBTru	Paid
2003 -	$75	-	$

- Set of 11 includes the manger, the Holy Family, the wisemen, and animals.

Use the spaces on the next page to update your guide when the midyear introductions are announced.

Photos of the midyear introductions will be included in the July-August issue of *the Village Chronicle* magazine.

	Dates _____ - _____	OSRP $_____	GBTru -	Paid $_____

	Dates _____ - _____	OSRP $_____	GBTru -	Paid $_____

	Dates _____ - _____	OSRP $_____	GBTru -	Paid $_____

	Dates _____ - _____	OSRP $_____	GBTru -	Paid $_____

	Dates _____ - _____	OSRP $_____	GBTru -	Paid $_____

The Easter Story Series

House Of The Last Supper Gift Set 59809

Dates	OSRP	GBTru	Paid
2001 -	$65	-	$_____

- First available during the 2002 Spring Discover Dept. 56 event.
- Set of 2 includes building and "Palm Sunday" accessory.

Tower Of David 59810

Dates	OSRP	GBTru	Paid
2002ᴹ -	$75	-	$_____

- Set of 3 includes Tower and 2 piece accessory, "Tower Guard & Garden Archway" and scroll.

Church Of The Holy Sepulcher 59814

Dates	OSRP	GBTru	Paid
2003ᴹ -	$85	-	$_____

Notes:

Heralding Angels		**Good Shepherd & His Animals**	
	59759 - Set of 3 1999 - OSRP: $20 GBTru: - Paid: $_____		59791 - Set of 6 1999 - OSRP: $25 GBTru: - Paid: $_____

Wise Men From The East		**Town Well & Palm Trees**	
	59792 - Set of 2 1999 - OSRP: $25 GBTru: - Paid: $_____ • Also included as part of Holy Night Nativity Gift Set.		59793 - Set of 3 1999 - OSRP: $45 GBTru: - Paid: $_____

Town Gate		**Palm Trees**	
	59794 - Set of 2 1999 - 2001 OSRP: $25 GBTru: $25 Paid: $_____		52820 - Set of 2 1999 - OSRP: $45 GBTru: - Paid: $_____ • Also included as part of Holy Night Nativity Gift Set.

Desert Oasis		**High Priests**	
	59901 - Set of 5 2000 - 2003 OSRP: $60 GBTru: $60 Paid: $_____		59799 - Set of 2 2000 - 2001 OSRP: * GBTru: * * Accessory contained in Herod's Temple.

Carpenter & Son

59801 - Set of 2

2000 - 2002

OSRP: *

GBTru: *

* Accessory contained in Carpenter's Shop.

Rug Merchant & Wool Spinner

59802 - Set of 2

2000 -

OSRP: *

GBTru: *

* Accessory contained in Rug Merchant's Colonnade.

Merchant Cart

59902 - Set of 2

2000 - 2003

OSRP: $30

GBTru: $30

Paid: $_____

Stonemason At Work

59903 - Set of 3

2000 - 2003

OSRP: $45

GBTru: $45

Paid: $_____

Desert Camp

59904 - Set of 4

2000 - 2003

OSRP: $52

GBTru: $55

Paid: $_____

Oil Lamps

59905 - Set of 2

2000 - 2002

OSRP: $25

GBTru: $28

Paid: $_____

• Battery operated.

Star Of Wonder

59906

2000 - 2003

OSRP: $20

GBTru: $20

Paid: $_____

• Battery/adapter operated.

Cypress Trees

59907 - Set of 3

2000 -

OSRP: $20

GBTru: -

Paid: $_____

• Originally released as "Cyprus" trees.

The Holy Land Accessories 272

Town Wall Sections

59908 - Set of 2

2000 -

OSRP: $16.50

GBTru: -

Paid: $_____

• Coordinates with Town Gate.

Desert Road

59909 - Set of 4

2000 -

OSRP: $22.50

GBTru: -

Paid: $_____

Desert Rocks

59910 - Set of 5

2000 - 2003

OSRP: $25

GBTru: $22

Paid: $_____

Limestone Outcropping

59911

2000 - 2003

OSRP: $40

GBTru: $40

Paid: $_____

Olive Harvest

59912 - Set of 3

2000 - 2003

OSRP: $40

GBTru: $38

Paid: $_____

The Holy Land Backdrop

52965

2001 - 2003

OSRP: $45

GBTru: $45

Paid: $_____

Palm Sunday

59809

2001 -

OSRP: *

GBTru: *

* The accessory contained in House Of The Last Supper.

Spice & Copper Vendors' Colonnade

59913 - Set of 3

2001 -

OSRP: $75

GBTru: -

Paid: $_____

Desert Caravan

59914 - Set of 5

2001 -

OSRP: $48

GBTru: -

Paid: $_____

Caravansary Drinking Well

59915

2001 - 2003

OSRP: $27.50

GBTru: $30

Paid: $_____

Caravansary Gate & Guard

59916 - Set of 2

2001 - 2003

OSRP: $42

GBTru: $45

Paid: $_____

Caravansary Wall

59917 - 2 Asst'd

2001 - 2003

OSRP: $30

GBTru: $30

Paid: $_____

Waterfall In The Wilderness

59918 - Set of 2

2001 - 2003

OSRP: $85

GBTru: $80

Paid: $_____

- Working fountain.
- Includes accessory "Man Drawing Water."

Tower Guard & Garden Archway

59810

2002ᴹ -

OSRP: *

GBTru: *

* The accessory contained in the Tower Of David.

Sand Road

59921 - Set of 2

2002ᴹ -

OSRP: $15

GBTru: -

Paid: $_____

- Includes road and bag of sand.

Pottery Craftsman

59812

2002 -

OSRP: *

GBTru: *

* The accessory contained in Potter's Shop.

Revolving Nativity Scene

59813

2002 -

OSRP: $130

GBTru: -

Paid: $_____

• Animated.

Holy Land Animals

59922 - Set of 3

2002 -

OSRP: $35

GBTru: -

Paid: $_____

The Prodigal Son

59923 - Set of 3

2002 -

OSRP: $35

GBTru: -

Paid: $_____

• Parables Series.

The Good Samaritan

59924 - Set of 3

2002 -

OSRP: $35

GBTru: -

Paid: $_____

• Parables Series.

The Sower And The Seed

59925 - Set of 2

2002 -

OSRP: $35

GBTru: -

Paid: $_____

• Parables Series.

Holy Night Fiber Optic Backdrop

59815

2003 -

OSRP: $150

GBTru: -

Paid: $_____

• Includes adapter.
• Both town and sky light up.

Use the following space(s) to update your guide when the midyear introductions are announced.

Photos of the midyear introductions will be included in the July-August issue of *the Village Chronicle* magazine.

_____

_____

_____ - _____

OSRP: $_____

GBTru: -

Paid: $_____

Notes:

North Pole Series™

From the time we first saw a Christmas tree, we each developed our own vivid images of Santa Claus, elves, flying reindeer, and a secret land called the North Pole. It seems safe to say that none of us—in our wildest imaginations—ever matched the Department 56 version of that fantasy place. When the village was introduced, there were the three buildings that we expected—Santa's Workshop, the Reindeer Barn, and the Elf Bunkhouse. The designs may have been different from the way we visualized them, but those were the buildings we all knew were there.

And then it grew. And grew. And grew. Over 70 buildings later, the North Pole is a very busy place. The famed "pitter patter of little feet" belongs not to children rushing downstairs on Christmas morning but to hundreds of little elves. In fact, the Pole has gotten so crowded that there is even a housing subdivision—Elf Land™ that is intended as a spot for the busy elves to relax.

Seven buildings have monogrammed letters on them that spell out North Pole. There are shops of every kind, places where everything is produced from dolls and bears to lights and ornaments. Even a few commercial vendors have moved in due to licensing agreements that have brought LEGO® blocks, Barbie®, Warner Bros®. characters, and the familiar Coca-Cola® polar bears to the frosty north. The famed Post Office is included, as is a Weather and Time Station to be certain that Santa reaches every home in one night. Elves make and test toys, bake, deliver mail and toys, sing, chart the night's course, skate and ski, and even use their tiny fingers to untangle lights and tinsel.

Santa's Workshop 56006

Dates	OSRP	GBTru	Paid
1990 - 1993	$72	$255	$____

• The original samples had a green roof.

NORTH POLE - Set of 2 56014

Dates	OSRP	GBTru	Paid
1990 - 1996/2000	$70	$75	$____

Reindeer Barn 56015

Dates	OSRP	GBTru	Paid
1990 - 2000	$35	$48	$____

• Variations exist with reindeer names duplicated and others omitted. The duplicated names vary.

Elf Bunkhouse 56016

Dates	OSRP	GBTru	Paid
1990 - 1996	$35	$40	$____

• The box and the bottomstamp both read "Elf Bunkhouse" while the sign above the door reads "Elves Bunkhouse."

NeeNee's Dolls And Toys 56200

Dates	OSRP	GBTru	Paid
1991 - 1995	$36	$50	$____

• The wreath on the front of the building contains the first letter spelling out "NORTH POLE."
• Early release to Showcase and GCC dealers.

NORTH POLE SHOPS - Set of 2 56219

Dates	OSRP	GBTru	Paid
1991 - 1995	$75	$100	$____

Orly's Bell & Harness Supply 56219

Dates	OSRP	GBTru	Paid
1991 - 1995	$37.50	$50	$_____

- The wreath on the front of the building contains the second letter spelling out "NORTH POLE."

Rimpy's Bakery 56219

Dates	OSRP	GBTru	Paid
1991 - 1995	$37.50	$60	$_____

- The wreath on the front of the building contains the third letter spelling out "NORTH POLE."

Tassy's Mittens & Hassel's Woolies 56227

Dates	OSRP	GBTru	Paid
1991 - 1995	$50	$68	$_____

- The wreaths on the front of the building contain the fourth and fifth letters spelling out "NORTH POLE."

Post Office 56235

Dates	OSRP	GBTru	Paid
1992 - 1999	$45	$55	$_____

- The wreath on the front of the building contains the sixth letter spelling out "NORTH POLE."
- Early release to Showcase Dealers.

Obbie's Books & Letrinka's Candy 56243

Dates	OSRP	GBTru	Paid
1992 - 1996	$70	$75	$_____

- The wreaths on the front of the building contain the seventh and eighth letters spelling out "NORTH POLE."
- The flag is fragile.

Elfie's Sleds & Skates 56251

Dates	OSRP	GBTru	Paid
1992 - 1996	$48	$55	$_____

- The wreath on the front of the building contains the last letter spelling out "NORTH POLE."

North Pole Chapel 56260

Dates	OSRP	GBTru	Paid
1993 - 2000	$45	$50	$_____

- Early release to Showcase Dealers and select buying groups.
- There is a bell in the tower.

North Pole Express Depot 56278

Dates	OSRP	GBTru	Paid
1993 - 1998	$48	$55	$_____

- The flags are fragile.

Santa's Woodworks 56286

Dates	OSRP	GBTru	Paid
1993 - 1996	$42	$50	$_____

Santa's Lookout Tower 56294

Dates	OSRP	GBTru	Paid
1993 - 2000	$45	$55	$_____

- Early samples have a completely red tower.
- Flags are easily damaged when removing from box.

Elfin Snow Cone Works 56332

Dates	OSRP	GBTru	Paid
1994 - 1997	$40	$50	$_____

Beard Barber Shop 56340

Dates	OSRP	GBTru	Paid
1994 - 1997	$27.50	$35	$_____

- A sign is separate in the box.

North Pole Dolls & Santa's Bear Works

56359

Dates	OSRP	GBTru	Paid
1994 - 1997	$96	$105	$_____

• Set of 3 includes two lit towers and a non-lit center piece.

Tin Soldier Shop

56383

Dates	OSRP	GBTru	Paid
1995^M - 1997	$42	$55	$_____

• Metal sign attached to the front is easily broken.

Elfin Forge & Assembly Shop

56384

Dates	OSRP	GBTru	Paid
1995 - 1998	$65	$75	$_____

Weather & Time Observatory

56385

Dates	OSRP	GBTru	Paid
1995 - 1999	$50	$55	$_____

Santa's Rooming House

56386

Dates	OSRP	GBTru	Paid
1995 - 1999	$50	$60	$_____

Elves' Trade School

56387

Dates	OSRP	GBTru	Paid
1995 - 1998	$50	$60	$_____

• Early pieces have signs that read "Evles Trade School."

Popcorn & Cranberry House 56388

Dates	OSRP	GBTru	Paid
1996ᴹ - 1997	$45	$85	$_____

• A lantern is separate in the box.

Santa's Bell Repair 56389

Dates	OSRP	GBTru	Paid
1996ᴹ - 1998	$45	$50	$_____

North Pole Start A Tradition Set 56390

Dates	OSRP	GBTru	Paid
1996ᴹ - 1996	$85	$90	$_____

• First available during the November 1996 Homes for the Holidays event. The price was reduced to $65 during the event.

• Set of 12 includes Candy Cane Lane set of 2 **Candy Cane & Peppermint Shop** (top) and **Gift Wrap & Ribbons** (bottom), a 2 piece accessory "Candy Cane Elves," 6 trees, Brick Road, and a bag of snow.

Route 1, North Pole, Home Of Mr. & Mrs. Claus 56391

Dates	OSRP	GBTru	Paid
1996 -	$110	-	$_____

• Earliest shipments had the two green gates included in the box. Later ones have the gates already inserted into the fence. 3 flags are separate in the box.

Hall Of Records 56392

Dates	OSRP	GBTru	Paid
1996 - 1999	$50	$55	$_____

Christmas Bread Bakers

56393

Dates	OSRP	GBTru	Paid
1996 - 2000	$55	$60	$_____

• A directional sign is separate in the box.

The Glacier Gazette

56394

Dates	OSRP	GBTru	Paid
1997ᴹ - 1999	$48	$50	$_____

Mrs. Claus' Greenhouse

56395

Dates	OSRP	GBTru	Paid
1997 - 2001	$68	$70	$_____

• A sign is separate in the box.

Glass Ornament Works

56396

Dates	OSRP	GBTru	Paid
1997 - 2003	$60	$60	$_____

• Glass ornaments and stands are extremely fragile.

Santa's Light Shop

56397

Dates	OSRP	GBTru	Paid
1997 - 2000	$52	$55	$_____

Elsie's Gingerbread

56398

Dates	OSRP	GBTru	Paid
1997 - 1998	$65	$90	$_____

• Limited to year of production.
• Uses Magic Smoke to create smoking effect rising from the chimney.

Custom Stitchers

56400

Dates	OSRP	GBTru	Paid
1998 - 2000	$37.50	$40	$_____

• Elf Land.
• 3 pieces of clothing and a bell are separate in the box.

Tillie's Tiny Cup Café

56401

Dates	OSRP	GBTru	Paid
1998 - 2000	$37.50	$45	$_____

• Elf Land.
• A bell is separate in the box.
• The sign on top of the building is easily snapped off.

The Elf Spa

56402

Dates	OSRP	GBTru	Paid
1998 - 2001	$40	$40	$_____

• Elf Land.
• A flag is separate in the box.

Real Plastic Snow Factory

56403

Dates	OSRP	GBTru	Paid
1998 - 2001	$80	$90	$_____

• A bell is separate in the box.

Reindeer Flight School

56404

Dates	OSRP	GBTru	Paid
1998 - 2002	$55	$60	$_____

• A weathervane and windsock are separate in the box.

Marie's Doll Museum

56408

Dates	OSRP	GBTru	Paid
1999ᴹ - 1999	$55	$75	$_____

• Inspired by Marie Osmond, the entertainer and avid doll designer and North Pole collector

Santa's Visiting Center

56407

Dates	OSRP	GBTru	Paid
1999ᴹ - 1999	$65	$75	$_____

- First available at the 1999 Discover Dept. 56 event.
- Set of 6 includes the Visiting Center, girl with dog, fence, tree, walkway, and bag of snow.
- Several national flags are separate in the box.

Elf Mountain Ski Resort

56700

Dates	OSRP	GBTru	Paid
1999 - 2002	$70	$75	$_____

- 2 flags are separate in the box.

The Peanut Brittle Factory

56701

Dates	OSRP	GBTru	Paid
1999 - 2002	$80	$80	$_____

- A sign is separate in the box.

Mini-Donut Shop

56702

Dates	OSRP	GBTru	Paid
1999 - 2001	$42	$50	$_____

- Elf Land.
- The umbrella is very fragile.

Cold Care Clinic

56703

Dates	OSRP	GBTru	Paid
1999 - 2000	$42	$45	$_____

- Elf Land.
- A sign and a bell are separate in the box.

Northern Lights Tinsel Mill 56704

Dates	OSRP	GBTru	Paid
1999 - 2002	$55	$60	$_____

Jack In The Box Plant No. 2 56705

Dates	OSRP	GBTru	Paid
1999 - 2000	$65	$70	$_____

- Limited to year of production.
- The smokestack is fragile.

Sweet Rock Candy Co. Gift Set 56725

Dates	OSRP	GBTru	Paid
2000ᴹ - 2000	$75	$90	$_____

- First available during the 2000 Discover Dept. 56 event.
- The silver bell honors Dept. 56's 25th anniversary.
- Set of 9 includes the building with silver bell, "Candy Mining" accessory, 3 Peppermint Trees, cobblestone walkway, 2 Candy Cane Fences, and a bag of snow.
- The sign is easily broken.

Crayola® Polar Palette Art Center 56726

Dates	OSRP	GBTru	Paid
2000ᴹ - 2002	$65	$70	$_____

- 2 signs are separate in the box.
- Licensed by Binney & Smith.

Toot's Model Train Mfg. 56728

Dates	OSRP	GBTru	Paid
2000 - 2001	$110	$190	$_____

- 25th Anniversary Limited Edition of 25,000.
- Includes animated model train that circles the smokestack.

ACME Toy Factory   56729

Dates	OSRP	GBTru	Paid
2000 - 2002	**$80**	**$85**	$_____

- Set of 5 includes Factory and 4 Looney Tunes characters—Bugs Bunny, Daffy Duck, Sylvester, and Taz.
- Pennant is packaged separately in the box.
- Licensed by Warner Bros.

Northern Lights Fire Station   56730

Dates	OSRP	GBTru	Paid
2000 -	**$64**	-	$_____

- Do not handle by candy cane pole.

Wedding Bells Chapel   56731

Dates	OSRP	GBTru	Paid
2000 - 2001	**$45**	**$55**	$_____

- Elf Land.

Ginny's Cookie Treats (Regular Issue)   56732

Dates	OSRP	GBTru	Paid
2000 -	**$50**	-	$_____

- Elf Land.
- This version includes only the building and 2 piece accessory "Gingerbread Corner."
- Sign is packaged separately in the box.

(Early Release)   56727

Dates	OSRP	GBTru	Paid
2000ᴹ - 2002	**$50**	**$55**	$_____

- This was an early release to the various May Co. department stores. It includes the building, accessory, 3 trees, and snow.

North Pole Beauty Shoppe   05733

Dates	OSRP	GBTru	Paid
2001ᴹ - 2001	**$40**	**$95**	$_____

- Elf Land.
- Was available only through the Avon cosmetics catalog.
- Includes 2 trees and a bag of snow.

North Pole

Design Works North Pole 56733

Dates	OSRP	GBTru	Paid
2001ᴹ - 2001	$75	$465	$____

- Each of the building's four sides depicts an aspect of the creative process.
- Only available at Dept. 56's silver anniversary event.
- Pennant and 4 signs separate in box.

Santa's Sleigh Launch 56734

Dates	OSRP	GBTru	Paid
2001ᴹ - 2001	$75	$90	$____

- First available during the 2001 Holiday Discover Department 56 event.
- Though box shows straight trees, this set includes curved trees.
- Set of 5 includes building, "All Clear For Take Off" accessory, 2 green glitter sisal trees, and a bag of snow.

LEGO® Building Creation Station 56735

Dates	OSRP	GBTru	Paid
2001ᴹ - 2003	$90	$100	$____

- Licensed by The LEGO® Group.

Caribou Coffee® Shop 56736

Dates	OSRP	GBTru	Paid
2001ᴹ - 2003	$62	$65	$____

- Set of 3 includes the Shop, a sign, and a reindeer.
- Licensed by Caribou Coffee® Co.

The Egg Nog Pub 56737

Dates	OSRP	GBTru	Paid
2001ᴹ - 2003	$40	$40	$____

- Elf Land.
- Sign is separate in the box.

Twinkle Brite Glitter Factory — 56738

Dates	OSRP	GBTru	Paid
2001 - 2003	$70	$70	$_____

Barbie™ Boutique — 56739

Dates	OSRP	GBTru	Paid
2001 -	$80	-	$_____

- Sign and flag are separate in the box.
- Licensed by Mattel, Inc®.

Beard Bros. Sleigh Wash — 56740

Dates	OSRP	GBTru	Paid
2001 - 2003	$70	$60	$_____

Polar Palace Theater — 56741

Dates	OSRP	GBTru	Paid
2001 - 2003	$40	$45	$_____

- Elf Land.
- Bell is separate in the box.

Starlight Dance Hall — 56742

Dates	OSRP	GBTru	Paid
2001 - 2002	$75	$80	$_____

- Numbered limited edition of 25,000.
- Sign is separate in the box.

Grandma's Bakery — 05841

Dates	OSRP	GBTru	Paid
2002ᴹ - 2002	$40	$85	$_____

- Elf Land.
- Was available only through the Avon cosmetics catalog.
- Set of 3 includes the Bakery and 2 sisal trees.
- Sign is separate in the box.

The Antler Inn 56744

Dates	OSRP	GBTru	Paid
2002ᴹ -	$75	-	$_____

• Two signs are separate in the box.

Glacier Park Pavilion 56745

Dates	OSRP	GBTru	Paid
2002ᴹ - 2002	$110	$110	$_____

• Holiday 2002 Special Edition.
• Limited to year of production.
• Animated.
• Set of 9 includes Pavilion with skating rink, "Skating With Santa" accessory, 2 elf skaters, 2 winter birch trees, 2 frosted topiaries, and snow.
• Four flags and sign are separate in the box.

Play-Doh® Sculpting Studio 56746

Dates	OSRP	GBTru	Paid
2002ᴹ - 2003	$80	$85	$_____

• Licensed by Hasbro Consumer Products.

Santa's Reindeer Rides 56748

Dates	OSRP	GBTru	Paid
2002ᴹ - 2002	$50	$55	$_____

• Holiday 2002 Special Edition.
• Limited to year of production.
• Animated.
• Set of 6 includes the building, "Look At Him Go!" accessory, frosted topiary tree, 2 frosted topiary bushes, and snow.

Polar Power Company

56749

Dates	OSRP	GBTru	Paid
2002 - 2003	$95	$100	$_____

- Limited to year of production.
- Animated with lighting effects.

Kringle Elfementary School

56750

Dates	OSRP	GBTru	Paid
2002 -	$45	-	$_____

- Elf Land.

Northwind Knitters

56751

Dates	OSRP	GBTru	Paid
2002 -	$65	-	$_____

- Set of 2 includes building and "Drying The Wool" accessory.

Frosty Pines Outfitters

56752

Dates	OSRP	GBTru	Paid
2002 - 2003	$60	$60	$_____

Hand Carved Nutcracker Factory

56753

Dates	OSRP	GBTru	Paid
2002 -	$65	-	$_____

North Pole

Coca-Cola® Fizz Factory 56754

Dates	OSRP	GBTru	Paid
2002 -	$85	-	$____

- Animated.
- If the bottle does not fizz, Dept. 56 suggests turning it over for 3 seconds, then upright before turning it on.
- Licensed by Coca-Cola®.

McElfin's Irish Restaurant & Gifts 56755

Dates	OSRP	GBTru	Paid
2002 -	$55	-	$____

Mitten Manor 56756

Dates	OSRP	GBTru	Paid
2002 -	$45	-	$____

- Set of 2 includes Manor and "Newt & Emma" accessory.

Checking It Twice Wind-Up Toys 56757

Dates	OSRP	GBTru	Paid
2003ᴹ - 2003	$75	$75	$____

- Holiday 2003 Special Edition.
- Limited to year of production.
- Animated. Includes adapter.
- Set of 5 includes the building, "Everything Looks A-Okay" accessory, walkway, sparkle glitter birch tree, and snow.

Naughty Or Nice Detective Agency 56758

Dates	OSRP	GBTru	Paid
2003ᴹ - 2003	$75	$55	$_____

- Holiday 2003 Special Edition.
- Limited to year of production.
- Animated. Includes adapter.
- Set of 6 includes the building, "Lots Of Good Children This Year" accessory, frosted pine tree, frosted pine shrubs, and snow.

Mickey's North Pole Holiday House 56759

Dates	OSRP	GBTru	Paid
2003ᴹ -	$85	-	$_____

- Disney Showcase Collection.
- Licensed by Disney Theme Parks.

KOLD Radio 56761

Dates	OSRP	GBTru	Paid
2003ᴹ -	$60	-	$_____

The Christmas Candy Mill 56762

Dates	OSRP	GBTru	Paid
2003 -	$75	-	$_____

- Animated.

Flurry's Snowglobe Maker 56763

Dates	OSRP	GBTru	Paid
2003 -	$68	-	$_____

Polar Roller Rink — 56764

Dates	OSRP	GBTru	Paid
2003 -	$65	-	$_____

- Animated.
- Includes "Elves On Wheels" accessory.

Red's Elf Land Diner — 56765

Dates	OSRP	GBTru	Paid
2003 -	$50	-	$_____

- Elf Land.

Pointy Toed Shoemaker — 56766

Dates	OSRP	GBTru	Paid
2003 -	$35	-	$_____

- Elf Land.
- Plays "Jingle Bells."

North Pole Town Hall — 56767

Dates	OSRP	GBTru	Paid
2003 -	$65	-	$_____

Santa's Castle — 56768

Dates	OSRP	GBTru	Paid
2003 -	$95	-	$_____

- Limited to year of production.
- Inspired by the Castle in the cartoon "Rudolph The Red-Nosed Reindeer."
- Licensed by Good-Times Merchandising & Licensing.

Rudolph's Misfit Headquarters — 56769

Dates	OSRP	GBTru	Paid
2003 -	$70	-	$_____

- Limited to year of production.
- Inspired by the location in the cartoon "Rudolph The Red-Nosed Reindeer."
- Licensed by Good-Times Merchandising & Licensing.

Use the space(s) below to update your guide when the midyear introductions are announced.

Photos of the midyear introductions will be included in the July-August issue of *the Village Chronicle* magazine.

Dates	OSRP	GBTru	Paid
____ - ____	$____	-	$____

Dates	OSRP	GBTru	Paid
____ - ____	$____	-	$____

Dates	OSRP	GBTru	Paid
____ - ____	$____	-	$____

Dates	OSRP	GBTru	Paid
____ - ____	$____	-	$____

Dates	OSRP	GBTru	Paid
____ - ____	$____	-	$____

Notes:

Trimming The North Pole

56081

1990 - 1993

OSRP: $10

GBTru: $30

Paid: $_____

Santa & Mrs. Claus

56090 - Set of 2

1990 -

OSRP: $15

GBTru: -

Paid: $_____

• Early samples had books that read "Good Boys" instead of "Good Kids."

Santa's Little Helpers

56103 - Set of 3

1990 - 1993

OSRP: $28

GBTru: $50

Paid: $_____

• The reindeer's antlers are very fragile.

Sleigh & Eight Tiny Reindeer

56111 - Set of 5

1990 -

OSRP: $40

GBTru: -

Paid: $_____

• The reindeer's antlers are very fragile.

Toymaker Elves

56022 - Set of 3

1991 - 1995

OSRP: $27.50

GBTru: $30

Paid: $_____

Baker Elves

56030 - Set of 3

1991 - 1995

OSRP: $27.50

GBTru: $35

Paid: $_____

Letters For Santa

56049 - Set of 3

1992 - 1994

OSRP: $30

GBTru: $55

Paid: $_____

• The reindeer's antlers are very fragile.

Testing The Toys

56057 - Set of 2

1992 - 1999

OSRP: $16.50

GBTru: $20

Paid: $_____

Woodsmen Elves

56308 - Set of 3
1993 - 1995
OSRP: $30
GBTru: $45
Paid: $_____

Sing A Song For Santa

56316 - Set of 3
1993 - 1998
OSRP: $28
GBTru: $36
Paid: $_____

North Pole Gate

56324
1993 - 1998
OSRP: $32.50
GBTru: $38
Paid: $_____

• The flags are fragile.

Last Minute Delivery

56367
1994 - 1998
OSRP: $35
GBTru: $40
Paid: $_____

• Though introduced in 1994, shipments were delayed due to production problems.

Snow Cone Elves

56375 - Set of 4
1994 - 1997
OSRP: $30
GBTru: $34
Paid: $_____

• Features the first "elfette" in North Pole.
• Porcelain and metal.

Charting Santa's Course

56364 - Set of 2
1995 - 1997
OSRP: $25
GBTru: $35
Paid: $_____

I'll Need More Toys

56365 - Set of 2
1995 - 1998
OSRP: $25
GBTru: $26
Paid: $_____

• Porcelain and acrylic.

A Busy Elf North Pole Sign

56366
1995 - 1999
OSRP: $20
GBTru: $24
Paid: $_____

• Porcelain and acrylic.

North Pole Express

56368 - Set of 3

1996 - 1999

OSRP: $37.50

GBTru: $45

Paid: $_____

• Some samples read "N.E. Express" on the side of the tender.

Early Rising Elves

56369 - Set of 5

1996 - 1999

OSRP: $32.50

GBTru: $33

Paid: $_____

End Of The Line

56370 - Set of 2

1996 - 1999

OSRP: $28

GBTru: $37

Paid: $_____

• Includes sign and signal packaged separately in the box.

Holiday Deliveries

56371

1996 - 2001ᴹ

OSRP: $16.50

GBTru: $20

Paid: $_____

Candy Cane Elves

56390 - Set of 2

1996ᴹ - 1996

OSRP: *

GBTru: *

* Accessory contained in the North Pole Start A Tradition Set.

Don't Break The Ornaments

56372 - Set of 2

1997 - 2001

OSRP: $27.50

GBTru: $28

Paid: $_____

• Ornaments are very fragile.

Delivering The Christmas Greens

56373 - Set of 2

1997 - 2001ᴹ

OSRP: $27.50

GBTru: $28

Paid: $_____

Untangle The Christmas Lights

56374

1997 - 2000

OSRP: $35

GBTru: $40

Paid: $_____

• Lit by battery/ adapter.

Peppermint Skating Party

56363 - Set of 6
1998[M] - 2000
OSRP: $64
GBTru: $65
Paid: $_____

Welcome To Elf Land Gateway Entrance

56431
1998 -
OSRP: $35
GBTru: -
Paid: $_____

Loading The Sleigh

52732 - Set of 6
1998 -
OSRP: $125
GBTru: -
Paid: $_____

• Animated—handcar runs back and forth along track. Lights on building flash.

Christmas Fun Run

56434 - Set of 6
1998 - 2000
OSRP: $35
GBTru: $38
Paid: $_____

Christmas FUN RUN

Delivering Real Plastic Snow

56435
1998 - 2001[M]
OSRP: $17
GBTru: $24
Paid: $_____

Reindeer Training Camp

56436 - Set of 2
1998 - 2002
OSRP: $27.50
GBTru: $28
Paid: $_____

• The reindeer's antlers are very fragile.

Have A Seat Elves

56437 - Set of 6
1998 -
OSRP: $30
GBTru: -
Paid: $_____

Dash Away Delivery

56438
1998 - 2001ᴹ
OSRP: $40
GBTru: $42
Paid: $_____

• The basket often comes unglued.
• Similar design made for Lord & Taylor. See Special Design section.

Tee Time Elves

56442 - Set of 2
1999ᴹ - 2001ᴹ
OSRP: $27.50
GBTru: $28
Paid: $_____

Happy New Year!

56443
1999ᴹ - 2000
OSRP: $17.50
GBTru: $20
Paid: $_____

A Happy Harley Day

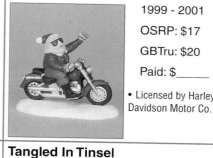

56706
1999 - 2001
OSRP: $17
GBTru: $20
Paid: $_____

• Licensed by Harley-Davidson Motor Co.

Downhill Daredevils

56707 - Set of 2
1999 - 2001
OSRP: $16.50
GBTru: $20
Paid: $_____

Tangled In Tinsel

56708
1999 -
OSRP: $25
GBTru: -
Paid: $_____

Canine Courier

56709 - Set of 3
1999 - 2002
OSRP: $32.50
GBTru: $33
Paid: $_____

Ski Bums

56710
1999 - 2001
OSRP: $22.50
GBTru: $26
Paid: $_____

Check This Out

56711
1999 - 2001
OSRP: $13.50
GBTru: $18
Paid: $_____

Marshmallows Around The Campfire

56712 - Set of 3
1999 - 2002
OSRP: $30
GBTru: $33
Paid: $_____

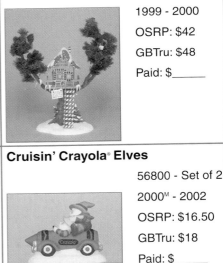

• The campfire is battery/adapter operated.

Open Wide!

56713
1999 - 2000
OSRP: $13
GBTru: $15
Paid: $_____

Elf Tree House

56446
1999 - 2000
OSRP: $42
GBTru: $48
Paid: $_____

Candy Mining

56725
2000ᴹ - 2000
OSRP: *
GBTru: *

* Accessory contained in the Sweet Rock Candy Co. Gift Set.

Cruisin' Crayola® Elves

56800 - Set of 2
2000ᴹ - 2002
OSRP: $16.50
GBTru: $18
Paid: $_____

• Licensed by Binney & Smith.

Leonardo & Vincent

56801
2000ᴹ - 2002
OSRP: $16.50
GBTru: $17
Paid: $_____

Party In The Hot Tub!

56802 - Set of 2
2000ᴹ - 2001
OSRP: $30
GBTru: $33
Paid: $_____

Gingerbread Corner

56732 - Set of 2

2000 -

OSRP: *

GBTru: *

* Accessory
contained in the
Ginny's Cookie Treats
Set.

All Aboard!

56803 - Set of 2

2000 - 2003

OSRP: $16.50

GBTru: $20

Paid: $_____

Rescue Ready

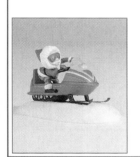

56804

2000 -

OSRP: $16.50

GBTru: -

Paid: $_____

Little Newlyweds

56805

2000 - 2001

OSRP: $13

GBTru: $24

Paid: $_____

Cutting The Trail

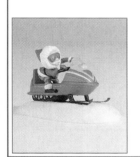

56806

2000 - 2003

OSRP: $14

GBTru: $14

Paid: $_____

Catch The Wind

56807

2000 - 2002

OSRP: $17.50

GBTru: $15

Paid: $_____

Icy Delights

56808

2000 - 2003

OSRP: $17.50

GBTru: $18

Paid: $_____

All Clear For Take Off

56734

2001ᴹ - 2001

OSRP: *

GBTru: *

* Accessory
contained in the
Santa's Sleigh Launch
Gift Set.

Brick Lift

56809

2001^M - 2003

OSRP: $17.50

GBTru: $20

Paid: $_____

• Licensed by the LEGO® Group.

Little Builders

56810

2001^M - 2003

OSRP: $16

GBTru: $17

Paid: $_____

• Licensed by the LEGO® Group.

Just A Cup Of Joe

56811

2001^M - 2003

OSRP: $22.50

GBTru: $24

Paid: $_____

• This was originally shipped in North Pole Woods sleeves.

Glitter Detail

56812 - Set of 2

2001 -

OSRP: $20

GBTru: -

Paid: $_____

Car Wash Cadets

56813

2001 - 2003

OSRP: $16.50

GBTru: $17

Paid: $_____

Two For The Show

56814

2001 - 2003

OSRP: $16.50

GBTru: $17

Paid: $_____

Kick Up Your Heels

56815

2001 - 2002

OSRP: $13.50

GBTru: $14

Paid: $_____

Peppermint Front Yard

56817

2001 -

OSRP: $42.50

GBTru: -

Paid: $_____

Wrap And Roll

56818

2001 - 2003

OSRP: $20

GBTru: $28

Paid: $_____

Raising The Flag At The North Pole

56820

2001 -

OSRP: $15.00

GBTru: -

Paid: $_____

LEGO® Warehouse Forklift

56819 - Set of 5

2001 - 2003

OSRP: $140.00

GBTru: $120

Paid: $_____

• Animated—forklift runs back and forth along track.
• Licensed by the LEGO® Group.

Skating With Santa

56745

2002ᴹ - 2002

OSRP: *

GBTru: *

* The accessory contained in Glacier Park Pavilion.

Look At Him Go!

56748

2002ᴹ - 2002

OSRP: *

GBTru: *

* The accessory contained in the Santa's Reindeer Rides.

More Play-Doh®, Please!

56822 - Set of 2

2002ᴹ - 2003

OSRP: $20

GBTru: $20

Paid: $_____

• Licensed by Hasbro Consumer Products.

North Pole Petting Zoo

56823

2002ᴹ -

OSRP: $35

GBTru: -

Paid: $_____

This Looks Like A Good Spot

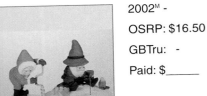

56831 - Set of 2

2002ᴹ -

OSRP: $16.50

GBTru: -

Paid: $_____

Kringle Street Snowman

56833

2002ᴹ - 2002

OSRP: $32.50

GBTru: $34

Paid: $_____

• Limited to year of production.
• Available only at Gold Key dealers.

Drying The Wool

56751

2002 -

OSRP: *

GBTru: *

* The accessory contained in the Northwind Knitters.

Newt & Emma

56756

2002 -

OSRP: *

GBTru: *

* The accessory contained in Mitten Manor.

S'mores & Hot Chocolate Stand

56835

2002 -

OSRP: $32.50

GBTru: -

Paid: $_____

• Elf Land.

Sparky The Plant Manager

56836

2002 - 2003

OSRP: $15

GBTru: $15

Paid: $_____

School Sleigh Express

56837

2002 -

OSRP: $25

GBTru: -

Paid: $_____

• Elf Land.

Running The Loom

56838

2002 -

OSRP: $12.50

GBTru: -

Paid: $_____

Ready For Adventure

56839

2002 - 2003

OSRP: $17.50

GBTru: $18

Paid: $_____

Frozen Veggies

56840

2002 -

OSRP: $15

GBTru: -

Paid: $_____

Coca-Cola® Taste Test

56841

2002 -

OSRP: $17.50

GBTru: -

Paid: $_____

• Licensed by Coca-Cola.

Nutcracker Delivery

56842 - Set of 2

2002 -

OSRP: $25

GBTru: -

Paid: $_____

Chimney Sweep For Hire!

56843

2002 -

OSRP: $13.50

GBTru: -

Paid: $_____

Frostbite Tree House Day Care

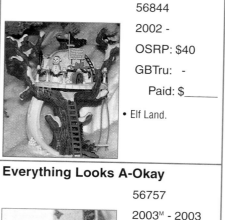

56844

2002 -

OSRP: $40

GBTru: -

Paid: $_____

• Elf Land.

Frosty Playground

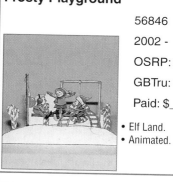

56846

2002 -

OSRP: $32.50

GBTru: -

Paid: $_____

• Elf Land.
• Animated.

Everything Looks A-Okay

56757

2003ᴹ - 2003

OSRP: *

GBTru: *

* The accessory contained in Checking It Twice Wind-Up Toys.

Lots Of Good Children This Year

56758

2003ᴹ - 2003

OSRP: *

GBTru: *

* The accessory contained in Naughty Or Nice Detective Agency.

Kringle Street Town Tree

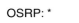

56847

2003ᴹ - 2003

OSRP: $35

GBTru: $35

Paid: $_____

• Includes adapter.
• Limited to year of production.

An Irish Cheer For Santa

56848 - Set of 2

2003ᴹ -

OSRP: $20

GBTru: -

Paid: $_____

Mickey Builds A Snowman

56849

2003ᴹ -

OSRP: $22.50

GBTru: -

Paid: $_____

• Licensed by Disney Theme Parks.

Bustin' A Move

56850 - Set of 2

2003ᴹ -

OSRP: $15

GBTru: -

Paid: $_____

Coca-Cola® Sliding Hill

56851

2003ᴹ -

OSRP: $60

GBTru: -

Paid: $_____

• Licensed by Coca-Cola.
• Includes adapter.

Reindeer Games

56853

2003 -

OSRP: $45

GBTru: -

Paid: $_____

• Limited to year of production.
• Licensed by Good-Times M & L.

Don't Let Go!

56854

2003 -

OSRP: $10

GBTru: -

Paid: $_____

Fillers & Flakers

56855

2003 -

OSRP: $20

GBTru: -

Paid: $_____

A Perfect Fit

56856

2003 -

OSRP: $16.50

GBTru: -

Paid: $_____

• Elf Land

The Key To The North Pole

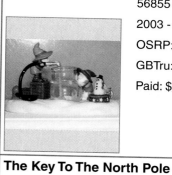

56857

2003 -

OSRP: $15

GBTru: -

Paid: $_____

Fly Through Elf

56858

2003 -

OSRP: $15

GBTru: -

Paid: $_____

• Elf Land

Candy Cane Shack

56859

2003 -

OSRP: $40

GBTru: -

Paid: $_____

• Working bubble lights.
• includes adapter.

The Misfits

56860

2003 -

OSRP: $35

GBTru: -

Paid: $_____

• Limited to year of production.
• Licensed by Good-Times M & L.

Mrs. Claus' Cookies & Milk

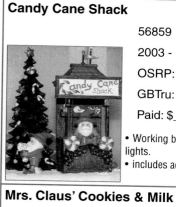

56861

2003 -

OSRP: $25

GBTru: -

Paid: $_____

Proud Papa & Mama

56862

2003 -

OSRP: $13.50

GBTru: -

Paid: $_____

• Elf Land

New Year's At The North Pole

56863

2003 -

OSRP: $20

GBTru: -

Paid: $_____

Ice & Snow Skating Pond

56867

2003 -

OSRP: $50

GBTru: -

Paid: $_____

• Animated.
• Includes adapter.

Use the space(s) on the following page to update your guide when the midyear introductions are announced.

Photos of the midyear introductions will be included in the July-August issue of *the Village Chronicle* magazine.

_____

_____ - _____

OSRP: $_____

GBTru: -

Paid: $_____

_____

_____ - _____

OSRP: $_____

GBTru: -

Paid: $_____

_____

_____ - _____

OSRP: $_____

GBTru: -

Paid: $_____

_____

_____ - _____

OSRP: $_____

GBTru: -

Paid: $_____

_____

_____ - _____

OSRP: $_____

GBTru: -

Paid: $_____

Small Collections

While most village collections seem to almost grow by leaps and bounds, there are a few that have followed a very different pattern. These small series were over almost as soon as they began, while two continuing collections are growing slowly.

Meadowland is a series of ceramic pieces that debuted—and retired—three years after Snow Village first appeared. It is the first instance of a village intended to be displayed other than during the winter.

Introduced in 1994, Disney Parks Village™ Series excited both village collectors and Disney fans with its reproductions of buildings from Orlando's Disney World and Anaheim's Disneyland. But within two years the relationship between the two companies abruptly ended.

Seasons Bay debuted in 1998 with six special first edition buildings and a series of seasonal accessories. The smaller pewter figures were created in scale to the buildings, a first for Department 56. A number of general accessories rounded out this Victorian village that retired after four years.

North Pole Woods™ began in 2000 and was produced for less than three years. It was treated by both Department 56 and collectors as a stepchild to the more popular North Pole Series™ and never seemed to acquire its own identity.

The two continuing series are the Historical Landmark® and Literary Classics® pieces. Each had its roots within other Heritage Villages. The Literary Calssics® pieces all include a building, accessory, and a copy of the book. Historical Landmarks® include several London structures as well as familiar American buildings.

THE HISTORICAL LANDMARK SERIES™

Initial Pieces were originally classified as part of Dickens'
Village Series®. This varied series depicts some of the most
well-known buildings in the world.

Tower Of London   58500

Dates	OSRP	GBTru	Paid
1997ᴹ - 1997	$165	$215	$_____

- Limited to year of production.
- This, the White Tower, is one of the many towers that comprise the Tower of London, famous for housing a prison as well as the Crown Jewels. Legend says six ravens must be at the tower to preserve the monarchy.
- The actual Tower of London is located along the Thames River in London.
- Set of 5 includes the Tower, a gate with tower, the raven master, a sign, and a wall with ravens.

The Old Globe Theatre   58501

Dates	OSRP	GBTru	Paid
1997 - 1998	$175	$150	$_____

- Limited to year of production.
- First samples of the building were made as two pieces. For production, it is one piece.
- Some early shipments have "The City Globe" stamped on the bottom.
- The Globe Theatre, located along the Thames River in London, was demolished in 1644 and was rebuilt in 1996 near the original site.

- Set of 4 includes the Theatre, two trumpeters, and a sign.

Independence Hall   55500

Dates	OSRP	GBTru	Paid
1998 - 2000ᴹ	$110	$115	$_____

- This replica of Philadelphia's Independence Hall was first Historical Landmark not associated with England.
- First available during the 1999 July event.
- Set of 2 includes Hall and sign.

Big Ben

58341

Dates	OSRP	GBTru	Paid
1998 - 2003	**$95**	**$95**	$_____

- It features a working clock on one of its faces. The other three read "5 of 6."
- It is a replica of London's Big Ben along the Thames River.
- Set of 2 includes Big Ben and sign.

The Old Royal Observatory Gold Dome Edition

58451

Dates	OSRP	GBTru	Paid
1999 - 2000	**Promo**	**$320**	$_____

- Limited to 5,500, Department 56 sent one to its valued retailers as a thank you for their support.

The Old Royal Observatory

58453

Dates	OSRP	GBTru	Paid
1999 - 2000	**$95**	**$100**	$_____

- Limited to 35,000.
- This is a replica of the Old Royal Observatory in Greenwich, England which keeps the world's time.
- Set of 2 includes Observatory and sign.

Cathedral Of St. Paul

58919

Dates	OSRP	GBTru	Paid
2001^M - 2001	**$150**	**$420**	$_____

- Replica of Cathedral of St. Paul in St. Paul, MN.
- Copper-colored roof.
- Only available at Dept. 56 25th Anniversary celebration.
- Christmas In The City bottomstamp. DV logo on box.

Cathedral Of St. Paul

58930

Dates	OSRP	GBTru	Paid
2001 -	**$150**	**-**	$_____

- Re-issue of the copper colored roof version that was available at the Dept. 56 25th Anniversary celebration.
- Also designated as a Christmas In The City design.

Temple Bar

58564

Dates	OSRP	GBTru	Paid
2002 - 2003	**$60**	**$55**	$_____

- This is a replica of a gate that once stood in London and is now on private property.
- Also designated as a Dickens' Village accessory.

Central Synagogue

59204

Dates	OSRP	GBTru	Paid
2002 - 2003	$110	$110	$_____

• Limited to year of production.
• This is a replica of Central Synagogue in New York City.
• Also designated as a Christmas In The City design.

Empire State Building

59207

Dates	OSRP	GBTru	Paid
2003ᴹ -	$185	-	$_____

• This is a replica of the Empire State Building in Manhattan.
• At 23 inches, this is the tallest building manufactured by Department 56.
• Features several holiday lighting effects, including different colors in detachable top section.
• Four American flags are separate in box.
• Also designated as a Christmas In The City design.

Tower Bridge Of London

58705

Dates	OSRP	GBTru	Paid
2003 -	$165	-	$_____

• Numbered limited edition of 20,000.
• Dickens' Village 20th Anniversary Series. Includes pin.
• It is a replica of London's Tower Bridge.
• Set of 4.

Historic Chicago Water Tower

59209

Dates	OSRP	GBTru	Paid
2003 -	$65	-	$_____

• Set of 2 includes Tower and sign.
• This is a replica of the Chicago Water Tower, one of the few buildings to survive the great Chicago fire of 1871.
• Also designated as a Christmas In The City design.

MEADOWLAND

This "non-winter" series was short-lived. Made of ceramic, it is considered by many collectors to be a companion series to the Original Snow Village®.

Thatched Cottage
50500

Dates	OSRP	GBTru	Paid
1979 - 1980	$30	$425	$_____

Countryside Church
50518

Dates	OSRP	GBTru	Paid
1979 - 1980	$25	$450	$_____

• This is a snowless version of the Snow Village 1979 Countryside Church.

Aspen Trees
50526

Dates	OSRP	GBTru	Paid
1979 - 1980	$16	$125	$_____

Sheep
50534

Dates	OSRP	GBTru	Paid
1979 - 1980	$12	$60	$_____

• Set of 12 includes 9 white and 3 black sheep.

LITERARY CLASSICS® COLLECTION

These designs are Department 56's interpretation of the buildings and characters that come to life in some of the literary world's most cherished works. Each set includes a specially printed copy of the classic in addition to a lit building and accessories which help to bring the stories to life. Other literary works have also been recognized in several of the villages, but none have been as comprehensive or detailed as these versions. Notice that none of the buildings have snow on them.

Great Expectations Satis Manor — 58310

Dates	OSRP	GBTru	Paid
1998 - 2001	$110	$85	$_____

- Charles Dickens used Restoration House in Rochester, England as the model for his Satis Manor.
- Set of 4 plus book includes the Manor and a 3 piece accessory "Miss Havisham, Estella, and Pip."

Little Women - The March Residence — 56606

Dates	OSRP	GBTru	Paid
1999ᴹ - 2000	$90	$10	$_____

- Louisa May Alcott based the March Residence on the Orchard House in Concord, MA. where she grew up.
- Set of 4 plus book includes the Residence and a 3 piece accessory "A Letter From Papa" which includes Marmie, Jo, Amy, Beth, and Meg.
- The water pump's handle is very fragile.

The Great Gatsby West Egg Mansion

Dates	OSRP	GBTru	Paid
1999 - 2001	**$135**	**$135**	$_____

- This is Department 56's interpretation of the Long Island mansion that F. Scott Fitzgerald depicted in his novel.
- Some pieces were shipped with extra statues in anticipation of breakage.
- Set of 4 plus book includes the Mansion, Jay Gatsby, Daisy Buchanan, and the infamous car.
- Licensed through the Fitzgerald Estate, LTD.

The Adventures Of Tom Sawyer, Aunt Polly's House   58600

Dates	OSRP	GBTru	Paid
2000ᴹ - 2001	**$90**	**$95**	$_____

- Inspired by Mark Twain's first book, this is a depiction of the home and characters made famous in the book.
- Set of 5 plus book includes the House, and a 4 piece accessory "Painting The White Picket Fence" which includes Tom Sawyer, two friends, and the fence.

Small Collections

Sherlock Holmes - 221B Baker Street   58601

Dates	OSRP	GBTru	Paid
2000 - 2003	**$90**	**$110**	$_____

- Inspired by Arthur Conan Doyle's famous works, this is Department 56's interpretation of the home of England's greatest fictional detective.
- Set of 3 plus book includes the house and 2 piece accessory "Elementary My Dear Watson."

DISNEY PARKS VILLAGE™ SERIES

Available for less than two years, this series reproduced familiar buildings at the Disney theme parks. First year releases
were more plentiful, while scarcity of later buildings resulted in
higher aftermarket values.

Mickey's Christmas Carol (10 Points)   53503

Dates	OSRP	GBTru	Paid
1994 - 1996	$144	$150	$_____

- This version has gold spires at the lower corners and peaks of the dormers.
- Replica of Disney World building.
- Set of 2 includes main building and outbuilding.
- Holiday Collection stamped piece (#07420) sold by Disney Parks has   **GBTru: $180** $_____

(6 Points)   53503

	GBTru	Paid
	$110	$_____

- Has no spires at the lower corners of the dormers.
- Holiday Collection has   **GBTru: $160** $_____

OLDE WORLD ANTIQUES SHOPS - Set of 2   53511

Dates	OSRP	GBTru	Paid
1994 - 1996	$90	$90	$_____

- Holiday Collection stamped piece (#07429) sold by Disney Parks has   **GBTru: $120** $_____

Olde World Antiques I   53511

Dates	OSRP	GBTru	Paid
1994 - 1996	$45	$50	$_____

- A similar building is in Disney World's Liberty Square.
- Holiday Collection stamped piece (#07429) sold by Disney Parks has   **GBTru: $65** $_____

Olde World Antiques II   53511

Dates	OSRP	GBTru	Paid
1994 - 1996	$45	$50	$_____

- A similar building is in Disney World's Liberty Square.
- Holiday Collection stamped piece (#07429) sold by Disney Parks has   **GBTru: $65** $_____

Disneyland Fire Department #105

53520

Dates	OSRP	GBTru	Paid
1994 - 1996	**$45**	**$55**	$_____

- Inspired by fire station on Main Street in Disneyland.
- Holiday Collection stamped piece (#07439) sold by Disney Parks has **GBTru: $80** $_____

Silversmith

53521

Dates	OSRP	GBTru	Paid
1995 - 1996	**$50**	**$195**	$_____

- Holiday Collection stamped piece (#07448) sold by Disney Parks has **GBTru: $225** $_____

Tinker Bell's Treasures

53522

Dates	OSRP	GBTru	Paid
1995 - 1996	**$60**	**$195**	$_____

- Holiday Collection stamped piece (#07449) sold by Disney Parks has **GBTru: $225** $_____

Mickey & Minnie

53538 - Set of 2
1994 - 1996
OSRP: $22.50
GBTru: $30
Paid: $_____

Disney Parks Family

53546 - Set of 3
1994 - 1996
OSRP: $32.50
GBTru: $30
Paid: $_____

Olde World Antiques Gate

53554
1994 - 1996
OSRP: $15
GBTru: $20
Paid: $_____

Balloon Seller

53539 - Set of 2
1995 - 1996
OSRP: $25
GBTru: $35
Paid: $_____

NORTH POLE WOODS™ SERIES

Available for only three years, these life-in-a-forest pieces were incorporated by many collectors into their North Pole villages, while others treated it as a separate area. The accessories were more readily placed within the North Pole Series™ than the lighted trees.

Town Meeting Hall

56880

Dates	OSRP	GBTru	Paid
2000ᴹ - 2002	$73	$50	$_____

• Adapter included.

Oakwood Post Office Branch

56881

Dates	OSRP	GBTru	Paid
2000ᴹ - 2002	$70	$40	$_____

• Adapter included.
• Set of 2 includes Post Office and elf.

Reindeer Care & Repair

56882

Dates	OSRP	GBTru	Paid
2000ᴹ - 2002	$65	$45	$_____

• Adapter included.

Trim-A-Tree Factory

56884

Dates	OSRP	GBTru	Paid
2000ᴹ - 2001	$55	$50	$_____

• Adapter included.
• Set of 2 includes Factory and elf.

Santa's Retreat

56883

Dates	OSRP	GBTru	Paid
2000 - 2002	$70	$60	$_____

• Early release to Parade of Gifts stores.
• Adapter included.
• Set of 2 includes tree and Mrs. Claus.

Rudolph's Condo   56885

Dates	OSRP	GBTru	Paid
2000 - 2002	**$50**	**$40**	$_____

• Licensed by GTM&L.

Reindeer Condo   56886

Dates	OSRP	GBTru	Paid
2000 - 2001	**$70**	**$50**	$_____

• Adapter included.
• Windsock separate in the box.

Chisel McTimber Art Studio   56887

Dates	OSRP	GBTru	Paid
2001 - 2002	**$65**	**$70**	$_____

• Adapter included.
• Set of 2 includes tree and "Elf Sculpting" accessory.

Welcome To North Pole Woods

Gateway Entrance
56920
2000ᴹ - 2002
OSRP: $25
GBTru: $20
Paid: $_____

Tailored For You
56921 - Set of 2
2000ᴹ - 2001
OSRP: $22.50
GBTru: $18
Paid: $_____

• The snowman's arms are fragile.

Elves
56922 - Set of 4
2000ᴹ - 2002
OSRP: $30
GBTru: $18
Paid: $_____

Scissors Wizards
56923 - Set of 2
2000ᴹ - 2001
OSRP: $25
GBTru: $20
Paid: $_____

• The reindeer's antlers are very fragile.

Nuts About Broomball
56926
2000ᴹ - 2001ᴹ
OSRP: $20
GBTru: $20
Paid: $_____

Birch Bench & Table
56927 - Set of 2
2000ᴹ - 2001ᴹ
OSRP: $9
GBTru: $9
Paid: $_____

Pinecone Path
52874 - Set of 6
2000 - 2002
OSRP: $15
GBTru: $12
Paid: $_____

• Straight and curved.

Acorn Street Lamps
52875 - Set of 4
2000 - 2002
OSRP: $15
GBTru: $12
Paid: $_____

• Battery/adapter operated.

Birch Bridge

52876
2000 - 2002
OSRP: $13.50
GBTru: $10
Paid: $_____

Birch Gazebo

52877
2000 - 2002
OSRP: $20
GBTru: $15
Paid: $_____

• Weathervane is very fragile.

Birch Fence

52878 - Set of 4
2000 - 2002
OSRP: $12
GBTru: $12
Paid: $_____

Star Of The Show

56928
2000 - 2002
OSRP: $25
GBTru: $20
Paid: $_____

• Licensed by Good-Times Merchandising & Licensing.

Polar Plowing Service

56929
2000 - 2002
OSRP: $30
GBTru: $20
Paid: $_____

Gone Fishing

56930
2000 - 2002
OSRP: $35
GBTru: $25
Paid: $_____

Ring Toss

56931 - Set of 2
2000 - 2002
OSRP: $17.50
GBTru: $18
Paid: $_____

• Licensed by Good-Times Merchandising & Licensing.

Balancing Act

56932 - Set of 3
2000 - 2002
OSRP: $25
GBTru: $20
Paid: $_____

• The reindeer's antlers are very fragile.

SEASONS BAY® SERIES

For many years Department 56 was famed for creating winter villages. But many collectors wanted to display their pieces for more than just a few months each year, and Seasons Bay met that need. The buildings were exceptionally crafted, but what made them different was the fact that they all lacked snow.

It was not the buildings, though, that made this a truly unique village. It was the accessories. Set in the Victorian era, the collection featured people engaged in year-round activities. A variety of plants and trees reinforced the seasonal designs. Another unique feature was the diminutive size of the people. Accessories were created in pewter in order to present them in proportion to their residences. This is the only village in which this is true.

Grandview Shores Hotel (First Edition)   53300

Dates	OSRP	GBTru	Paid
1998 - 1999	**$150**	**$175**	$_____

• This version is identified by its gold flags, weathervane, and First Edition decal on its bottom.

(Open Edition)   53400

Dates	OSRP	GBTru	Paid
1998 - 2000	**$150**	**$125**	$_____

Bay Street Shops (First Edition)   53301

Dates	OSRP	GBTru	Paid
1998 - 1999	**$135**	**$150**	$_____

• This version is identified by its gold flags and First Edition decal on its bottom.
• Set of 2 includes two buildings—Maggie's Millinery and Bayside Clothiers/Book Nook—that fit together.

(Open Edition)   53401

Dates	OSRP	GBTru	Paid
1998 - 2002	**$135**	**$120**	$_____

• Set of 2 includes two buildings—Maggie's Millinery and Bayside Clothiers/Book Nook—that fit together.

Chapel On The Hill (First Edition)   53302

Dates	OSRP	GBTru	Paid
1998 - 1999	**$72**	**$80**	$_____

• This version is identified by its gold cross and First Edition decal on its bottom.

(Open Edition)   53402

Dates	OSRP	GBTru	Paid
1998 - 2001	**$72**	**$65**	$_____

Side Porch Café (First Edition)   53303

Dates	OSRP	GBTru	Paid
1998 - 1999	**$50**	**$65**	$_____

• This version is identified by the First Edition decal on its bottom.

(Open Edition)   53403

Dates	OSRP	GBTru	Paid
1998 - 2002	**$50**	**$50**	$_____

Inglenook Cottage #5 (First Edition)   53304

Dates	OSRP	GBTru	Paid
1998 - 1999	**$60**	**$75**	$_____

• This version is identified by the First Edition decal on its bottom.

(Open Edition)   53404

Dates	OSRP	GBTru	Paid
1998 - 2000	**$60**	**$50**	$_____

The Grand Creamery (First Edition)   53305

Dates	OSRP	GBTru	Paid
1998 - 1999	**$60**	**$65**	$_____

• This version is identified by its gold flag and First Edition decal on its bottom.

(Open Edition)   53405

Dates	OSRP	GBTru	Paid
1998 - 2001	**$60**	**$45**	$_____

Parkside Pavilion   53411

Dates	OSRP	GBTru	Paid
1999 - 2002	**$65**	**$55**	$_____

• Set of 2 includes the Pavilion and fountain.

Parkside Pavilion Gift Set   53412

Dates	OSRP	GBTru	Paid
1999 - 2000	**$75**	**$75**	$_____

• Available during the 2000 Spring Discover Department 56 event.
• Set of 9 includes the Pavilion, a 4 piece accessory "Art Classes At Morning's Light," and stick-on floral arrangements.

Springlake Station   53413

Dates	OSRP	GBTru	Paid
1999 - 2002	**$90**	**$85**	$_____

• Early shipments had "filled-in" windows. Later shipments had the bottom half of the windows cut-out.
• Clock and 4 potted plants are separate in box.

Stillwaters Boathouse

53414

Dates	OSRP	GBTru	Paid
1999 - 2002	$70	$75	$_____

• Weathervane separate in box.

Mystic Ledge Lighthouse

53445

Dates	OSRP	GBTru	Paid
2000ᴹ - 2000	$96	$125	$_____

• Limited Edition - 5,600 pieces.

Garden Valley Vineyards

53446

Dates	OSRP	GBTru	Paid
2000 - 2001	$125	$150	$_____

• 25th Anniversary Limited Edition of 5,600.

Breezy Hill Stables

53447

Dates	OSRP	GBTru	Paid
2000 - 2002	$68	$70	$_____

• Weathervane and potted plant are separate in box.

East Cape Cottages

53448

Dates	OSRP	GBTru	Paid
2000 - 2002	$95	$90	$_____

• Set of 2.
• Do not handle by railings or columns.
• Ladders are very fragile.
• Boats are easily damaged.

Seaside Inn

53449

Dates	OSRP	GBTru	Paid
2001ᴹ - 2002	$68	$60	$_____

• Weathervane and potted plant are separate in box.

Bayport Souvenir And Kite Shop

53450

Dates	OSRP	GBTru	Paid
2001 - 2002	$60	$50	$_____

• Pilings and fence are fragile.

SEASONS BAY ACCESSORIES

Relaxing In A Garden

53307 - Set of 3
1998 - 2001
OSRP: $25
GBTru: $20
Paid: $_____

• Spring

A Stroll In The Park

53308 - Set of 5
1998 - 2002
OSRP: $25
GBTru: $20
Paid: $_____

• Spring

I'm Wishing

53309
1998 - 2001ᴹ
OSRP: $13
GBTru: $10
Paid: $_____

• Spring

Sunday Morning At The Chapel

53311 - Set of 2
1998 - 2001
OSRP: $17
GBTru: $14
Paid: $_____

• Spring

Fishing In The Bay

53313
1998 - 2002
OSRP: $13
GBTru: $11
Paid: $_____
• Summer

Here Comes The Ice Cream Man

53314 - Set of 4
1998 - 2002
OSRP: $35
GBTru: $30
Paid: $_____
• Summer

4th Of July Parade

53317 - Set of 5
1998 - 2002
OSRP: $32.50
GBTru: $30
Paid: $_____
• Summer

Trick Or Treat

53319 - Set of 4
1998 - 2002
OSRP: $25
GBTru: $22
Paid: $_____
• Fall

Back From The Orchard

53320
1998 - 2001
OSRP: $27.50
GBTru: $22
Paid: $_____
• Fall

Afternoon Sleigh Ride

53322
1998 - 2001^M
OSRP: $27.50
GBTru: $22
Paid: $_____
• Winter

Fun In The Snow

53323 - Set of 2
1998- 2001^M
OSRP: $15
GBTru: $12
Paid: $_____
• Winter

Skating On The Pond

53324 - Set of 2
1998 - 2002
OSRP: $20
GBTru: $15
Paid: $_____
• Winter

A Day At The Waterfront	The Garden Cart

A Day At The Waterfront

53326 - Set of 2

1998 - 2002

OSRP: $20

GBTru: $20

Paid: $_____

• Summer

The Garden Cart

53327

1998 - 2002

OSRP: $27.50

GBTru: $24

Paid: $_____

• Spring

Art Classes At Morning's Light

53412 - Set of 4

1999 - 2000

OSRP: *

GBTru: *

* Accessory contained in the 1999 Parkside Pavilion Gift Set.

The Garden Swing

53415

1999 - 2002

OSRP: $13

GBTru: $10

Paid: $_____

• Spring

Arriving At The Station

53416 - Set of 5

1999 - 2002

OSRP: $32.50

GBTru: $26

Paid: $_____

• Spring

The Perfect Wedding

53417 - Set of 7

1999 - 2002

OSRP: $25

GBTru: $24

Paid: $_____

• Summer
• Includes the book "Wedding Customs And Keepsakes."

Gently Down The Stream

53418

1999 - 2002

OSRP: $25

GBTru: $20

Paid: $_____

• Summer

A Grand Day Of Fishing

53419

1999 - 2002

OSRP: $25

GBTru: $24

Paid: $_____

• Summer

An Afternoon Picnic

53420 - Set of 3

1999 - 2002

OSRP: $18

GBTru: $15

Paid: $_____

• Fall

A Bicycle Built For Two

53421

1999 - 2002

OSRP: $17.50

GBTru: $15

Paid: $_____

• Fall

Rocking Chair Readers

53422 - Set of 2

1999 - 2002

OSRP: $15

GBTru: $13

Paid: $_____

• Fall

Lifeguard On Duty

53423

1999 - 2002

OSRP: $20

GBTru: $18

Paid: $_____

• Summer

A Day Of Holiday Shopping

53425 - Set of 3

1999 - 2002

OSRP: $25

GBTru: $20

Paid: $_____

• Winter

The First Snow

53426

1999 - 2002

OSRP: $15

GBTru: $15

Paid: $_____

• Winter

Singing Carols In Town

53427

1999 - 2002

OSRP: $22.50

GBTru: $18

Paid: $_____

• Winter

Pull Together

53600

2000 - 2002

OSRP: $35

GBTru: $28

Paid: $_____

• Summer

Evening Of Horseback Riding

53601 - Set of 2
2000 - 2002
OSRP: $30
GBTru: $25
Paid: $_____
• Summer

Gathering Grapes

53602 - Set of 2
2000 - 2001
OSRP: $25
GBTru: $20
Paid: $_____
• Fall

A Sleigh Ride With Santa

53603 - Set of 2
2000 - 2002
OSRP: $35
GBTru: $27
Paid: $_____
• Winter

Fresh Seafood By The Shore

53604
2000 - 2002
OSRP: $27.50
GBTru: $28
Paid: $_____
• Summer

The Kite of Spring

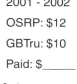

53608
2001 - 2002
OSRP: $12
GBTru: $10
Paid: $_____
• Spring

Seasons Bay Flag Raising

53611
2001 - 2002
OSRP: $12.50
GBTru: $12
Paid: $_____
• Spring

SEASONS BAY GENERAL VILLAGE ACCESSORIES

Mini Sisal Evergreens
Set of 12
$13   52763
1998 - 2002

Garden Fountain
Set of 9
$40   53330
1998 - 2001

Potted Flowers
8 Assorted
$12.50   53331
1998 - 2001ᴹ

Flowering Potted
Tree - 2 Assorted
$20   53332
1998 - 2001

Garden Park Bench
Set of 4
$12   53333
1998 - 2001ᴹ

Planter Box
Topiaries - Set of 4
$15   53334
1998 - 2001ᴹ

Garden Gazebo
$15   53338
1998 - 2002

Seasons Bay Sign
$10   53343
1998 - 2001

Flowering Vine
2 Assorted
$20   53344
1998 - 2001

Geranium Window
Box
$12   53345
1998 - 2001

Beach Front
Set of 3
$15   53355
1998 - 2001

Park Street Lights
Set of 4
$15   53366
1998 - 2002

Potted Topiaries
Set of 4
$15   53370
1998 - 2001ᴹ

Beach Front
Extensions - Set of 4
$15   53374
1998 - 2001

Stone Footpath
Sections - Set of 12
$15   53375
1998 - 2002

Lattice Obelisk
Set of 2
$8.50   53376
1998 - 2001ᴹ

Ivy Vine
Set of 4
$7.50   53377
1998 - 2001^M

Spring/Summer
Trees - Set of 4
$24   53382
1998 - 2001

Autumn Trees
Set of 4
$24   53383
1998 - 2001

Winter Trees
Set of 4
$24   53384
1998 - 2001

Amusement Park
Carousel
$75   53410
1999 - 2002

Seasons Bay Park
Set of 8
$70   53428
1999 - 2002

Christmas Garlands
& Wreaths - Set of 14
$10   53429
1999 - 2002

Sandy Beach
$7.50   53433
1999 - 2001

Adirondack Chairs
Set of 4
$10   53436
1999 - 2002

Harvest Decorations
Set of 12
$22.50   53431
2000^M - 2002

Patriotic Decorations
Set of 7
$12   53605
2000 - 2002

Small Collections

Heritage Village® Collection

The term Heritage Village Collection® has sometimes confused collectors. It is not a separate village but an umbrella term that encompasses six porcelain villages—Dickens' Village Series®, New England Village® Series, Alpine Village Series®, Christmas in the City® Series, North Pole Series™, and Little Town of Bethlehem™ Series, as well as smaller series such as Disney Parks Village™ Series, Historical Landmark Series®, and Literary Classics® Collection.

Most of these pieces clearly belong to a specific village, and often can only be displayed in that series. This is true for most buildings and accessories. There is not too much flexibility when it comes to placing elves, taxicabs, or the angels and wise men. But there are some (usually) porcelain pieces that are more versatile and can equally well be placed in two or more of the villages. Many of those pieces are from the earlier years of the collection. Today Department 56 "assigns" most pieces to a specific village or considers them as General Village Accessories. That was not always the case, as some accessories were seemingly designed with the intention of crossing village lines. Even today an occasional piece is actually designated for this category. Recently a number of the ubiquitous Village Vans have begun appearing to celebrate holidays. The Crystal Ice Palace is the only lit building in this category.

The items in this section are more versatile than those in the individual village sections. That does not mean that each of them can go in every village, but none are restricted to a single location. Among the most versatile are a number of porcelain trees, porcelain fences, and several Event Pieces.

Sleighride (Version 1)   (Version 2)

65110

1986 - 1990

OSRP: $19.50

GBTru: $50

Paid: $_____

GBTru: $40

Paid: $_____

• Early pieces have sleeves that read "Dickens' Sleighride," and the man has a narrow white scarf with red polka dots.

• Later pieces have a man with red polka dots on his scarf and lapels.

Porcelain Trees

65374 - Set of 2

1986 - 1992

OSRP: $14

GBTru: $24

Paid: $_____

Skating Pond

65455

1987 - 1990

OSRP: $24

GBTru: $50

Paid: $_____

• Early shipments were made in Taiwan and had blue-streaked ice. Later shipments were made in the Philippines and had all blue ice.

Stone Bridge

65463

1987 - 1990

OSRP: $12

GBTru: $50

Paid: $_____

• Varies from light to dark color.

Snow Children ✓

59382 - Set of 3

1988 - 1994

OSRP: $15

GBTru: $22

Paid: $_____

Village Train Trestle

59811

1988 - 1990

OSRP: $17

GBTru: $45

Paid: $_____

• Sleeves read "Stone Train Trestle."

One Horse Open Sleigh ✓

59820

1988 - 1993

OSRP: $20

GBTru: $30

Paid: $_____

Village Sign With Snowman

55727

1989 - 1994

OSRP: $10

GBTru: $12

Paid: $_____

Heritage Village Promotional Sign

99538

1989 - 1990

OSRP: $5

GBTru: $12

Paid: $_____

• Variation features green lettering on green facade.

Porcelain Pine, Large

52183

1992 - 1997

OSRP: $12.50

GBTru: $15

Paid: $_____

Porcelain Pine, Small

52191

1992 - 1997

OSRP: $10

GBTru: $12

Paid: $_____

Churchyard Fence & Gate

55638 - Set of 3

1992 - 1992

OSRP: $15

GBTru: $34

Paid: $_____

• Samples have gray stonework; production pieces have brown.
• Early release to GCC.

Churchyard Gate And Fence ✓

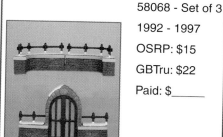

58068 - Set of 3

1992 - 1997

OSRP: $15

GBTru: $22

Paid: $_____

Churchyard Fence Extensions ✓

58076 - Set of 4

1992 - 1997

OSRP: $16

GBTru: $20

Paid: $_____

Porcelain Pine Trees

52515 - Set of 2

1994 - 1997

OSRP: $15

GBTru: $18

Paid: $_____

Christmas Bells

98711

1996^M - 1996

OSRP: $35

GBTru: $35

Paid: $_____

• 1996 Homes for the Holidays event piece.

Village Square Clock Tower ✓

52591

1996 - 2000

OSRP: $32.50

GBTru: $25

Paid: $_____

• Battery-operated.

The Holly & The Ivy

56100 - Set of 2

1997^M - 1997

OSRP: $17.50

GBTru: $16

Paid: $_____

• 1997 Homes for the Holidays event piece.

Poinsettia Delivery Truck

59000

1997 - 1999

OSRP: $32.50

GBTru: $34

Paid: $_____

• Similar designs were produced for retailers. See the Special Design section.

Porcelain Pines

59001 - Set of 4

1997 -

OSRP: $17.50

GBTru: -

Paid: $_____

Our Own Village Park Bench

02211

1997 - 1999

OSRP: $10

GBTru: $10

Paid: $_____

• Sold plain or with retailer name on the back of the bench as a promotional piece.

Painting Our Own Village Sign

55501

1998 - 2000

OSRP: $12.50

GBTru: $10

Paid: $_____

• Sold plain or with retailer name on the sign as a promotional piece.

Stars And Stripes Forever

55502

1998 - 1999

OSRP: $50

GBTru: $55

Paid: $_____

• July 1999 event piece.
• Plays "Stars and Stripes Forever."
• Includes 3 flags.

Dorothy's Skate Rental

55515
1999 - 2002
OSRP: $35
GBTru: $40
Paid: $_____

• Named after Olympic Gold Medal winner, Dorothy Hamill.
• Early release to only two stores.
• Lighted. Includes skates.

Hear Ye, Hear Ye

55523
1999 - 2001ᴹ
OSRP: $13.50
GBTru: $10
Paid: $_____

• Includes stickers so the scroll can be personalized.

Village Monuments

55524 - Set of 3
1999 - 2001ᴹ
OSRP: $25
GBTru: $22
Paid: $_____

Christmas Carolers

58631 - Set of 3
2000 -
OSRP: $27.50
GBTru: -
Paid: $_____

Crystal Ice Palace

58922 - Set of 9
2001ᴹ - 2001
OSRP: $165
GBTru: $135
Paid: $_____

• Set of 9 includes Palace, 2 piece accessory "Palace Bears," 4 trees, snow crystals, and ice path. Pennant separate in box.
• Although this design is considered a Heritage village design, it was shipped with an Original Snow Village Collection hang tag.
• This was a 25th Anniversary celebration design and, therefore, should have been stamped as such. When Department 56 became aware that it had not been stamped, it supplied decals to retailers who in turn could provide them to collectors.

Crystal Ice King & Queen

58976 - Set of 2

2001ᴹ - 2001

OSRP: $20

GBTru: $24

Paid: $_____

• Limited edition of 25,000.
• 25th Anniversary celebration design.

Mountie

58632

2001 - 2003

OSRP: $24

GBTru: $28

Paid: $_____

• Available only in Canada.

Village Memorial

53028

2002ᴹ - 2003

OSRP: $35

GBTru: $28

Paid: $_____

• Be careful removing from box; the globe is separate.

Halloween Village Express

58634

2002ᴹ - 2002

OSRP: $25

GBTru: $20

Paid: $_____

• Club 56 and Gold Key dealer exclusive.

Christmas Village Express

58635

2002ᴹ - 2002

OSRP: $25

GBTru: $26

Paid: $_____

• Club 56 and Gold Key dealer exclusive.

Village Square Snowman

58638

2002ᴹ - 2002

OSRP: $32.50

GBTru: $28

Paid: $_____

• Limited to year of production.
• Available only at Gold Key dealers.

Valentine Village Express

58639

2002 - 2003

OSRP: $25

GBTru: $25

Paid: $_____

St. Patrick's Village Express

58640

2002 - 2003

OSRP: $25

GBTru: $25

Paid: $_____

Easter Village Express

58641

2002 - 2003

OSRP: $25

GBTru: $25

Paid: $_____

Happy Birthday Village Express

58642

2002 - 2003

OSRP: $25

GBTru: $24

Paid: $_____

Walter's Hot Dog Stand

No Photo Available

58643

2002 - N/A

OSRP: $45

GBTru: N/A

Paid: $_____

• This design was never produced.

Village Square Town Tree

58644

2002ᴹ - 2003

OSRP: $35

GBTru: $33

Paid: $_____

• Limited to year of production.

Use the following space(s) to update your guide when the midyear introductions are announced.

Photos of the midyear introductions will be included in the July-August issue of *the Village Chronicle* magazine.

_____

_____

____ - ____

OSRP: $_____

GBTru: -

Paid: $_____

_____

_____

____ - ____

OSRP: $_____

GBTru: -

Paid: $_____

_____

_____

____ - ____

OSRP: $_____

GBTru: -

Paid: $_____

Notes:

Special Designs

It could be argued that all designs are special…and they are. In this case, the reference is to individual pieces or small groupings designed for specific organizations, businesses, or retailers. They are not available to collectors through traditional resources but must be acquired directly from a single source. Although they may be difficult to obtain, virtually every item in this section has been adopted into one or more villages by enthusiastic displayers.

The earliest pieces—the Bachman's Hometown Series—were produced for only a year. They have traits similar to Heritage Village® Collection pieces; in fact one piece served as the mold for a building in the Christmas In The City® Series.

The Profiles Department 56® pieces are manufactured by Department 56 for other corporations to distribute through their own marketing approaches, to stockholders, employees, or the general public.

The National Council of Clubs, an umbrella organization for collectors clubs, has released a number of pieces that have only been available at special events or through local collecting clubs that are affiliated with the national organization.

The largest grouping involves contract arrangements with retailers or companies who have specially designed variations of regular village pieces. At times a single piece has been adapted for a number of retailers; other times only one variation has been created. These unique yet familiar pieces have often found their way into village displays where sometimes they are more appreciated than those they imitated. After all, something different always draws the attention of fellow collectors.

BACHMAN'S HOMETOWN SERIES

This short-lived series was produced for Bachman's of Minneapolis, MN, the original parent company of Department 56. Three buildings were manufactured and distributed, but a fourth, a bookstore, never made it past the drawing board.

Boarding House   06700

Dates	OSRP	GBTru	Paid
1987 - 1988	**$34**	**$250**	$_____

• Inspired by the Sprague House in Red Wing, MN.

Church   06718

Dates	OSRP	GBTru	Paid
1987 - 1988	**$40**	**$275**	$_____

• Designed after a St. Paul, MN church.

Drugstore   06726

Dates	OSRP	GBTru	Paid
1988 - 1989	**$40**	**$555**	$_____

• Same mold as the Christmas In The City 1988 Variety Store And Barber Shop. See the CIC section.
• Inspired by a store in Stillwater, MN.

NATIONAL COUNCIL OF CLUBS (NCC)

The National Council of Clubs is an umbrella organization that dispenses information and advice to local Department 56 collectors' clubs.

Collectors Club House   54800

Dates	OSRP	GBTru	Paid
1998 - 1998	**$56**	**$125**	$_____

- An exclusive for members of National Council of Clubs related collectors clubs, this set was available directly to clubs from Department 56.
- Collectors who purchased the Club House could have decals of their clubs' logos affixed to the signs.
- Set of 2 includes House and man & woman accessory.

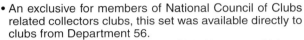

Under The NCC Umbrella   See below

Dates	OSRP	GBTru	Paid
2000 - 2001	**$20**	**$40**	$_____

- Based on Dickens' Village Under The Bumbershoot, this accessory was sold by the NCC at Dept 56 events.
- Available in 5 colors—yellow (02100), green (02101), red (02102), blue (02103), and silver (02104).

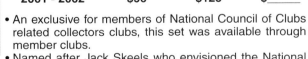

Jack's Umbrella Shop   05826

Dates	OSRP	GBTru	Paid
2001 - 2002	**$56**	**$125**	$_____

- An exclusive for members of National Council of Clubs related collectors clubs, this set was available through member clubs.
- Named after Jack Skeels who envisioned the National Council of Clubs, an organization that would assist and support local clubs.
- Set of 2 includes Shop, "Is It Raining?" accessory, and pin.
- The umbrella stand is very fragile.

PROFILES DEPARTMENT 56®

This is a series produced by Department 56 for use as promotional pieces by other companies. Many collectors, however, have adapted them into some of the Heritage Village Collections®.

Heinz® House — 07826

Dates	OSRP	GBTru	Paid
1996ᴹ - 1996	$28	$75	$___

• A replica of the home and first Heinz production building, this was given as a gift to Heinz vendors in late 1996 and sold by direct mail to its stockholders in 1997.

State Farm® - Main Street Memories — 56000

Dates	OSRP	GBTru	Paid
1997 - 1997	$35.50	$95	$___

• Made available to State Farm employees, this building depicts one similar to a Randy Souder painting.
• The gumball machine, broom, and awnings are fragile.
• Spire and sign are separate in box.

Heinz® Grocery Store — 05600

Dates	OSRP	GBTru	Paid
1998 - 1998	$34	$70	$___

• This corner grocery store was used by Heinz as a gift to Heinz vendors in late 1998 and sold by direct mail to its stockholders in 1999.
• Pickle sign is separate in the box.

Heinz® Hitch — 02291

Dates	OSRP	GBTru	Paid
1999 - 1999	$31	$55	$___

• Based on The Pumpkin Wagon, this was used by Heinz as a gift to Heinz vendors in late 1999 and sold by direct mail to its stockholders in 2000.

Heinz® Evaporated Horse Radish Factory — 02291

Dates	OSRP	GBTru	Paid
2000 - 2000	$40	$75	$___

• This design was used by Heinz as a gift to Heinz vendors in late 2000 and sold by direct mail to its stockholders in 2001.

State Farm® - Main Street Fire Station No. 1 05709

Dates	OSRP	GBTru	Paid
2000 - 2000	**$37**	**$85**	$_____

- Made available to its employees, this building depicts a similar one in Randy Souder's painting Main Street Memories that was commissioned by State Farm.
- Spire and lamppost are separate in the box.

Heinz® Town Clock 05834

Dates	OSRP	GBTru	Paid
2001ᴹ - 2001	**$15**	**$25**	$_____

- This working Clock was used by Heinz as a gift to Heinz vendors in late 2001 and sold by direct mail to its stockholders in 2002.

Wells Fargo® Historic Office 05930

Dates	OSRP	GBTru	Paid
2002ᴹ - 2002	**$42.50**	**$55**	$_____

- This building was used by Wells Fargo as a promotional item to celebrate its 150th anniversary.

Spam® Museum 06956

Dates	OSRP	GBTru	Paid
2003ᴹ - 2003	**$63.25**	**$64**	$_____

- This building was used by Hormel's Spam division as a promotional item.
- It is a replica of the Spam Museum in Austin, MN.
- Licensed by Hormel Foods Corporation.

MISCELLANEOUS

Designs in this category include those that were made for one retailer or company or a select group of retailers. In almost all instances, they were based on existing pieces.

John Deere® Water Tower — 25104

Dates	OSRP	GBTru	Paid
1988 - 1988	$24	$660	$_____

- Produced exclusively for the John Deere catalog.
- The tower reads "Moline Home of John Deere."
- Licensed by Deere & Co.

Bachman's For Sale Sign — 05398

Dates	OSRP	GBTru	Paid
1989 - 1989	$4.50	$10	$_____

- This version of the For Sale Sign was produced exclusively for Bachman's of Minneapolis, MN. to sell during its 1990 Village Gathering.

To date 27 versions of the **VILLAGE EXPRESS VAN** have been produced. A green edition in Christmas in the City was one of the regular releases in 1992. That same year a black promotional edition was created, followed by the rarest, a gold version. Seventeen retailers' versions were produced in 1994 and 1995. A silver edition was created in 2001 to celebrate Department 56's 25th anniversary. Several holiday versions are recent additions.

Village Express Van - Black — 99511

Dates	OSRP	GBTru	Paid
1992 - 1992	Promotional	$50	$_____

- This van was originally given to Department 56 sales representatives as a gift at their National Sales conference in 1992. It was later used as a special event piece at the 1993 Bachman's Village Gathering.

Village Express Van - Gold — 99775

Dates	OSRP	GBTru	Paid
1993 - 1993	Promotional	$420	$_____

- Packed in a special gold box, this promotional "Road Show" edition was presented to potential investors before the company's initial public offering.

Village Express Van - Gatherings   See below

Dates	OSRP	GBTru	Paid
1994 - 1994	**$25**	**See below**	

- The right side of each van features the Department 56 logo. The left side has the specific retailer's logo. 14 vans were produced—13 for Department 56 sponsored Village Gatherings and one for The Lemon Tree which sold it to its Collector's Club members.

Item #	Van	GBTru	Paid
07293	Bachman's	**$40**	$_____
07374	Bronner's	**$35**	$_____
07307	Christmas Dove	**$38**	$_____
07390	European Imports	**$38**	$_____
07358	Fortunoff	**$55**	$_____
07323	Incredible Christmas	**$40**	$_____
07218	Lemon Tree	**$30**	$_____
07331	Limited Edition	**$35**	$_____
07315	Lock, Stock & Barrel	**$40**	$_____
07366	North Pole City	**$40**	$_____
07340	Robert's	**$36**	$_____
07412	Stat's	**$30**	$_____
07382	William Glen	**$32**	$_____
07404	Windsor Shoppe	**$30**	$_____

Village Express Van   See below

Dates	OSRP	GBTru	Paid
1995 - 1995	**See below**	**See below**	

- The Parkwest van was a gift to retailers who were members of the Parkwest catalog group. It features the Department 56 logo on the right side, and Parkwest's logo on the left side.
- St. Nick's van features the Department 56 logo on the right side and its logo on the left.
- The Canadian van was produced for retailers in Canada. It features the Department 56 logo on the right side, and a red maple leaf on the left side.

Item #	Van	OSRP	GBTru	Paid
07522	Parkwest	**Promo**	**$360**	$_____
07560	St. Nick's	**$25**	**$36**	$_____
21637	Canadian	**$40**	**$45**	$_____

Squash Cart   07536

Dates	OSRP	GBTru	Paid
1995ᴹ - 1995	**$50**	**$75**	$_____

- Produced exclusively for Bachman's of Minneapolis, MN, this commemorated the company's 110th anniversary and notes this with a bottomstamp. It was first sold at the 1995 Bachman's Village Gathering.

A Visit With Santa
See below

Dates	OSRP	GBTru	Paid
1995 - 1995	$25	**See below**	

• Eight stores had this piece personalized with their names and choice of colors for the packages.

Item #	Store	GBTru	Paid
07544	Bachman's	$35	$_____
07676	Fortunoff	$40	$_____
07684	Lemon Tree	$30	$_____
07641	Limited Edition	$38	$_____
07730	Pine Cone Christmas	$36	$_____
07650	Stat's	$30	$_____
07668	William Glen	$30	$_____
07692	Young's Ltd.	$30	$_____

Here Comes Santa
See below

Dates	OSRP	GBTru	Paid
1996 - 1996	$25	**See below**	

• 24 stores had this piece personalized with their names on the banner. One store, Bachman's, had "Joy to the World" on the banner.

Item #	Store	GBTru	Paid
07744	Bachman's	$40	$_____
07745	Bronner's	$40	$_____
07748	Broughton Christmas	$32	$_____
07752	Cabbage Rose	$36	$_____
07753	Calabash Nautical Gifts	$40	$_____
07751	Calico Butterfly	$35	$_____
07763	Carson Pirie Scott	$35	$_____
07755	Christmas Loft	$35	$_____
07750	Dickens' Gift Shoppe	$40	$_____
07762	European Imports	$40	$_____
07747	Fibber Magee's	$38	$_____
07741	Fortunoff	$45	$_____
07759	Gustaf's	$38	$_____
07754	Ingle's Nook	$38	$_____
07746	Limited Edition	$40	$_____
07742	North Pole City	$35	$_____
07740	Pine Cone Christmas	$30	$_____
07760	Royal Dutch Collectibles	$35	$_____
07756	Russ Country Gardens	$35	$_____
07757	St. Nick's	$38	$_____
07758	Seventh Avenue	$30	$_____
07749	Stat's	$30	$_____
07743	William Glen	$38	$_____
07761	Young's Ltd.	$38	$_____

St. Nick's Pick-up And Delivery　　　07821

Dates	OSRP	GBTru	Paid
1996ᴹ - 1996	$10	$20	$_____

- Limited to 1,080 pieces, this personalized version of the Snow Village piece was produced exclusively for St. Nick's of Littleton, Co.

Bachman's Flower Shop　　　08802

Dates	OSRP	GBTru	Paid
1997ᴹ - 1997	$50	$95	$_____

- A personalized version of the Snow Village Secret Garden Florist, this was produced exclusively for Bachman's of Minneapolis, MN and was first sold at its 1997 Village Gathering.

Bachman's Wilcox Truck　　　08803

Dates	OSRP	GBTru	Paid
1997ᴹ - 1997	$30	$45	$_____

- A personalized version of the Heritage Village Poinsettia Truck, this replica of a Bachman's 1919 Wilcox was produced exclusively for Bachman's of Minneapolis, MN and was sold at its 1997 Gathering.

Lionel® Electric Train Shop　　　02202

Dates	OSRP	GBTru	Paid
1998ᴹ - 1998	$55	$155	$_____

- Limited to 5,000, this personalized Snow Village design was produced exclusively for Allied Model Trains of Culver City, CA. 1946 is the year Allied opened, and 4411 is its actual street number. Licensed by Lionel.

Bachman's Greenhouse　　　02203

Dates	OSRP	GBTru	Paid
1998ᴹ - 1998	$60	$85	$_____

- A personalized version of the Snow Village Secret Garden Greenhouse, this was produced exclusively for Bachman's of Minneapolis, MN and was first sold at its 1998 Village Gathering.

Say It With Flowers　　　02204

Dates	OSRP	GBTru	Paid
1998ᴹ - 1998	$30	$40	$_____

- A personalized version of the Snow Village Christmas Visit To The Florist, this set was produced exclusively for Bachman's of Minneapolis, MN and was first sold at its 1998 Village Gathering.

Bachman's Tending The Cold Frame — 02208

Dates	OSRP	GBTru	Paid
1998ᴹ - 1998	$35	$45	$_____

• This personalized version of the Dickens' Village Tending The Cold Frame was produced exclusively for Bachman's of Minneapolis, MN and was first sold at its 1998 Village Gathering.

North Pole City's Father Christmas's Journey — 02244

Dates	OSRP	GBTru	Paid
1998ᴹ - 1998	$30	$35	$_____

• This personalized version of the Dickens' Village design was produced exclusively for North Pole City of Oklahoma City, OK to honor its 10th anniversary.

William Glen Delivery Truck — 02300

Dates	OSRP	GBTru	Paid
1998ᴹ - 1998	$37.50	$35	$_____

• This personalized version of the Heritage Village Poinsettia Delivery Truck was produced exclusively for William Glen of Sacramento, CA and was first sold at its 1998 Village Gathering.

Lord & Taylor Delivery Wagon — 07880

Dates	OSRP	GBTru	Paid
1998ᴹ - 1998	$32.50	$45	$_____

• This personalized version of the Dickens' Village Fezziwig Delivery Wagon was produced exclusively for Lord & Taylor department stores.

Lord & Taylor Flower Cart — 02250

Dates	OSRP	GBTru	Paid
1999ᴹ - 1999	$27.50	$45	$_____

• This personalized version of the Dickens' Village Chelsea Market Flower Monger & Cart was produced exclusively for Lord & Taylor department stores.

William Glen Grocery Delivery — 02413

Dates	OSRP	GBTru	Paid
1999 - 1999	$18	$25	$_____

• This personalized version of the Christmas In The City Johnson's Delivery Wagon was produced exclusively for William Glen of Sacramento, CA and was first sold at its 1999 Village Gathering.

Bachman's Original Homestead, 1885   02255

Dates	OSRP	GBTru	Paid
1999ᴹ - 1999	$75	$100	$_____

- Limited to 7,500, it is the first numbered limited edition Snow Village design. Inspired by a Bachman family home, it was sold as a commemorative piece during the 1999 Bachman's Village Gathering.

Lilac City Water Tower   02423

Dates	OSRP	GBTru	Paid
1999 - 2000	$40	$50	$_____

- Limited to 500 pieces. Produced exclusively for Lock, Stock And Barrel of Rochester, NY.
- The tower reads "Lilac City… Rochester, New York, Incorporated 1834."

William Glen Taxi   02270

Dates	OSRP	GBTru	Paid
2000ᴹ - 2000	$12.50	$15	$_____

- This personalized version of the Christmas In The City City Taxi was produced exclusively for William Glen of Sacramento, CA and was first sold at its 2000 Village Gathering.

Feeney's Delivery Of Dreams   02272

Dates	OSRP	GBTru	Paid
2000ᴹ - 2000	$12.50	$15	$_____

- This personalized version of the Christmas In The City City Taxi was produced exclusively for Feeney's of Feasterville, PA.

Lord & Taylor Hot Air Balloon 2000   02440

Dates	OSRP	GBTru	Paid
2000ᴹ - 2000	$40	$45	$_____

- This personalized version of North Pole Dash Away Delivery was produced exclusively for Lord & Taylor department stores.
- The basket often comes unglued from the base.

Town Tree Carolers   05702

Dates	OSRP	GBTru	Paid
2000ᴹ - 2000	$65	$70	$_____

- Produced exclusively for NALED/Parkwest dealers.
- Set of 6 includes tree, set of 3 carolers, lampposts, and bench.
- Battery/adapter operated.

Village Express Van - Silver
52911

Dates	OSRP	GBTru	Paid
Dates	OSRP	GBTru	Paid
2001M - 2001	$25	$60	$_____

- Special issue for Department 56's silver anniversary.
- Only available at that event.

25th Anniversary Village Footbridge
52910

Dates	OSRP	GBTru	Paid
2001M - 2001	$15	$25	$_____

- Special issue for Department 56's silver anniversary.
- Only available at that event.

Toys For Tots
05746

Dates	OSRP	GBTru	Paid
2001M - 2001	$50	$50	$_____

- Produced exclusively for the Carson Pirie Scott department stores.

Feeney's Our Sign For All Seasons
05832

Dates	OSRP	GBTru	Paid
2001M - 2001	$15	$15	$_____

- This personalized version of the Village Sign And Bench was produced exclusively for Feeney's of Feasterville, PA.

Wegmans Delivery Wagon
05838

Dates	OSRP	GBTru	Paid
2001M - 2001	$22.50	$25	$_____

- Based on Christmas In The City Johnson's Delivery Wagon, this piece was produced exclusively for Lock, Stock And Barrel of Rochester, NY. It features the name of a well known regional grocery chain.

Feeney's Anniversary Lamppost
06001

Dates	OSRP	GBTru	Paid
2002M - 2002	$5	$5	$_____

- This personalized Lamppost was produced exclusively for Feeney's of Feasterville, PA.

ALLIED MODEL TRAINS DEPARTMENT 56 TRAINS

Allied Model Trains, one of the largest model train stores in the world, has produced a unique train set that has become highly collectible. Manufactured by Lionel Trains, each car features village-related artwork.

Snow Village Box Car

Dates	OSRP	GBTru	Paid
1995 - 1995	$45	$70	$_____

- Limited Edition of 5,000.
- Produced by Lionel Trains.
- Licensed by Department 56.

Heritage Village Box Car

Dates	OSRP	GBTru	Paid
1996 - 1996	$50	$70	$_____

- Limited Edition of 5,000.
- Produced by Lionel Trains.
- Licensed by Department 56.

Department 56 Caboose

Dates	OSRP	GBTru	Paid
1997 - 1997	$60	$90	$_____

- Limited Edition of 3,000.
- Produced by Lionel Trains.
- Licensed by Department 56.

Holly Bros. Tank Car

Dates	OSRP	GBTru	Paid
1998 - 1998	$60	$70	$_____

- Limited Edition of 3,000.
- Produced by Lionel Trains.
- Licensed by Department 56.

Department 56 Locomotive

Dates	OSRP	GBTru	Paid
1999 - 1999	$380	$535	$_____

- Limited Edition of 1,717.
- Includes tender.
- Produced by Lionel Trains.
- Licensed by Department 56.

Real Plastic Snow Hopper

Dates	OSRP	GBTru	Paid
2000 - 2000	**$60**	**$65**	**$____**

- Limited Edition of 3,000.
- Produced by Lionel Trains.
- Licensed by Department 56.

Happy Holidays Gondola

Dates	OSRP	GBTru	Paid
2001 - 2001	**$50**	**$55**	**$____**

- Limited Edition of 3,000.
- Produced by Lionel Trains.
- Licensed by Department 56.

General Village Accessories

Items in this category are designed to accompany virtually any village. They are the final decorating touches that add character to a scene, or help to bring it to life. In this guide these accessories have been divided into five categories:

TREES: You can never have too many trees, and virtually all of them are here. A few, like Bethlehem's palm trees and the porcelain pieces can be found elsewhere, but all the other trees, shrubs, and hedges are in this section. If it's a tree—even if it lights—it's found in this category, not under the "Electrical" section.

ELECTRICAL: Both the pieces on display and the cords, bulbs, adapters, and multiple plugs that activate them are found under "Electrical." This includes all animated pieces, trains, Brite Lites, streetlights, and colored lights. The sole exception is trees with lights, which may be found in the "Trees" category.

FENCES, GATES, AND WALLS: With the exception of a few porcelain pieces, all the boundary markers and their entrances are located in this section.

SNOW: The final finishing touches to every winter village are located in this frosty area.

MISCELLANEOUS: If it didn't appear in any of the above sections—and it's not made of porcelain or ceramic, this is the catchall category where you'll find roads, mountains, trim pieces, bridges, resin animals, and Mill Creek pieces.

Those General Village Accessories that have unique application to North Pole or Halloween displays are listed in separate color-coded pages at the conclusion of this section.

TREES
TREES
TREES
TREES
TREES
TREES
TREES
TREES
TREES

Spruce Forest
$90   65943
1987 - 1990

Spruce Tree With
Wooden Base, Sm
$3.50   65951
1987 - 1995

Spruce Tree With
Wooden Base, Med
$5   65978
1987 - 1995

Spruce Tree With
Wooden Base, Lg
$7   65986
1987 - 1995

Christmas Wreaths
$5   51110
1988 - 1991

Frosted Topiary
Village Garden
$16   51152
1988 - 1990

Sisal Topiary
Garden
$50   51853
1988 - 1992

Frosted Cone Tree
w/Wood Base, Lg
$10   51934
1988 - 1989

Frosted Norway
Pines
$12   51756
1989 - 1998

Winter Oak Tree
With 2 Red Birds
$16   51845
1989 - 1990

**Photo Not
Available**

Sisal Topiary, Lg
N/A   51861
1989 - 1989

**Photo Not
Available**

Sisal Topiary, Med
N/A   51870
1989 - 1989

**Photo Not
Available**

Sisal Topiary, Sm
N/A   51888
1989 - 1989

**Photo Not
Available**

Sisal Topiary, Mini
N/A   51896
1989 - 1989

Potted Topiary Pair
$5   51926
1989 - 1994

Frosted Topiary
Trees, S/2
$12   52000
1989 - 1999

Frosted Topiary, s/4
$10   52019
1989 - 1999

Frosted Topiary, s/8,
Lg
$12   52027
1989 - 1999

Frosted Topiary, s/8,
Sm
$7.50   52035
1989 - 1999

Mini Spruce Forest
$50   65790
1989 - 1990

Winter Oak, Sm
$4.50   51810
1990 - 1994

Winter Oak, Lg
$8   51829
1990 - 1994

Sisal Trees, s/7
$16   51837
1990 - 1990

Frosted Evergreen Papier-Maché, s/3
$16   65820
1990 - 1996

Evergreen Trees
$13   52051
1991 - 1997

Sisal Wreaths
$4   54194
1991 - 1998

Winter Birch Tree
$12.50   52167
1993 - 1996

Pine Cone Trees
$15   52213
1993 - 1995

Frosted Spruce Tree 15"
$12.50   52310
1994 - 1996

Frosted Spruce Tree 22"
$27.50   52329
1994 - 1996

Bare Branch Tree With 25 Lights
$13.50   52434
1994 - 2001

Pencil Pines
$15   52469
1994 - 1998

Autumn Maple Tree
$15   52540
1994 - 1997

Frosted Bare Branch Tree, Sm
$6.50   52418
1995 - 1996

Frosted Bare Branch Tree, Lg
$12.50   52426
1995 - 1996

Spruce Tree Forest
$25   52485
1995 - 1996

Frosted Zig–Zag Tree, White
$15   52493
1995 - 1996

Frosted Zig–Zag Tree, Green
$15   52507
1995 - 1996

Snowy White Pine Tree, Sm
$15   52558
1995 - 1996

Snowy White Pine
Tree, Lg
$20   52566
1995 - 1996

Landscape
$16.50   52590
1995 -

Flexible Sisal Hedge
$7.50   52596
1995 - 2001^M

Hybrid Landscape
$35   52600
1995 -

Lighted Snowcapped
Revolving Tree
$35   52603
1995 - 1997

Lighted
Snowcapped Trees
$45   52604
1995 - 1997

Frosted Fir Trees
$15   52605
1995 - 1998

Cedar Pine Forest
$15   52606
1995 - 1998

Ponderosa Pines
$13   52607
1995 - 1998

Arctic Pines
$12   52608
1995 - 1998

Fallen Leaves
$5   52610
1995 -

Snowy Evergreen
Trees, Sm
$8.50   52612
1995 - 2000

Snowy Evergreen
Trees, Med
$25   52613
1995 -

Snowy Evergreen
Trees, Lg
$32.50   52614
1995 - 2001

Snowy Scotch
Pines
$15   52615
1995 -

Autumn Trees
$13.50   52616
1995 - 1998

Wagon Wheel Pine
Grove
$22.50   52617
1995 - 1998

Pine Point Pond
$37.50   52618
1995 - 1999

Double Pine Trees
$13.50   52619
1995 - 1998

Jack Pines
$18   52622
1996 -

Bare Branch Trees
$22.50   52623
1996 -

Holly Tree
$10   52630
1996 - 2000

Birch Tree Cluster
$20   52631
1996 - 2001

Towering Pines
$13.50   52632
1996 - 1999

Winter Birch
$22.50   52636
1996 -

Frosted Spruce
$25   52637
1996 -

Frosted Hemlock Trees
$32.50   52638
1996 - 1998

Town Tree
$35   52639
1996 -

Autumn Birch/ Maple Trees
$27.50   52655
1997 -

Wintergreen Pines, s/3
$7.50   52660
1997 -

Wintergreen Pines, s/2
$15   52661
1997 - 2003

Flexible Sisal Hedge, Lg
$10   52662
1997 -

Lighted Snowy Tree
$27.50   52683
1997 - 2000

Lighted Christmas Tree
$48   52690
1997 - 1998

Flexible Autumn Hedges
$10   52703
1998 - 2000

Decorated Sisal Trees
$12.50   52714
1998 - 2001

Craggy Oak Tree
$12.50   52748
1998 - 2001

Swinging Under The Old Oak Tree
$30   52769
1998 - 2001ᴹ

Pine Trees With Pine Cones
$15   52771
1998 - 2001

Winter Pine Trees With Pine Cones
$15   52772
1998 - 2001

Flocked Pine Trees. s/3
$15   53367
1998 - 2000

Twinkling Tip Tree
$17.50   52781
1999 - 2001

Pequot Pines
$50   52818
1999 -

Pequot Pine, XLg
$32.50   52819
1999 -

Twinkling Lit Town Tree
$35   52837
1999 - 2001

Frosted Topiaries
$40   52842
1999 - 2001

Frosted Shrubbery
$20   52843
1999 - 2001

Frosty Light Trees
$20   52844
1999 - 2001

Up In The Apple Tree
$27.50   56640
1999 - 2000

Flocked Pine Trees, s/2
$16   56715
1999 - 2001

Icicle Trees
$27.50   56722
1999 - 2001

Twinkling Lit Trees, White
$32.50   56723
1999 - 2001

Twinkling Lit Shrubs, White
$15   56724
1999 - 2001

Twinkling Lit Trees, Green
$32.50   52823
1999 - 2001^{M}

Twinkling Lit Shrubs, Green
$15   52824
1999 - 2001^{M}

Celebration Tree 2000
$30   52850
2000^{M} -

Pinewood Trees, Lg
$17   56924
2000^{M} - 2002

Pinewood Trees, Sm
$13.50   56925
2000^{M} - 2002

Natural Evergreens, s/8
$24   52885
2000 -

Natural Evergreens, s/16
$45   52886
2000 - 2003

Fiber Optic Trees
$17.50   52888
2000 - 2002

Icy Trees, Sm
$17.50   52889
2000 - 2003

Icy Trees, Med
$25   52890
2000 - 2003

Icy Tree, Lg
$27.50   52891
2000 - 2002

Winter Green Spruce
$17   52892
2000 - 2001

Landscape Starter
Set
$6.50   52898
2000 -

Holly Topiaries
$12.50   52899
2000 - 2002

Holly Hedges
$15   52900
2000 - 2003

Holly Tree & Bush
$20   52901
2000 - 2001

Metal Bare Branch
Trees
$25   52931
2001ᴹ - 2002

Village Twinkle Brite
Tree, Lg
$22.50   52301
2001 -

City Lit Bare Branch
Tree
$12.50   52973
2001 -

Village Spring/
Summer Trees, s/4
$22.50   52974
2001 -

Village Autumn
Trees, s/4
$22.50   52975
2001 -

Village Winter
Trees, s/4
$22.50   52976
2001 -

Village Twinkle Brite
Tree, Sm
$17.50   52983
2001 -

Fiber Optic Woods,
Green Trees
$48   52985
2001 -

Fiber Optic Woods,
White Trees
$48   52986
2001 - 2003

Bag-O-Frosted
Topiaries, s/10
$8.50   52996
2001 -

Fiber Optic Woods
Grn Trees/Multi-lights
$48   53001
2001 - 2003

Tinsel Trees, s/4
$15   53012
2001 -

Bag-O-Frosted
Topiaries, s/2
$6.50   53018
2001 -

Acrylic Green Glitter
Trees, s/3
$25   53032
2002ᴹ -

Lighted Acrylic
Trees, s/2
$25   53033
2002ᴹ - 2003

Ice Crystal Pines, s/3
$50   53081
2002 -

Lighted Crystal
Pines, s/3
$75   53083
2002 -

Spring Oaks, s/2
$17.50   53084
2002 -

Village Frosted
Spruce, Small, s/3
$20   53085
2002 -

Fall Oaks, s/2
$17.50   53086
2002 -

Photo Not
Available

Willow Trees, s/2
$17.50   53134
2003 -

ELECTRICAL
ELECTRICAL
ELECTRICAL
ELECTRICAL
ELECTRICAL
ELECTRICAL
ELECTRICAL
ELECTRICAL
ELECTRICAL

Multi Color 10 Light Set
N/A   36323
1987 - 1989

Multi Colored 10 Light Set
N/A   36331
1987 - 1989

Amber 10 Light Set
N/A   36358
1987 - 1989

Street Lamps
$10   36366
1987 - 2000

Village Express Train - Black
$90   59978
1987 - 1988

Village Express Train - Red, Green
$95   59803
1988 - 1996

Streetlamp Wrapped In Garland
$10   59935
1988 - 1988

Streetlamp With Garland
$18   59943
1988 - 1988

Replacement Light Bulb
$2.50   99002
1988 - 1990

Single Cord Set
$3.50   99028
1988 -

6 Socket Lite Set
$13   99279
1988 -

Traffic Light
$10   55000
1989 - 2001

Railroad Crossing Sign
$10   55018
1989 - 2000

AC/DC Adapter
$10   55026
1989 -

Old World Streetlamp
$22   55034
1989 - 1991

Turn Of The Century Lamppost
$16   55042
1989 -

Turn Of The Century Lamppost
$22   55050
1989 - 1991

Double Street Lamps
$13   59960
1989 -

Candles By The Doorstep
$7   52060
1990 - 1994

General Village Accessories

365

Battery Operated
Light
$2.50   99260
1990 - 1991

Lights Out Remote
Control
$25   52132
1991 - 1994

Mini Lights
$12.50   52159
1991 - 2000

Replacement Light
Bulbs
$2.50   99244
1991 -

Multi-Outlet Plug
Strip, 6 Outlets
$10   99333
1991 -

Yard Lights
$13   54160
1992 - 1994

I Love My Village
Brite Lites
$15   52221
1993 - 1997

Merry Christmas
Brite Lites
$13.50   52230
1993 - 2000

Reindeer Brite Lites
$10   52248
1993 - 1999

Brite Lites Adapter
$10   52256
1993 -

Fence Brite Lites
$19   52361
1993 - 1999

Snowman Brite
Lites
$15   52370
1993 - 1999

Tree Brite Lites
$10   52388
1993 - 1999

Santa Brite Lites
$15   52396
1993 - 1999

Department 56 Brite
Lites
$10   98469
1993 - 1997

Animated Skating
Pond
$60   52299
1994 -

Streetcar ✔
$65   52400
1994 - 1998

Waving Flag Brite
Lites
$15   52442
1994 - 1997

Set of 20 Red
Lights Brite Lites
$9   52450
1994 - 1997

Animated All
Around The Park
$95   52477
1994 - 1996

Coca-Cola Neon Sign
$16.50   54828
1994 - 1998

Let It Snow Machine
$85   52592
1995 - 1997

Up, Up & Away
$40   52593
1996 - 2001

Spotlight
$7   52611
1996 - 2000

Mini Lights
$10   52626
1996 - 1998

Boulevard
Lampposts
$15   52627
1996 -

Country Road
Lampposts, s/2
$12   52628
1996 - 1997

Revolving Turntable
$50   52640
1996 - 1999

Animated Ski
Mountain
$75   52641
1996 - 1998

Animated
Accessory Track
$65   52642
1996 - 1999

Waterfall W/Electric
Pump
$65   52644
1996 - 1999

Replacement Round
Light Bulbs
$2   99245
1996 -

LED Light Bulb
$6.50   99247
1996 - 2000

20 Socket Light Set
With Bulbs
$25   99278
1996 -

Animated Sledding
Hill
$65   52645
1997 -

Country Road
Lampposts, s/4
$15   52663
1997 - 2001

Candy Canes Brite
Lites
$18   52670
1997 - 1999

Angel Brite Lites
$15   52671
1997 - 1999

Snow Dragon Brite
Lites
$20   52672
1997 - 1999

Santa In Chimney
Brite Lites
$15   52673
1997 - 1999

General Village Accessories

367

Candles Brite Lites
$17   52674
1997 - 1999

Holly Archway Brite
Lites
$25   52675
1997 - 1999

45 LED Light Strand
$22.50   52678
1997 -

Lighted Christmas
Pole
$32.50   52679
1997 - 2000

Road Construction
Sign
$12   52680
1997 - 2001ᴹ

Walkway Lights
$12   52681
1997 - 2000

Frosty Light Sprays
$12   52682
1997 - 1999

String Of Starry
Lights
$12.50   52684
1997 - 2000

Spotlight
Replacement Bulbs
$2.50   99246
1997 - 2000

Double Light Socket
Adapter
$4   99280
1997 -

Camden Park
Fountain
$84   52705
1998 - 2000

Carnival Carousel
LED Light Set
$20   52706
1998 - 2001

Replacement Light
Bulb, Clear
$3   52707
1998 -

Replacement Light
Bulb, Yellow
$3   52708
1998 -

Village Express
Electric Train Set
$270   52710
1998 -

Christmas
Luminaries
$15   52715
1998 - 2002

Fireworks
$25   52727
1998 -

String Of 25 Mini
LED Lights
$10   52728
1998 -

Biplane Up In The
Sky
$50   52731
1998 - 2000

Ski Slope
$75   52733
1998 -

Railroad Lamps
$15   52760
1998 - 2001ᴹ

String Of Spotlights
$15   52779
1998 - 2002

Replacement
Incandescent Bulbs
$4   13638
1999 -

Animated Photo
With Santa
$90   52790
1999 - 2001ᴹ

Through The Woods
Mountain Trail
$75   52791
1999 - 2003

Fireworks
Replacement Bulbs
$3.50   52800
1999 -

Remote Switches,
Right & Left
$20   52807
1999 -

Nativity Creche
$20   52822
1999 -

Fieldstone
Footbridge
$40   52827
1999 -

Frosted Fountain
$20   52831
1999 -

3 Socket Light Set
$7.50   52835
1999 -

Stadium Lights
$22.50   52845
1999 -

Bumper Fun Ride
$98   52500
2000ᴹ - 2002

Look, It's The
Goodyear Blimp
$45   52501
2000ᴹ - 2001

Santa's On His Way
$65   52502
2000ᴹ -

Replacement
Lightning Bulbs
$3   52846
2000ᴹ -

Electric Foam Cutter
$25   52847
2000ᴹ -

Light Adapter for
NPW
$5   52852
2000ᴹ - 2000

Light Adapter With
3 Jacks for NPW
$6   52853
2000ᴹ - 2002

Mill Falls Working
Waterfall
$75   52503
2000 -2001

General Village Accessories

369

Holiday Singers
$75   52505
2000 -

Festive Front Yard
$75   52506
2000 -

Perfect Putt
$65   52508
2000 - 2001

Woodland Carousel
$75   52509
2000 - 2001

Village Junkyard
$85   52861
2000 -

Repl Bulbs For 52779
String Of Spotlights
$15   52893
2000 - 2002

Repl Flickering Bulb
For Creepy Creek Hs
$5   52904
2000 -

Santa's Sleigh
$68   58630
2000 -

Gondola Animated
Scene
$85   52511
2001ᴹ -

Santa By The Light
of The Moon
$37.50   52984
2001 - 2003

Hockey Practice,
s/3
$37.50   52512
2001 -

Valentine's
Decorating Set, s/5
$22.50   53020
2002ᴹ -

Easter Decorating
Set, s/5
$22.50   53021
2002ᴹ -

St. Patrick's Day
Decorating Set, s/5
$22.50   53022
2002ᴹ -

4th Of July
Decorating Set, s/5
$22.50   53024
2002ᴹ -

Sounds Of The
North Woods
$85   53025
2002ᴹ -

Repl. Halogen Bulb
Starlight Dance Hall
$4   53027
2002ᴹ -

Packages Delivery
$50   53038
2002 -

Replacement Aux.
Cord With Light
$4.50   53039
2002 -

Snowflake Light
Poles, s/4
$17.50   53049
2002 -

String Of 12
Snowman Lights
$10   53053
2002 -

City Trolley, s/6
$75   53054
2002 -

Lighted Tiered
Platform
$250   53089
2002 -

Sounds Of The City
$65   53111
2003 -

Replacement 3 Volt
Light Bulb, s/2
$4   53121
2003 -

String Of 12
Snowflake Lights
$10   53122
2003 -

String Of 12 Santa
Lights
$10   53123
2003 -

Year Round Lighted
Lawn Orns , s/6
$20   53125
2003 -

Lighted Street
Boulevard
$17.50   53137
2003 -

Village Twinkling
Snow Tree Skirt
$50   53152
2003 -

Village Twinkling
Blanket Of Snow
$30   53153
2003 -

Holiday Streetlights,
s/2
$10   59427
2003 -

WALLS
FENCES
GATES
WALLS
FENCES
GATES
WALLS
FENCES
GATES

White Picket Fence
$3   51004
1987 - 2000

White Picket Fence
s/4
$12   51012
1987 - 1997

Lamp Post Fence
$13   55069
1989 - 1991

Photo Not
Available

Lamp Post Fence
$13   55077
1989 - 1989

Lamp Post Fence
Extension
$10   55085
1989 - 1991

Photo Not
Available

Lamp Post Extension
$10   55093
1989 - 1989

Wrought Iron Fence
$2.50 each   59986
1989 - 1998

Snow Fence
$7   52043
1991 - 1998

Frosty Tree-Lined
Picket Fence
$6.50   52078
1991 - 1997

Tree-Lined
Courtyard Fence
$4   52124
1990 - 1998

Wrought Iron Gate
And Fence
$15   55140
1991 - 1998

Wrought Iron Fence
Extensions ③
$12.50   55158
1991 - 1998

Wrought Iron Fence
$10   59994
1991 - 1999

Courtyard Fence
With Steps
$4   52205
1992 - 1998

Chain Link Fence
With Gate
$12   52345
1993 - 1998

Chain Link Fence
Extensions
$15   52353
1993 - 1998

Victorian Wrought
Iron Fence w/Gate
$15   52523
1994 - 2001ᴹ

Victorian Wrought
Iron Fence Extension
$15   52531
1994 - 2001ᴹ

Split Rail Fence,
With Mailbox
$12.50   52597
1995 - 1997

Twig Snow Fence,
Wood
$6   52598
1995 - 2000

White Picket Fence
With Gate
$10   52624
1996 - 1998

White Picket Fence
Extensions
$10   52625
1996 - 1998

Stone Wall
$2.50   52629
1996 -

Stone Curved
Wall/Bench
$15   52650
1997 - 2001

Snow Fence
$7   52657
1997 -

Camden Park
Square Stone Wall
$2.50   52689
1997 - 2000

Fieldstone Wall
$3.50   52717
1998 -

Fieldstone Entry
Gate
$10   52718
1998 - 2001ᴹ

Holly Split Rail
Fence
$18   52722
1998 - 2001

Holly Split Rail Fence
w/Seated Children
$13.50   52723
1998 - 2001

Stone Wall With
Sisal Hedge
$5   52724
1998 - 2001

Corral Fence
$32   52746
1998 - 2001

Fieldstone Wall
With Apple Tree
$25   52768
1998 - 2001ᴹ

Ice Crystal Gate &
Walls
$32.50   56716
1999 - 2002

Ice Crystal Walls
$15   56717
1999 - 2001

Tall Stone Walls
$20   52825
1999 -

Fieldstone Curved
Wall/Bench, s/4
$15   53009
2001 -

General Village Accessories

SNOW
SNOW
SNOW
SNOW
SNOW
SNOW
SNOW
SNOW
SNOW

Real Plastic Snow
7 oz. Bag
$3   49981
1977 -

Real Plastic Snow
2 lb. Box
$10   49999
1977 - 2000

Blanket Of New
Fallen Snow
$7.50   49956
1991 -

Photo
Not Available
At Press Time

Let It Snow
Crystals, 8 oz. Box
$6.50   49964
1991 - 1992

Fresh Fallen Snow
7 oz. Bag
$3.20   49979
1995 -

Fresh Fallen Snow
2 lb. Box
$12   49980
1995 - 2000

Glistening Snow
$10   53362
1998 - 2001

Ice Crystal Blanket
Of Snow
$6   52841
1999 -

Pine Scented Fresh
Fallen Snow
$4.30   52848
2000 -

First Frost Snow
Crystals
$3.50   52906
2000 -

Real Removable
Snow, s/10
$5   53101
2003 -

MISCELLANEOUS
MISCELLANEOUS
MISCELLANEOUS
MISCELLANEOUS
MISCELLANEOUS
MISCELLANEOUS
MISCELLANEOUS
MISCELLANEOUS
MISCELLANEOUS

Park Bench
$3.20   51098
1987 - 1993

Town Clock
$3   51101
1988 - 1998

SV Garland Trim
$4.50   51128
1988 - 1991

Up On A Roof Top
$6.50   51390
1988 - 1999

Birds
$3.50   51802
1989 - 1994

Christmas Eave Trim
$3.50   55115
1989 -

Town Square
Gazebo
$19   55131
1989 - 1997

Acrylic Icicles
$4.50   52116
1990 - 2000

Mylar Skating Pond
$6   52086
1991 - 2000

Brick Road
$10   52108
1991 -

"It's A Grand Old
Flag"
$4   54178
1991 - 1997

Greetings
$5   54186
1991 - 1994

Cobblestone Road
$10   59846
1991 -

Tacky Wax
$2.50   52175
1992 -

"Village Sounds"
Tape With Speakers
$25   55247
1992 - 1994

"Village Sounds"
Tape
$8   55255
1992 - 1994

Mountain, Sm
$32.50   52264
1992 - 2000

Mountain, Med
$65   52272
1992 - 2000

Mountain, Lg
$150   52280
1992 -

General Village Accessories

375

Heritage Banners
$6   55263
1992 - 1995

Heritage Village
Promotional Banner
$0   09482
1992 - 1992

Wrought Iron Park
Bench
$5   52302
1993 -

Sled & Skis
$6   52337
1993 - 2000

Mountain Backdrop
$65   52574
1994 -

Mountain Tunnel
$37.50   52582
1994 - 2000

Let It Snow
Snowman Sign
$12.50   52594
1995 - 1998

Pink Flamingos
$7.50   52595
1995 -

Election Yard Signs
$10   52599
1995 - 1997

Brick Town Square
$15   52601
1995 -

Cobblestone Town
Square
$15   52602
1995 -

Magic Smoke
$2.50   52620
1996 - 2000

Mill Creek
(Straight Section)
$12.50   52633
1996 - 2001

Mill Creek
(Curved Section)
$12.50   52634
1996 - 2001

Mill Creek Bridge
$35   52635
1996 - 2000

Mountain
Centerpiece
$45   52643
1996 - 2000

Stone Footbridge
$16   52646
1997 -

Stone Trestle Bridge
$37.50   52647
1997 - 2001ᴹ

Stone Holly Corner
Posts And Archway
$20   52648
1997 -

Stone Holly Tree
Corner Posts
$8.50   52649
1997 - 2000

Mill Creek Pond
$55   52651
1997 - 2002

Village Gazebo
$22.50   52652
1997 - 2000

Mill Creek Wooden
Bridge
$32.50   52653
1997 - 2002

Mill Creek Park
Bench
$14   52654
1997 - 1999

Telephone Poles
$15   52656
1997 - 2001

Television Antenna
$5   52658
1997 - 1999

Weather Vane
$6.50   52659
1997 - 1999

Log Pile
$3   52665
1997 -

Two Lane Paved
Road
$15   52668
1997 -

Blue Skies Backdrop
$7.50   52685
1997 - 2000

Starry Night Sky
Backdrop
$7.50   52686
1997 - 2000

Camden Park
Square
$75   52687
1997 - 2000

Camden Park
Cobblestone Road
$10   52691
1997 - 2001

Holiday Tinsel Trims
$8   52712
1998 - 2000

Tinsel Trims
$8   52713
1998 -

Slate Stone Path
Straight
$3   52719
1998 -

Woodland Animals
At Mill Creek
$32.50   52720
1998 - 2001

Stone Stairway
$16.50   52725
1998 -

Clear Ice
$6.50   52729
1998 - 2001^M

Green
$12.50   52739
1998 -

Putting Green
$22.50   52740
1998 - 2002

Moose In The Marsh
$25   52742
1998 - 1999

Bears In The Birch
$25   52743
1998 - 2003

Foxes In The Forest
$22.50   52744
1998 - 2000

Thoroughbreds
$45   52747
1998 - 2001

Gray Cobblestone Section
$7.50   52751
1998 - 2000

Gray Cobblestone Archway
$10   52752
1998 - 2000

Gray Cobblestone Tunnel
$6.50   52753
1998 - 2000

Real Gray Gravel
$5   52754
1998 - 2000

Gray Cobblestone Capstones
$6   52755
1998 - 2000

Gravel Road
$10   52756
1998 - 2000

Wolves In The Woods
$25   52765
1998 - 2001

Wooden Pier
$32.50   52766
1998 -

Slate Stone Path Curved
$3   52767
1998 -

Grassy Ground Cover
$7.50   53347
1998 -

Nativity Sand
$6.50   41430
1999 - 2001ᴹ

Craggy Cliff Platform
$65   52794
1999 - 2003

Craggy Cliff Extensions
$25   52795
1999 - 2003

Wooden Rowboats
$20   52797
1999 - 2002

Autumn Moss
$7.50   52802
1999 - 2001

Spring/Summer
Moss
$7.50   52803
1999 - 2001

9" Straight Track
$12.50   52808
1999 -

18" Radius Curved
Track
$12.50   52809
1999 -

Personalize Your
Village Accessories
$16.50   52811
1999 - 2001

Woodland Wildlife
Animals, Lg
$32.50   52813
1999 -

Majestic Woodland
Birds
$25   52814
1999 - 2002

Woodland Animals
At Cliff's Edge
$75   52816
1999 -2001

Fieldstone Stairway
$10   52826
1999 - 2001

Cats & Dogs
$15   52828
1999 -

Lookout Tower
$32.50   52829
1999 - 2001

Wooden Canoes
$20   52830
1999 - 2003

The Trout Stream
$50   52834
1999 -

Real Gravel
$5   52839
1999 - 2001ᴹ

Ground Cover
$12.50 ea.   52840
1999 -

Family Winter
Outing
$10   55033
1999 - 2001

Woodland Wildlife
Animals, Sm
$27.50   55525
1999 -

North Pole Photo
With Santa
$7.50   56444
1999 - 2000

Red Wrought Iron
Park Bench
$5   56445
1999 -

Park Bench
$7.50   52851
2000 - 2001

The Dockhouse
$40   52863
2000 -

Mountain Lion's Den
$22.50   52864
2000 - 2001

Buffalo On The
Prairie
$22.50   52865
2000 - 2001

Birds Out Back
$30   52866
2000 - 2003

Smokehouse
Incense Burner
$15   52880
2000 - 2001

Balsam Fir Incense
$5   52881
2000 - 2001

Village Sign and
Bench
$8.50   52882
2000 - 2001

Fabric Cobblestone
Road
$10   52884
2000 -

Light Hole Protectors
$7.50   52887
2000 -

Mill Creek Campsite
$55   52894
2000 -

The Woodshed &
Chopping Block
$40   52895
2000 - 2003

Personalize Pen
$5   52897
2000 - 2003

Crushed Ice
$5   52908
2000 - 2003

Mountain Stream
$150   52909
2000 -

Good Fishing
$35   56643
2000 -

Winter Scene
Backdrop
$45   52930
2001 - 2003

Here Fishy Fishy Ice
House
$37.50   52937
2001 -

Watching For Ducks,
s/2
$30   52938
2001 -

Turkeys/Geese In
The Field, s/2
$27.50   52939
2001 -

Village Lamppost
And Sign
$7.50   52940
2001 - 2002

American Flags, s/7
$12.50   52943
2001 -

Village Flea Market,
s/38
$65   52945
2001 - 2003

Mountain Creek Y
Shape
$42.50   52946
2001 -

Dog And Puppies,
Cat And Kittens, s/2
$20   52948
2001 -

Village Bicycle And
Tricycle, s/2
$12.50   52950
2001 -

Deer In The Woods
$22.50   52953
2001 -

Bald Eagle Nesting
$18.50   52972
2001 - 2003

Village Mountain
High
$75   52977
2001 -

Village Moss 4
Asst'd Colors
$7.50   52979
2001 -

Woodland
Landscape Set, s/9
$35   52989
2001 - 2003

Snowy Landscape
Set, s/5
$35   52990
2001 - 2002

City Landscape Set,
s/13
$35   52993
2001 -

Mallard And Wood
Duck, s/2
$12.50   53002
2001 - 2003

Mountain Creek
Waterfall
$42.50   53003
2001 -

Mountain Creek
Curved Section
$17.50   53005
2001 -

Mountain Creek
Straight Section, s/2
$25   53006
2001 -

Fieldstone Fireplace
$12.50   53010
2001 - 2003

Mountain Creek
Bear/Moose, s/2
$22.50   53017
2001 - 2003

A Christmas Eve
Flight Backdrop
$45   53037
2002 -

Holiday Trimmings,
s/14
$10   53042
2002 -

Village Boats, s/2
$20   53043
2002 -

A Harvest Feast
$35   53045
2002 -

Rocky Mt. Wildlife-
Bears/Bobcat, s/2
$30   53047
2002 -

Seasonal
Lampposts, s/4
$17.50   53048
2002 -

Village Santa Sign
$7.50   53051
2002 - 2003

Village Roll Of Moss
$20   53052
2002 -

Spring/Summer
Landscape Set, s/10
$35   53076
2002 -

Acrylic Ice Block
Display Piece
$20   53088
2002 -

Real Acylic Ice,
mini, bag of 12
$10   44476
2003ᴹ -

Real Acylic Ice,
small, bag of 6
$10   44477
2003ᴹ -

Real Acylic Ice,
medium, bag of 4
$12.50   44478
2003ᴹ -

Create A Scene
Village Platform
$25   53093
2003ᴹ -

Snowy Platform, s/3
$20   53094
2003ᴹ -

Summer Platform, s/3
$20   53095
2003ᴹ -

Fall Platform, s/3
$20   53096
2003ᴹ -

Potted Poinsettias,
s/4
$7.50   53105
2003 -

Fresh Flower Cart
$20   53106
2003 -

Winter Trimmings
$45   53107
2003 -

Harvest Bounty
$45   53108
2003 -

Spring Is
Everywhere!
$45   53109
2003 -

Fishing At Trout
Lake
$35   53110
2003 -

Brick Path, s/6
$15   53136
2003 -

Autumn Landscape
Set, s/27
$35   53138
2003 -

Winter Wonderland
Landscape Set, s/11
$35   53140
2003 -

Village Real Acrylic
Ice, s/22
$10   53141
2003 -

Real Acrylic Icicles
$5   53151
2003 -

Several buildings and accessories have been produced within the North Pole Series.

These General Village pieces can be used by themselves or in combination with those items.

NORTH POLE
NORTH POLE
NORTH POLE
NORTH POLE
NORTH POLE
NORTH POLE
NORTH POLE
NORTH POLE
NORTH POLE

Pole Pine Forest
$48   55271
1991 - 1998

Pole Pine Tree, Sm
$10   55280
1991 - 1998   2

Pole Pine Tree, Lg
$12.50   55298
1991 - 1998   5

Elves On Ice
$9   52298
1996 - 2000

North Pole Candy
Cane Lampposts
$13   52621
1996 - 2001ᴹ

Candy Cane Fence
$8.50   52664
1997 -

Peppermint Road
(Straight Section)
$5   52666
1997 -

Peppermint Road
(Curved Section)
$5   52667
1997 -

Candy Cane Bench
$5   52669
1997 -

Downhill Elves
$9   56439
1998 - 2000

Holiday
Cobblestone Road
$10   56447
1999 - 2001

Peppermint Trees
$17.50   56721
1999 - 2003

Elves On Track
$10   56714
1999 - 2001

Bridge Over The Icy
Pond
$40   56720
1999 - 2002

Gumdrop Street
Lamps
$20   52871
2000 - 2001

Green Glitter Sisal
Trees
$17.50   52902
2000 - 2001

North Pole Backdrop
$45   52962
2001 - 2002

Gumdrop Street
Lamp, s/4
$18   52966
2001 -

Gumdrop Tree
w/LED Lights, 9 inch
$25   52967
2001 -

Gumdrop Tree Non-
Lit, 9"
$12   52968
2001 -

Gumdrop Tree Non-
Lit, 12"
$15   52969
2001 - 2003

Tinsel Ball Trees, s/5
$15   52971
2001 -

Village Gumdrop
Road, s/4
$10   52978
2001 -

Peppermint
Landscape Set, s/7
$35   52991
2001 - 2003

Peppermint Trees
s/2
$15   53011
2001 - 2003

Faces Of The Season
Picket Fence
$42.50   53029
2002^M -

North Pole Animated
Train With Track, s/7
$42.50   53030
2002^M - 2003

Village Peppermint
Sign
$7.50   53114
2003 -

Curved Village
Gumdrop Road, s/4
$10   53135
2003 -

Several Halloween buildings and accessories have been produced within the Original Snow Village Collection.

These General Village pieces can be used by themselves or in combination with those items.

String Of 12
Pumpkin Lights
$13   52700
1998 - 2001

Jack-O' Lanterns
$10   52701
1998 - 2002

Up, Up & Away
Witch - Animated
$50   52711
1998 - 2003

Halloween
Luminaries
$15   52738
1998 - 2002

Halloween Fence
$12.50   52702
1998 -

Halloween Accessories
$50   52704
1998 - 2001

Halloween Spooky
Tree
$15   52770
1998 - 2002

Witch By The Light
Of The Moon
$30   52879
2000 -

Lit Spooky Tree
$30   52896
2000 -

Haunted Front Yard
$65   52924
2001ᴹ -

Halloween Scene
$45   52933
2001ᴹ -

Haunted Graveyard
$36   52513
2001 -

Village Swinging
Skeleton - Animated
$36   52514
2001 - 2003

Hocus Pocus Witch
- Animated
$30   52516
2001 -

Halloween Pumpkin
Stand
$35   52956
2001 -

Halloween Village
Set, s/24
$35   52957
2001 - 2003

Halloween Full Moon
$30   52960
2001 - 2003

Gothic Street Lamp,
s/2
$17.50   52961
2001 -

Spooky Black Bare
Branch Trees, s/3
$12.50   52964
2001 - 2002

Spooky Wrought
Iron Fence, s/6
$15   52982
2001 -

Autumn/Halloween
Landscape Set, s/6
$35   52992
2001 - 2002

Jack-O'-Lantern
String of 12 Lights
$7.50   53000
2001 -

Candy Corn String
of 20 Lights
$10   53013
2001 - 2003

Halloween Village
Sign
$7.50   53044
2002 - 2003

Witch Crash
$36   53056
2002 -

Haunted Hearse
$42.50   53057
2002 -

Skeleton Fence
$12.50   53059
2002 -

Gravely Landscape
Set, s/8
$45   53060
2002 -

Lighted Halloween
Scarecrows, s/2
$25   53061
2002 -

Halloween
Topiaries, s/3
$17.50   53062
2002 - 2003

Spooky Totem
$12.50   53063
2002 - 2003

Tombstones, s/6
$10   53065
2002 -

Spooky Black Glitter
Tree, s/3
$17.50   53067
2002 -

Haunted Outhouse
$25   53068
2002 -

Creepy Creek Bridge
$35   53071
2002 -

Over The Hill
Tombstone
$12   53072
2002 -

Haunted Fiber Optic
Backdrop
$65   53075
2002 -

Jack-O-Lantern
Pumpkins, s/12
$7.50   53077
2002 -

Skull Street Lamps,
s/4
$17.50   53079
2002 -

Glowing String of
Scary Lights, 2 Astd
$12.50   53080
2002 -

Spooky Willows, s/2
$17.50   53087
2002 -

Ghostly Landscape
Set, s/12 (Exclusive)
$35   04771
2003 -

Eerie Rocks & Road,
s/8
$35   53119
2003 -

Phantom Of The
Organ
$65   53126
2003 -
.

Rock-A-Bye Vampire
$36   53128
2003 -

Lit Graveyard Tree
$17.50   53129
2003 -

Halloween Yard
Decorations, s/22
$12.50   53130
2003 -

Scary Twisted Trees,
s/2
$20   53131
2003 -

Scaredy Bat
$45   53132
2003 -

Swinging Ghoulies
$55   53133
2003 -

Ghostly Landscape
Set, s/12
$35   53143
2003 -

Spooky Village Sign
$7.50   53144
2003 -

Harvest Gourds, s/10
$7.50   53145
2003 -

Resting My Bones
$25   53146
2003 -

Mummy Mischief
$30   53148
2003 -

Bubble Light Ghosts
s/2
$25   53149
2003 -

Pumpkin Street
Lamps, s/2
$12.50   53150
2003 -

ITEM NUMBER INDEX

HOW DESIGNS ARE LISTED:

For years Department 56 used hyphens in its item numbers. For instance, a design's item number may have been 1234-5. However, several years ago, the company stopped using the hyphens. Therefore, we have omitted all hyphens in both the index as well as in the content of the book. That same design's number would now appear as 12345.

Item Number Index

395

Item Number Index

399

ALPHABETICAL INDEX

HOW DESIGNS ARE LISTED:

A, An, or The: A design with a name beginning with "A," "An," or "The" is listed by the second word in its name. For instance, "The Emily Louise" is listed as "Emily Louise, The."

Nicknames: Some designs are often referred to by more than one name. For instance, "C. Fletcher Public House" is also called "Public House." In order to make this index easier to use, the designs' common references are listed in addition to their proper names.

Index

405

Index

Index

414

Index

418

Index

423